Publication No. 10
of the Mathematics Research Center
United States Army
The University of Wisconsin

STOCHASTIC MODELS IN MEDICINE AND BIOLOGY

STOCHASTIC MODELS IN MEDICINE AND BIOLOGY

Proceedings of a Symposium Conducted by the Mathematics Research Center, United States Army, at the University of Wisconsin, Madison, June 12-14, 1963.

edited by

JOHN GURLAND

MADISON · THE UNIVERSITY
OF WISCONSIN PRESS · 1964

Published by
THE UNIVERSITY OF WISCONSIN PRESS
430 Sterling Court, Madison, Wisconsin 53706

Typescript by Technical Publication Staff,
Mathematics Research Center, U. S. Army
Printed in the United States of America by
North American Press, Milwaukee, Wisconsin
Library of Congress Catalog Card Number 64-14509

LECTURERS

NIELS ARLEY
Professor, Department of Biophysics,
Norsk Hydro's Institute for Cancer Research
Montebello, Norway

ANTHONY F. BARTHOLOMAY
Assistant Professor, Mathematical Biology, Harvard University
Medical School and Associate on Staff, Peter Bent Brigham Hospital
Boston, Massachusetts

CHIN LONG CHIANG
Associate Professor, Biostatistics Department,
University of California
Berkeley, California

WILLIAM G. COCHRAN
Professor, Department of Statistics, Harvard University
Cambridge, Massachusetts

MILES DAVIS*
Graduate Student, Department of Statistics, Harvard University
Cambridge, Massachusetts

JOSEPH O. IRWIN
Member, Medical Research Council, Statistical Research Unit
London School of Hygiene and Tropical Medicine, University of London
Keppel Street, London, England

SAMUEL KARLIN
Professor, Department of Mathematics and Statistics,
Stanford University
Stanford, California

---

* Co-author. The paper was presented by the other author listed. See Table of Contents.

BRUCE R. LEVIN*
Graduate Student, Department of Human Genetics
University of Michigan Medical School
Ann Arbor, Michigan

HENRY L. LUCAS
Professor, Department of Experimental Statistics,
North Carolina State College
Raleigh, North Carolina

JAMES McGREGOR*
Instructor, Applied Mathematics and Statistical Laboratory
Stanford University
Stanford, California

JERZY NEYMAN
Professor and Director, Statistical Laboratory,
University of California
Berkeley, California

IZAAK OPATOWSKI
Professor, Committee on Mathematical Biology,
University of Chicago
Chicago, Illinois

ANATOL RAPOPORT
Professor, Mathematical Biology, Mental Health Research Institute
University of Michigan
Ann Arbor, Michigan

WILLIAM J. SCHULL
Associate Professor, Department of Human Genetics
University of Michigan Medical School
Ann Arbor, Michigan

ELIZABETH L. SCOTT*
Associate Professor, Statistical Laboratory,
University of California
Berkeley, California

---

* Co-author. The paper was presented by the other author listed. See Table of Contents.

NORBERT WIENER
Professor Emeritus, Department of Mathematics,
Massachusetts Institute of Technology
Cambridge, Massachusetts

SEWALL WRIGHT
Professor Emeritus, Department of Genetics,
University of Wisconsin
Madison, Wisconsin

FOREWORD

This volume is the outgrowth of a symposium that was conducted by the Mathematics Research Center, U. S. Army, at the University of Wisconsin, June 12-14, 1963. The purpose of the symposium was the presentation and discussion of results in a field of increasing interest and importance--stochastic models in medicine and biology. The wide scope of this field is evident from the many types of stochastic models which have been conceived and developed for various applications. The present volume includes all the papers that were presented, and, in addition, one paper, that by Professor J. Neyman, which was invited but not presented because of unforeseen and unavoidable circumstances that prevented him from attending.

The symposium was opened on the morning of June 12 with welcoming addresses by Professor R. A. Alberty, Dean of the Graduate School and on behalf of the Mathematics Research Center by Professor R. E. Langer, Director. Opening remarks were made by Professor John Gurland, program chairman. The lectures were presented in the auditorium of the Wisconsin Center on the University campus. They were about forty-five minutes in length and each was followed by a discussion period of about fifteen minutes.

The chairmen of the respective morning and afternoon sessions were:

Dr. A. R. Curreri, Professor of Surgery, School of Medicine, University of Wisconsin.

Dr. J. Berkson, Chief, Section of Biometry and Medical Statistics, Mayo Clinic.

Dr. G. E. P. Box, Professor and Chairman, Department of Statistics, University of Wisconsin.

Dr. J. F. Crow, Professor of Medical Genetics and Acting Dean, School of Medicine, University of Wisconsin.

Dr. W. J. Dixon, Professor Biostatistics, Department of Preventive Medicine, University of California.

Dr. D. B. Delury, Professor and Chairman, Department of Mathematics, University of Toronto.

The second session of the first day was adjourned in mid afternoon to permit attendance at a specially arranged picnic at Picnic Point on the beautiful shores of Lake Mendota. The weather (also specially arranged) during the picnic and also during most of the symposium was extremely pleasant.

The papers are arranged in the order in which they appeared on the printed program despite some minor deviations from the order in the actual presentation. Through the kind co-operation of the speakers and of the persons who raised questions during the discussion period it has been possible to include a record of the discussions. Due to the limited time for discussion some questions were submitted later in writing which the speakers graciously consented to answering.

Sincere thanks are extended to Professor Langer for his extremely helpful guidance and direction, and to the speakers, chairmen, discussants, attendants for their pleasant co-operation which was so instrumental in making this symposium a great success. The persevering efforts and extensive co-operation provided by the clerical staff of the Mathematics Research Center is also deeply appreciated.

John Gurland

PREFACE

An important and fundamental aspect of physical science consists in the formulation and development of models in man's attempt to understand the universe in which he finds himself. It also characterizes his attempts to understand man himself, society, and the whole interrelated complex of biology, sociology, and medical science. One can hardly imagine any scientific subject which does not depend on some sort of model to aid man in grappling with the vast array of problems thrust before him and in gaining some insight into the important, essential underlying relations.

The success of a model depends heavily on whether the factors which the scientist regards as important and which he has included in the model are actually relevant and essential. This will, of course, be reflected in how close the conclusions based on the model are in accordance with observation. A great improvement has been accomplished in many applications as a result of models in which are incorporated a stochastic mechanism of one sort or another. In such a model, for example, the knowledge of a system being in a certain state at one specific time does not determine uniquely its state at others but merely the probability of possible states at other times.

Through their realistic assessment of the important role of chance and the resulting increase of flexibility, stochastic models provide a tremendous potential for successful applications in medicine and biology. The topics presented at this symposium in their diverse nature are but a few examples of the wide scope of scientific problems which may be effectively studied through the use of stochastic models. It is hoped this volume of papers will stimulate an even greater interest in this timely subject and lead to fruitful applications and developments of the ideas presented.

John Gurland

Madison, Wisconsin, 1963

CONTENTS

STOCHASTIC MODELS IN MEDICINE AND BIOLOGY

NIELS ARLEY

Applications of Stochastic Models for the Analysis of the Mechanisms of Carcinogenesis

Introduction

I wish to start with some general remarks to elucidate the subject of this symposium: in what way can quantitative mathematical considerations help us to a deeper insight in Nature's structure and functioning. In our time of rapid technological progress and social change I think it is first of all well to keep in mind constantly the modest remarks about our basic knowledge of Nature which Einstein made to his friend M. v. Laue a few months before he died:

"Wenn ich in den Grübeleien eines langen Lebens etwas gelernt habe, so ist es dies, dass wir von einer tiefen Einsicht in die elementaren Vorgänge viel weiter entfernt sind, als die meisten Zeitgenossen glauben" [1].

("If I have learned something from the speculations of a long life, then it is that we are a much longer distance away from a deep insight in the elementary processes of Nature than most of the colleagues of our time believe").

Actually all those basic problems in physics mentioned by Einstein in 1938 as unsolved [2], are still as unsolved today as they were 25 years ago. It is also a conspicuous fact that we do not yet know the basic causes of such elementary biological phenomena as every individual of Man has observed throughout 100,000's of years and still observes today: why we are all going to die, why the growth of every child stops at maturity, why we all need sleep every day.

It is, therefore, no wonder that we still know so little about the basic biological problems of both normal and pathological cells, such as why cells divide, why cells differentiate into various tissues, and why some cells develop into the abnormal cells we call tumor or neoplastic cells. Consequently, it is not surprising that in spite of the fact that such vast sums of money, of man-power, and of study has been devoted to cancer research during the last half century or so, that sometimes it is jokingly said that now more people live on cancer than die of cancer, even today we still really do not know what cancer is, nor what distinguishes a normal cell from a tumor cell.

At my institute we have recently tried to give a comprehensive review of what we know, of what we do not know, and of what experimental and theoretical methods of investigation we may today hope to be most fruitful for extending our knowledge about these basic biological problems [3]. I shall here give you a very short report of this paper, referring you to the paper itself for more details, both experimental and theoretical, and for an extensive bibliography which we hope contains practically all the essential papers in this field of the worlds literature, including Soviet literature.

Now the research of the last decade or so has made it more and more probable that the reason why it has turned out to be so difficult to fill all the gaps in our biological knowledge discussed at length in our paper is that all the basic cell processes, both those of normal cells and those of tumor cells, take place at a submicroscopic level, and, more specifically, between and within single biologically important macromolecules called DNA, RNA, and protein molecules. However, only recently it has been possible to begin developing the experimental techniques necessary for attacking somatic cell problems at the molecular level. Before such direct experimental attacks become possible, the finer details can only be studied by applying theoretical analyses. In this connection it is interesting to note that a similar situation is met with in another frontier field of research, viz. cosmology where theoretical studies have to be used in the exploration of regions of the universe which are at present unattainable for direct observation even with the strongest telescopes, but which nevertheless make their effects felt indirectly here on the earth, e.g. in such phenomena as inertia and the darkness of the night sky [4]. So at both ends of our knowledge of the universe, in the infinitely small world of the atoms as well as in the infinitely large world of the galaxies, theory is the vanguard which gives us guides for the later experimental exploration. For a theoretician this is really a very pleasant situation and it may give rise to much philosophical speculation, how it comes about that the human brain is constructed by Nature in such a marvellous way that by pure thinking we seem to be able to learn something about Nature itself [5]. Incidentally, it is worth mentioning that our understanding of the processes of the infinitely small world of the atoms seems to be intimately connected with our understanding of the infinitely large world of the galaxies, as you will find discussed e.g. in the fascinating book of Dr. Sciama just quoted [4].

Before showing you the detailed results of theoretical studies of the mechanisms of how tumors arise, or carcinogenesis, I wish to give you an impression of the experimental background for the assumptions underlying such theoretical studies.

Experimental studies of the role of chromosomes

It is now generally thought that the genetical experiments of the last decade or so show beyond doubt that both for normal and for pathological cells most of the genetical information carried by both sex cells and somatic cells is contained in the sequence of certain atomic groups called bases of the macromolecules we call DNA molecules located in the chromosomes and now thought to be the genes of genetics. It turns out that hereby the two most important and previously distinct theories of carcinogenesis, viz. the so-called somatic mutation theory and the virus theory, are both reduced to one and the same problem, viz. that of the control of cellular development and differentiation by the DNA and the so-called messenger RNA molecules which latter carry the genetic information of the former out to certain particles called ribosomes in the cytoplasm where protein synthesis takes place. Furthermore, recent biochemical results on certain diseases, the so-called sickle-cell anemia and hemoglobin C disease, makes it probable that many other diseases, both somatic and psychic, and especially both benign and malignant tumors, may have an etiology similar to that of sickle-cell anemia and hemoglobin C disease, viz. to be due to a specific atomic deletion, substitution, or rearrangement in the so-called nucleotides in specific DNA molecules, and to consist of a specific atomic deletion, substitution, or rearrangement in specific protein molecules.

I think it is of great interest to mention that both these and other basic biological phenomena such as ageing and death of all living organisms may be the results of one and the same typical quantum mechanical phenomenon, the so-called tunnel effect whereby particles, here the protons in the so-called hydrogen bonds between the pairing bases within the DNA molecules, may pass through potential energy barriers which are in classical physics impenetrable [6].

However, sofar we have not developed experimental methods for directly observing such and other atomic changes within the DNA molecules, but it seems natural to expect changes on the molecular level in the DNA molecules to give rise to observable changes already on the next level, viz. that of the chromosomes which carry the DNA molecules, although there is reason to assume that what can be seen in the microscope is just a fraction of the changes really occurring on the molecular level within the DNA molecules.

Up to about 1950 observations of the number and structure of single chromosomes in cells of mammals including Man were hardly technically feasible, but during the last decade such detailed observations have been made possible by new cytological techniques developed in Levan's laboratory in Lund, Sweden, and elsewhere [7, 8, 12]. In 1956 one obtained for the first time a clear picture of the chromosomes of Man. To give you some idea of the results of the

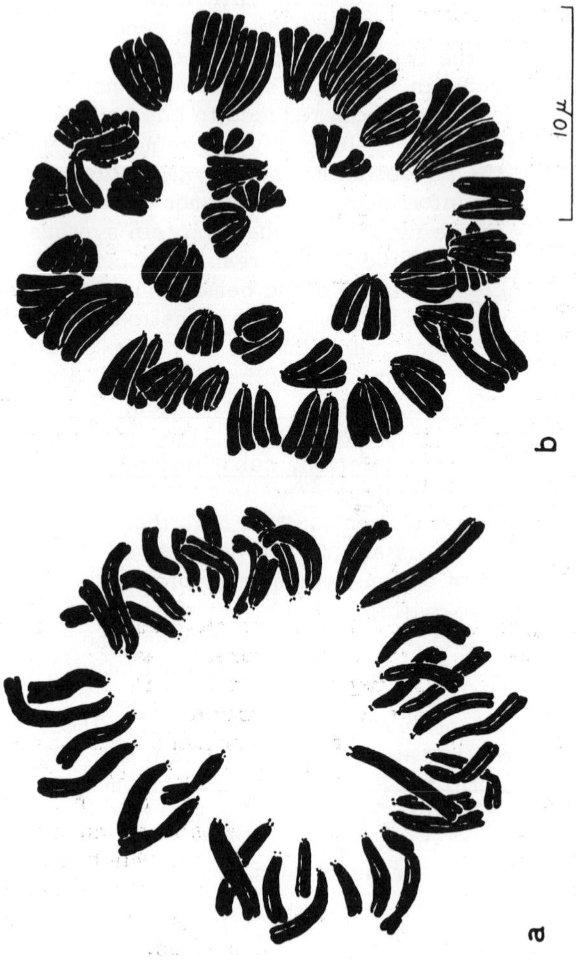

Figure 1. (Levan [12] figure 5).

Normal (a) and endoreduplicated (b) mitosis of a mouse ascites tumor (the TA_3 carcinoma).

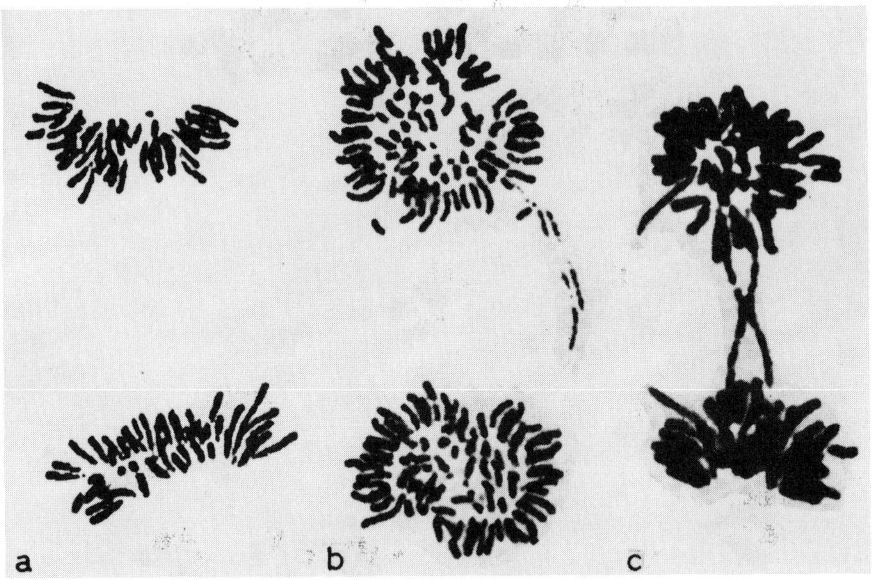

Figure 2. (Levan [12] figure 6).

Normal anaphase (a), and anaphases with structural rearrangements (b and c) of a mouse ascites tumor (the EL carcinoma).

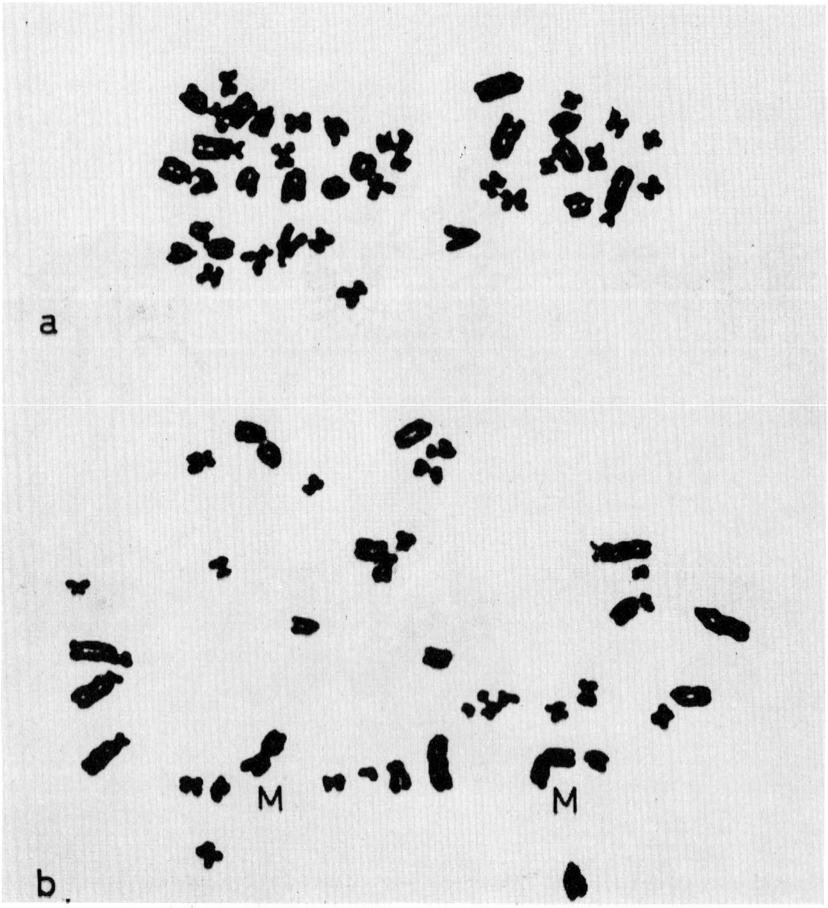

Figure 3. (Levan [12] figure 7).

The karyotype of normal rat tissue (a), and of the stemline of the Yoshida rat sarcoma (b). The latter deviates from the normal karyotype in chromosome number, 40 instead of 42 and in many structural rearrangements, the most striking of which are the two big metacentrics, marked M in the figure.

studies of the role of chromosomes in cancer research I show you in figures 1-3 three microphotographs obtained by Levan, Tjio, and co-workers comparing the chromosome pattern, the socalled karyotype, of normal cells with that of tumor cells in mice and rats. You will see here that in certain cases the differences are obvious even to non-experts, but that in other cases the differences are so minute that they can be noticed only by specially experienced experts. Recently Levan has also observed similar chromosomal changes in early tumors induced by viruses, viz. by Rous sarcoma virus in rats. In figures 4-6 I show you three graphs prepared by Levan showing the frequency distribution of the number of chromosomes in normal cells of man, rat, and mouse, in ascitestumors of mice, and in virus-induced tumors in mice. Taking into account Levan's quoted recent findings the chromosome studies seem to show beyond doubt that:

(a) cells of normal tissues of a given species have very uniform karyotypes characteristic for the given species,
(b) populations of tumor cells consist of a continuously and randomly changing genetic mosaics of cell clones with different karyotypes being in a dynamic equilibrium, which changes mostly so that the cells tend towards increased autonomy,
(c) every change in the interior or exterior environment initiates selective displacements of the equilibrium between the different karyotypes in such a way that the tumor cell population as a whole adapts itself to the new environment in a way resembling the adaptation by natural selection of the natural species in evolution.

Thus, on the one hand, random genotype variation seems to be a prerequisite for cells to attain adaptation to permanent growth, and, on the other hand, ageing and death seem to be the price that cells have to pay for keeping their genotype and their natural genetical balance system intact. This is analogous to the fact that individual organisms and species with constant genotypes all have to age and die, whereas the whole living kingdom has attained adaptation to permanent growth by the gradual random genotype variation of natural evolution. There seems to be a limit both in cells and in whole organisms and species to the capacity of keeping up the required balance system within the frame of a fixed amount of genetic information constituting a genotype. As mentioned above these facts may be the necessary macroscopic results of the quantum mechanical tunnel effect due to which there is always built into any DNA molecule a non-vanishing error probability so that its content of genetic information cannot keep constant indefinitely, but must necessarily undergo changes with certain small but non-vanishing probabilities in the course of time [6].

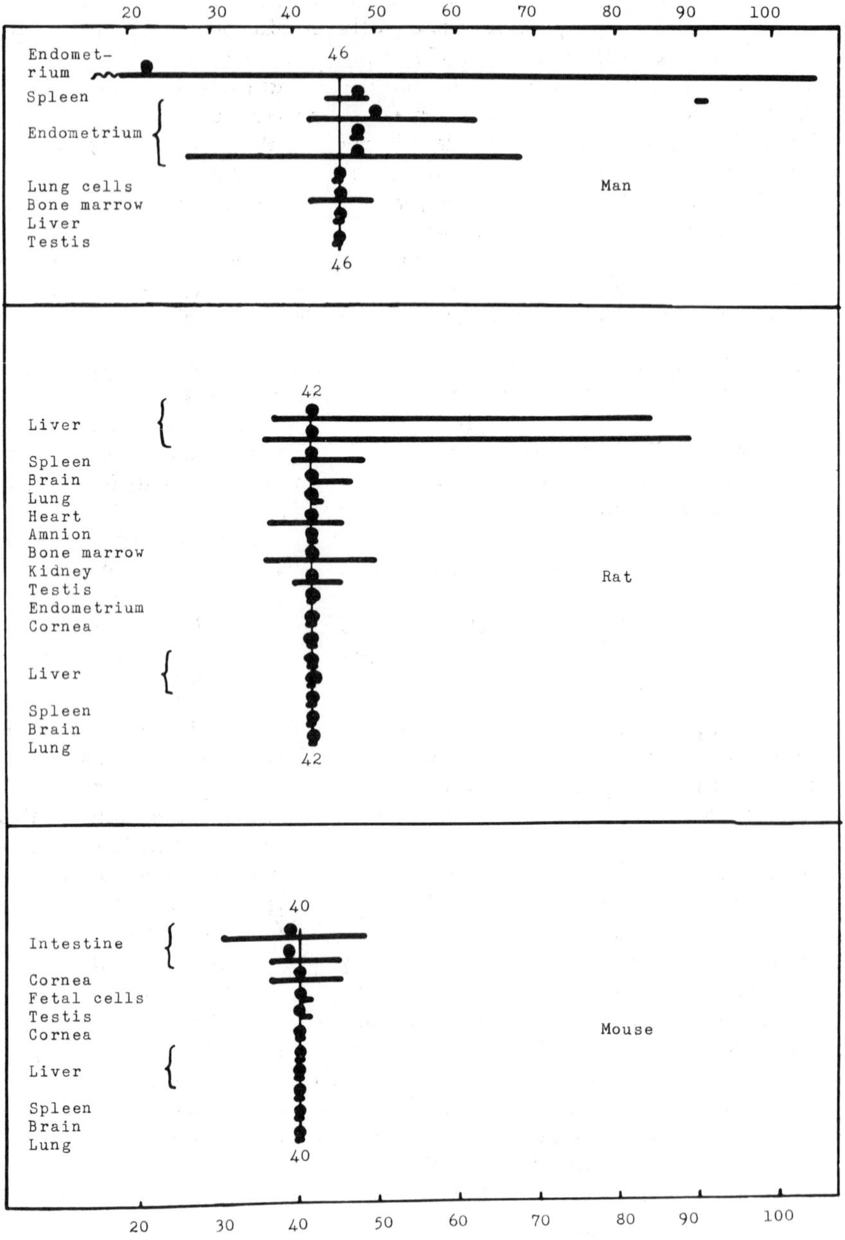

Figure 4. (Levan [12] figure 2).

Chromosome numbers of mammalian normal tissues.

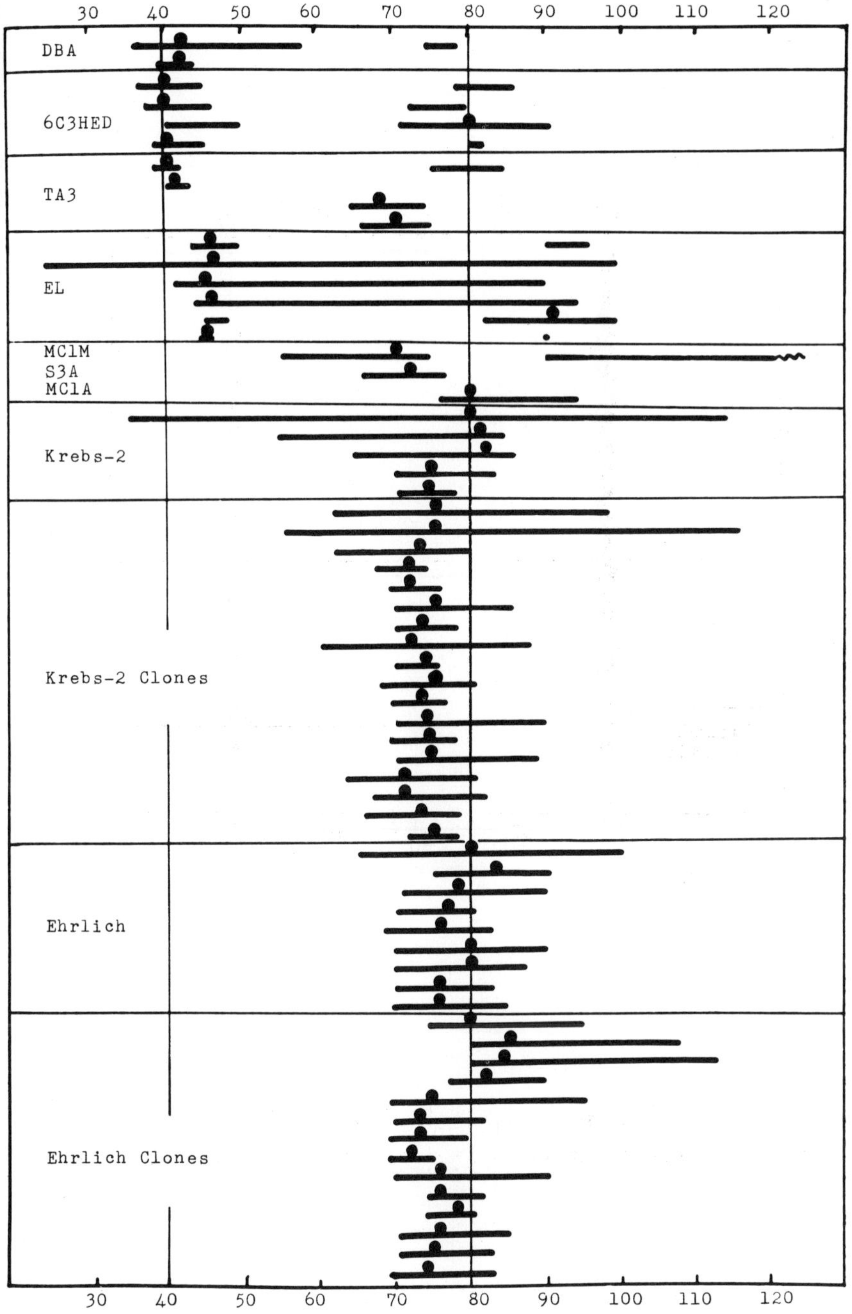

Figure 5. (Levan [12] figure 3).

Chromosome numbers of mouse ascites tumors.

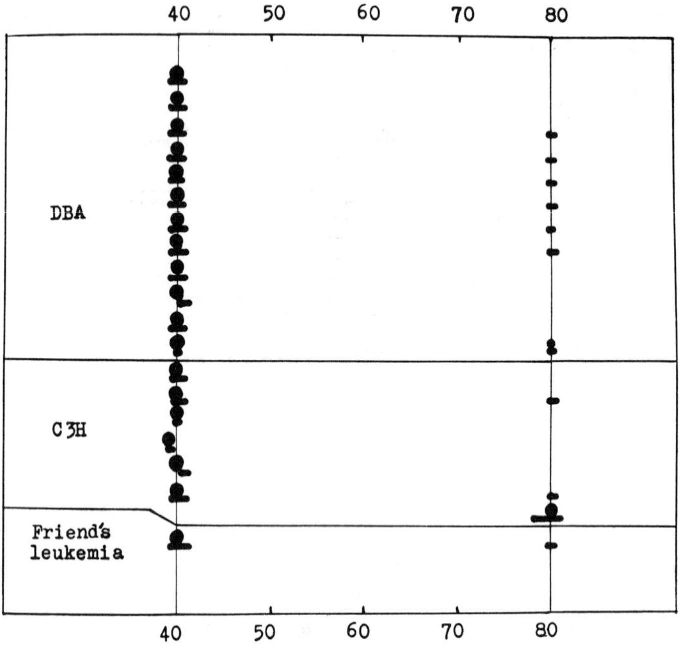

Figure 6. (Levan [12] figure 10).

Chromosome numbers of virus-induced primary tumors of the mouse.

Experimental studies of tumor growth

The second type of experiments I wish to mention, is some observations of tumor growth in vivo as function of time made by means of a casting technique on living animals developed by Andreasen and Mrs. Borum at the Fibiger Laboratory in Copenhagen, Denmark [9,10]. In figures 7-9 I show you some of the casts made by Andreasen and Borum, and in figure 10 I show you the quantitative growth curves of the tumors shown in figure 9. As you will see from both the cast pictures and the growth curves also the growth of tumors, once they have been initiated, is a highly random phenomenon showing great fluctuations as would be expected from the chromosome findings just mentioned, viz. that a population of tumor cells is a continuously and randomly changing genetic mosaic of cell clones with different karyotypes. As you see, the figures actually show that a tumor may at any time make a transition from one morphological type into quite another one by incessant minor changes and by growth and regression, being sometimes gradual, but more often abrupt. Also for other types of tumors the growth seems to be of a similar complicated multistage type, being formed by continued random genotype variation, adaptation, and selection.

Furthermore it seems that, once a tumor has been initiated, either experimentally by internal or external carcinogenic agents or spontaneously, the growth rate, morphology, and other observable characteristics of any tumor are independent both of the nature and the quantity of the applied carcinogenic agent, and of the time of occurrence, being also the same for induced and for spontaneous tumors.

The initiation of spontaneous tumors may, like genetical mutations, be the results of the quantum mechanical tunnel effect mentioned above whereby a DNA molecule goes over into an isomeric molecule in which certain of the protons in the hydrogen-bonds between the bases have changed places [6]. In the experimentally induced tumors it is possible that the formation by the carcinogenic agents of these same isomeric forms of the DNA molecules also form the primary step in the transition of normal cells to tumor cells. However that may be, it seems that the problem of how tumors arise reduces to the question of the finer details of certain molecular processes regarding DNA, RNA, and protein molecules, which processes are governed by the stochastic laws of quantum theory.

Theoretical studies of carcinogenesis

The main problem is, consequently, to make from our present physico-chemical knowledge of basic atomic and molecular processes as realistic assumptions as possible of how the primary random change occurs when a normal cell turns into a tumor cell. Next, to work out from these assumptions as detailed quantitative predictions as

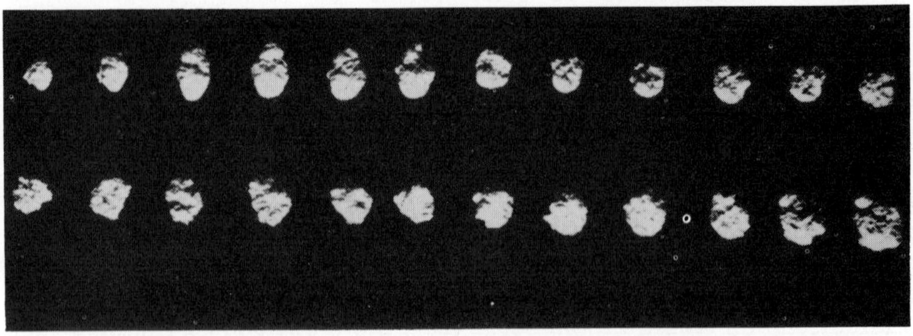

Casts of a skin papilloma, made twice weekly, showing the development of the tumour through 12 weeks.

Figure 7. (Andreasen and Borum [9] figure 1).

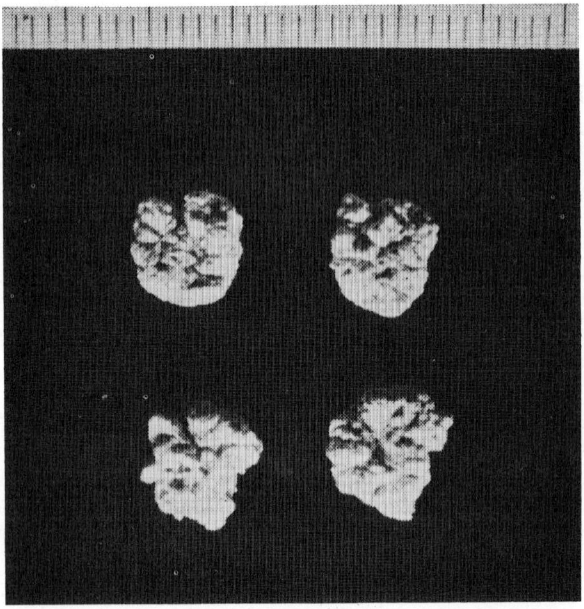

Hand lens magnification of casts Nos. 11-14 from figure 7 illustrating minute changes of the tumour during two weeks.

Figure 8. (Andreasen and Borum [9] figure 2).

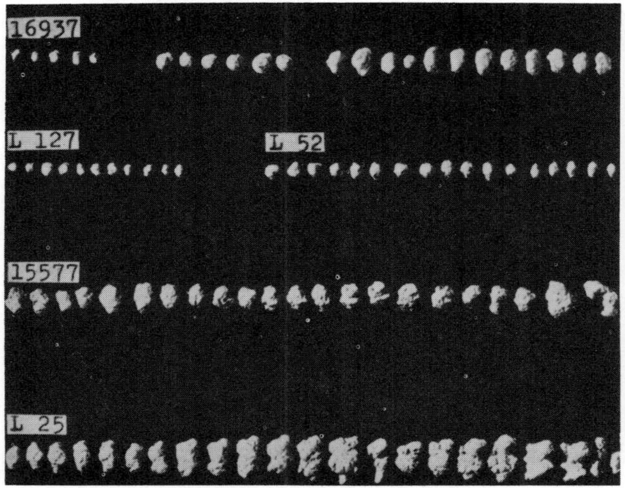

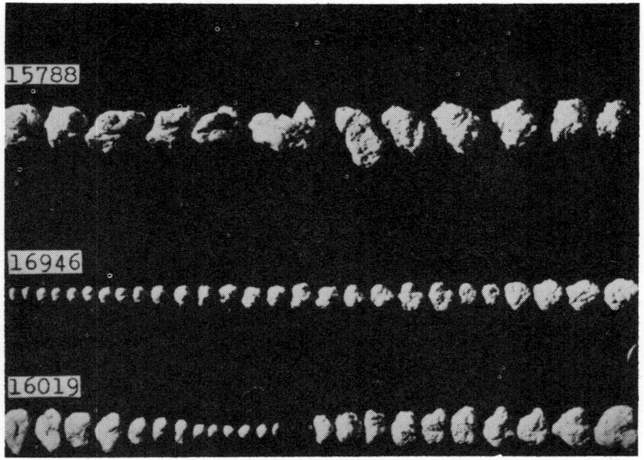

Series of casts illustrating the development of the papillomas on eight mice. A number of casts were omitted for lack of space, the illustration showing only representative casts, selected at fairly uniform intervals within each series: 16937: A predominantly plate-shaped papilloma. L. 127: A pinhead-shaped papilloma. L. 52: A bun-shaped papilloma with smooth surface. 15577: A bun-shaped papilloma with rough surface. L. 25: A lobular papilloma. 15788: A horny papilloma. 16946: Papilloma passing through the following stages in the course of its development: Pinhead-shaped to smooth bun-shaped to horny to lobular to bun-shaped with rough surface. 16019: Papilloma passing the following stages: Plate-shape to bun-shaped with smooth surface to bun-shaped with rough surface.

Figure 9. (Borum [10] plate 1.

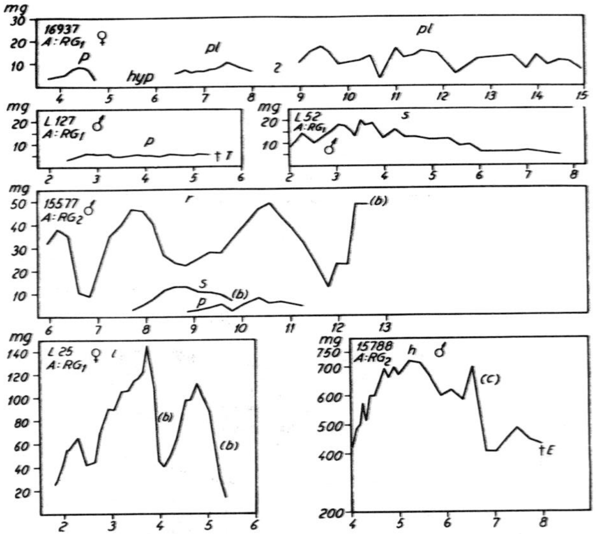

Growth curves of the papillomas shown in Plate I. Abscissa: Age of mouse in months. Ordinate: Volume of papilloma in arbitrary units, in this study in terms of the weight of the papilloma cast in mg. (Since the specific gravity of the cement material was constant throughout the experiment (3.1 g/cu cm), the actual volume of the papilloma in cubic cm may be found by dividing the cast weight by a factor 3100).

16937: Growth curve of a predominantly plate-shaped papilloma.
L. 127: Growth curve of a pinhead-shaped papilloma.
L. 52: Growth curve of a bun-shaped papilloma with smooth surface.
15577: Growth curve of a bun-shaped papilloma with rough surface.
L. 25: Growth curve of a lobular papilloma.
15788: Growth curve of a horny papilloma.
16946: Growth curve of a papilloma passing through the stages: pinhead-shaped, bun-shaped with smooth surface, horny, lobular, to bun-shaped with rough surface.
16019: Growth curve of a papilloma passing through the stages: plate-shaped, bun-shaped with smooth surface, and bun-shaped with rough surface.

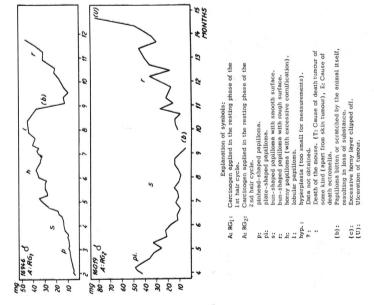

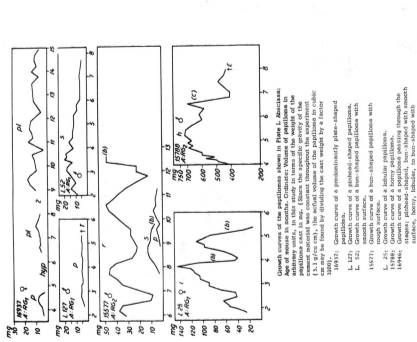

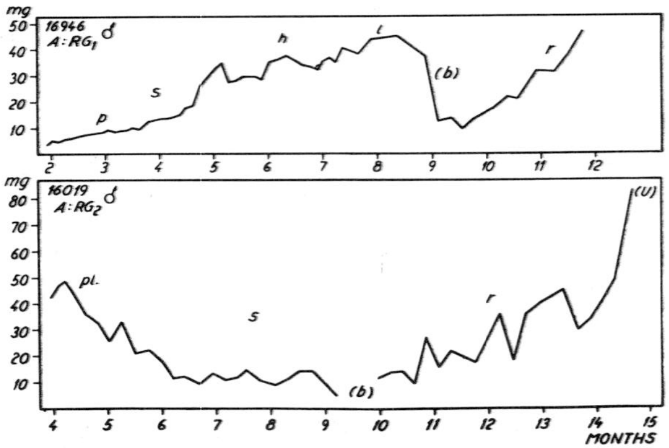

Explanation of symbols:

A: RG_1: Carcinogen applied in the resting phase of the 1st hair cycle.
A: RG_2: Carcinogen applied in the resting phase of the 2nd hair cycle.
p: pinhead-shaped papilloma.
pl: plate-shaped papilloma.
s: bun-shaped papilloma with smooth surface.
r: bun-shaped papilloma with rough surface.
h: horny papilloma (with excessive cornification).
l: lobular papilloma.
hyp.: hyperplasia (too small for measurements).
?: Data not obtained.
†: Death of the mouse. (T: Cause of death tumour of some kind (apart from skin tumour), E: Cause of death ectromelia.
(b): Papilloma bitten or scratched by the animal itself, resulting in loss of substance.
(c): Excessive horny layer clipped off.
(U): Ulceration of tumour.

Figure 10. (Borum [10] plate 2).

possible about all the results of a quantitative nature which may with present techniques be obtained experimentally. It should hereby be stressed that the purpose of any theoretical studies in natural science, be it in physics, biology, cosmology or other fields, is to obtain new knowledge about Nature, in the ideal case by narrowing down the possibilities to just those which are actually realized in Nature. Consequently, only such models fulfill their purpose which allow the deduction of quantitative predictions about all experimentally measurable quantities.

Now, in studies of carcinogenesis, as in most other fields of research, models may be constructed in various ways depending on which basic assumptions we start from. As discussed above, it is with present experimental techniques beyond our powers to check these assumptions in direct experimentation. The best procedure is, therefore, to investigate how the phenomenon might have been formed from each set of assumptions. If one set of results looks more like the real phenomenon than another set we shall probably have discovered not only how the phenomenon is actually formed, but also which basic assumptions are correct.

In the case of carcinogenesis a closer analysis shows that there exists four and only four possibilities for the construction of models, as will be understood from figure 11. I have here illustrated the sequence of events now thought to take place in the experimental induction of tumors by ionizing radiation, but the same picture applies to

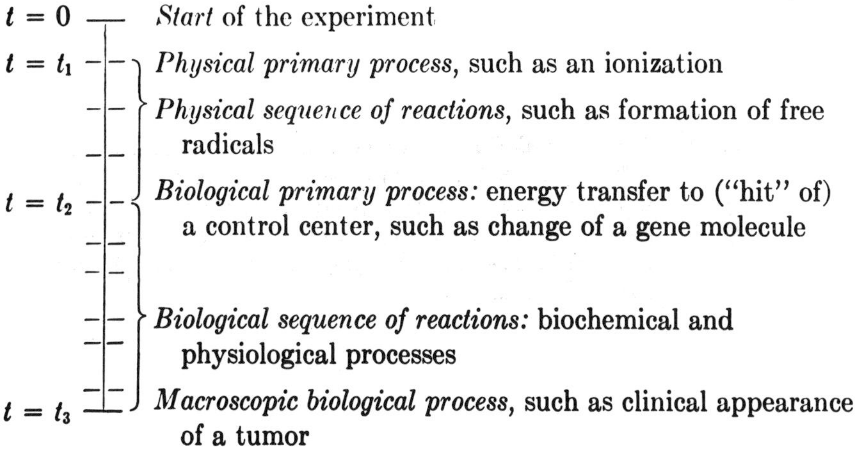

Figure 11. The sequence of events in carcinogenesis. (Arley and Eker [3] figure 1).

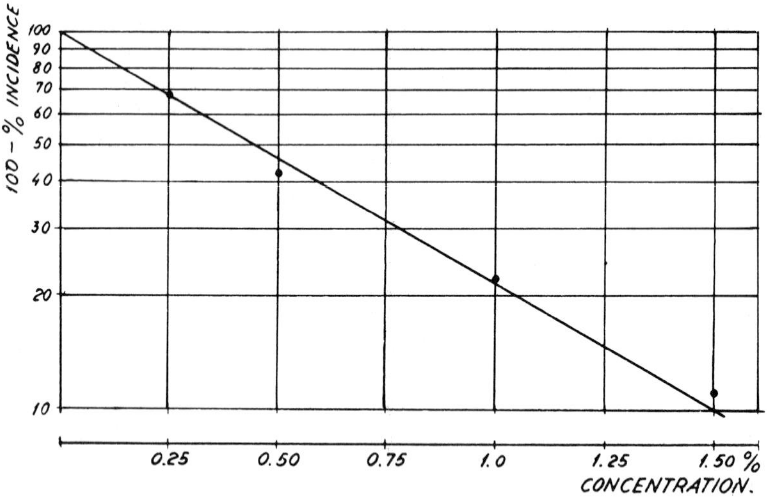

Figure 12. Theoretical final relative incidence F plotted as 100−F% on a logarithmic scale versus the applied concentration of a chemical carcinogen. Experimental points from Engelbreth-Holm and Iversen 1951 for DMBA painted once on mice. (Arley and Eker [3] figure 2).

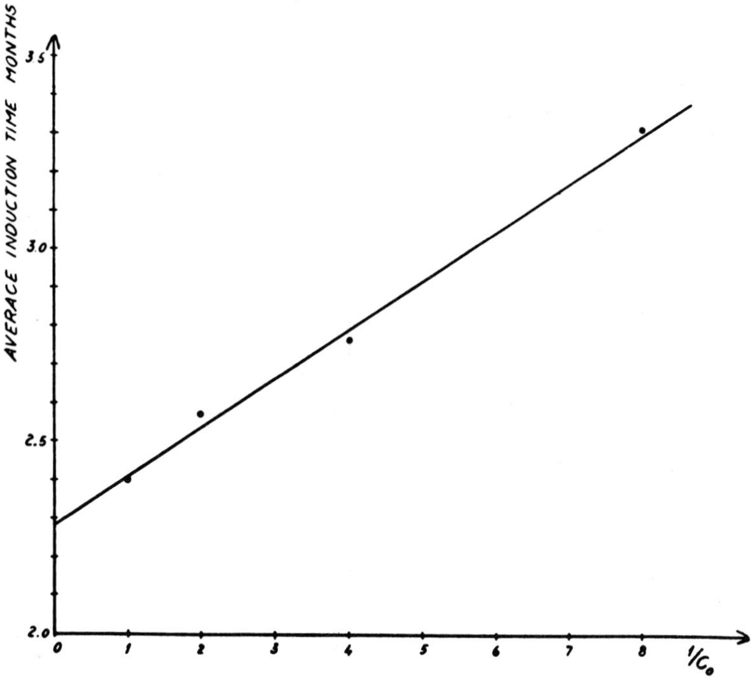

Figure 13. Theoretical average induction time plotted versus the reciprocal of the applied concentration of a chemical carcinogen. Experimental points from Bryan and Shimkin 1941 for MC injected once subcutaneously to mice. (Arley and Eker [3] figure 3).

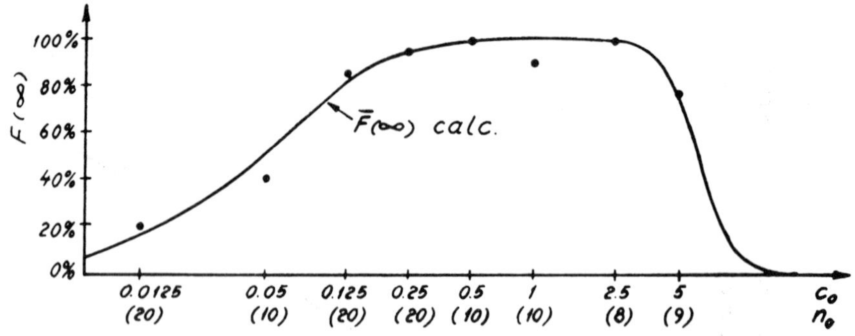

Figure 14. Theoretical final relative incidence plotted versus the logarithm of the applied concentration of a chemical carcinogen. Experimental points from Lettinga 1937 for DBA injected once subcutaneously to mice. (Arley and Eker [3] figure 4).

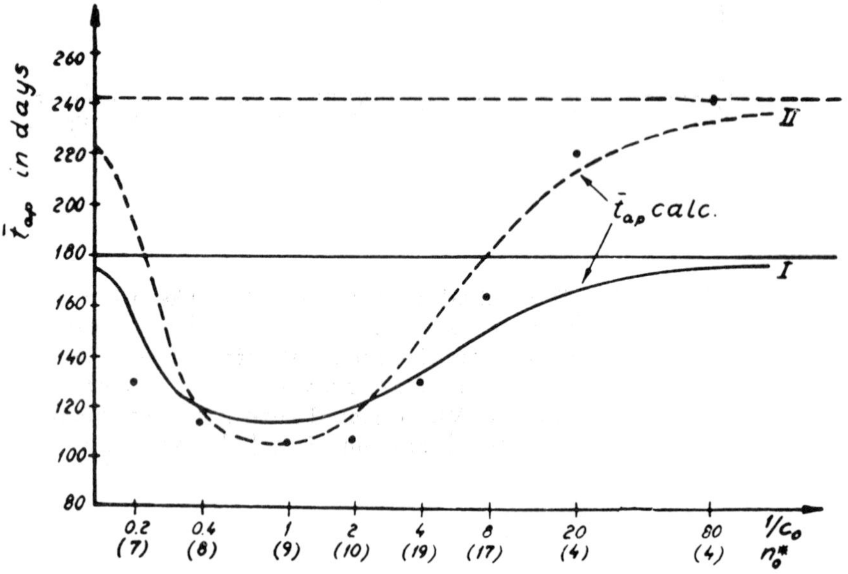

Figure 15. Theoretical average induction time plotted versus the logarithm of the reciprocal of the applied concentration of a chemical carcinogen. Experimental points from Lettinga 1937 for DBA injected once subcutaneously to mice. (Arley and Eker [3] figure 5).

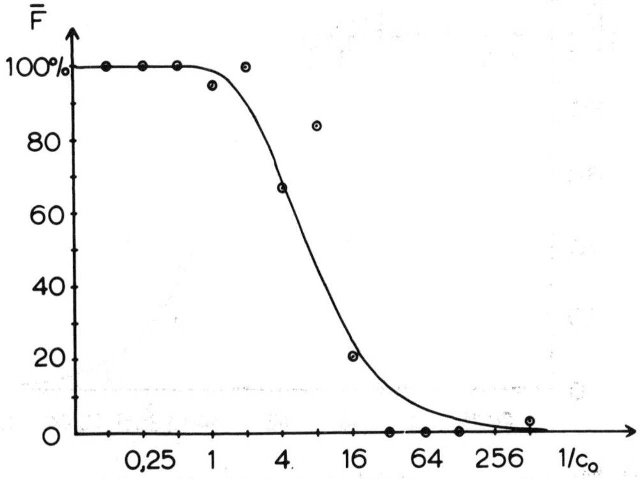

Figure 16. Theoretical final relative incidence plotted versus the logarithm of the reciprocal of the applied concentration of a chemical carcinogen. Experimental points from Bryan and Shimkin 1943 for BP injected once subcutaneously to mice. (Arley and Eker [3] figure 6).

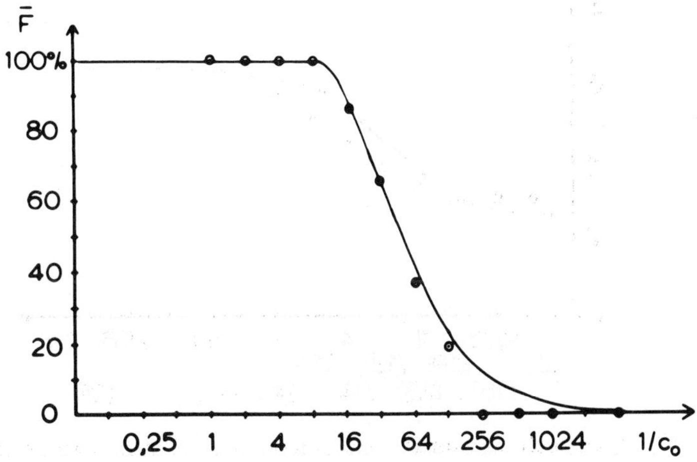

Figure 17. Theoretical final relative incidence as in figure 16 but for MC. (Arley and Eker [3] figure 7).

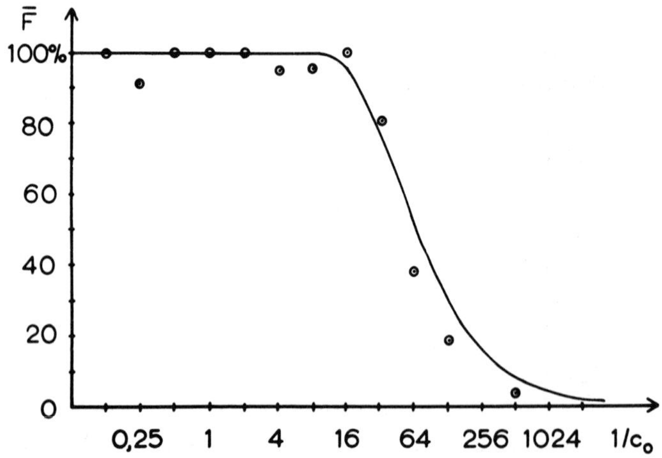

Figure 18. Theoretical final relative incidence as in figure 16 but for DBA. (Arley and Eker [3] figure 8).

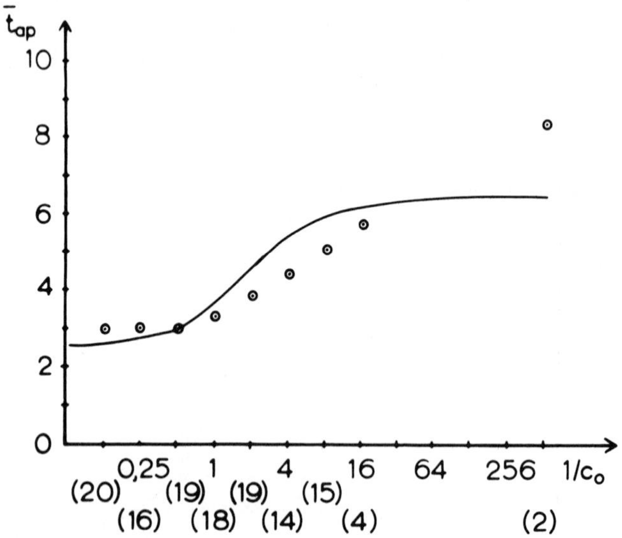

Figure 19. Theoretical average induction time plotted versus the logarithm of the applied concentration of a chemical carcinogen. Experimental points from Bryan and Shimkin 1943 for BP injected once subcutaneously to mice. (Arley and Eker [3] figure 9).

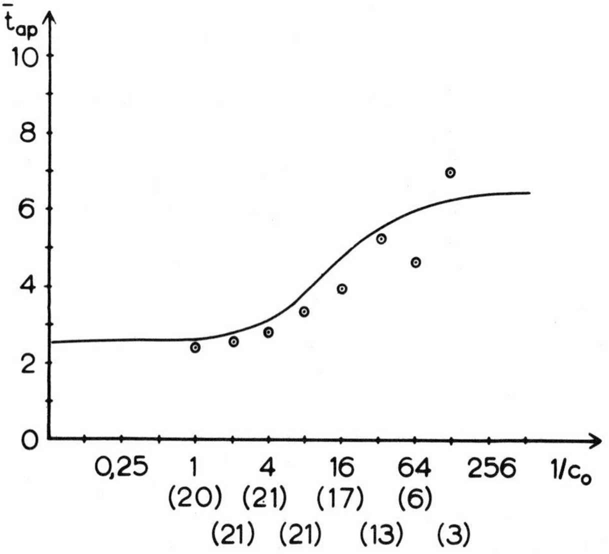

Figure 20. Theoretical average induction time as in figure 19 but for MC . (Arley and Eker [3] figure 10).

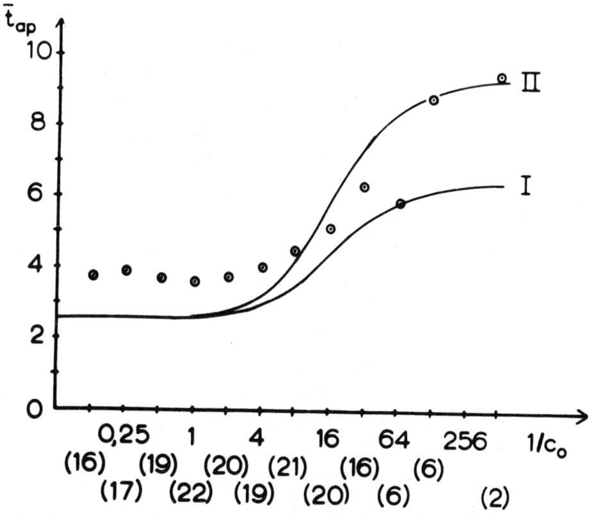

Figure 21. Theoretical average induction time as in figure 19 but for DBA . (Arley and Eker [3] figure 11).

all other types of tumor induction. For those who know the terminolog used, the figure speaks for itself, and those who do not may refer to the detailed explanation given in an extensive paper I am reporting [3]. In any case you will see that we have the two possibilities for the two time instants denoted t_1 and t_2 in the figure, that either $t_1 = t_2$ or $t_1 < t_2$. In the former case we speak of a direct mechanism, in the latter of an indirect mechanism. Also you will see that we have the two possibilities that either one transfer of energy from the carcinogenic agent to a suitable macromolecule, a socalled "hit", is able -- but need not necessarily be sufficient -- to induce neoplasia, or more than one "hit" is required. In the former case we speak of a one-hit mechanism, in the latter of a multi-hit mechanism.

By combination we thus get exactly four possibilities, viz.
(1) a direct one-hit type mechanism,
(2) an indirect one-hit type mechanism,
(3) a direct multi-hit type mechanism,
(4) an indirect multi-hit type mechanism of carcinogenesis.

In my institute's paper which I am reporting here [3] you will find, I hope, a complete description of all work found in the world literature of such models and their comparison with present experimental knowledge. In case we should have overlooked any such work we shall be most happy if you will kindly inform us of any further work.

Without going into details you may easily guess that mathematically by far the simplest of the four possibilities mentioned is the first one, the direct one-hit mechanism. I shall now show you the quantitative deductions from this type of model and their comparison with experiments. It must, of course, here be a very schematic review and again I beg to refer you to the extensive paper for all the details behind the figures 12-39. All what is necessary for you here is to note that actually in most of the figures the theoretical curves do fit the experimental points quite well. Just by looking at the figures I hope you will agree that they lead to the following conclusions:

1. A stochastic model assuming that neoplasia can be initiated by one single energy transfer directly from each carcinogenic agent to a suitable macromolecule of the somatic cells can, on the whole, give both a fair qualitative and quantitative description of all the experimental findings for chemical carcinogens, carcinogenic viruses, ultraviolet radiation, radioisotopes, and ionizing radiations.
2. In some cases the comparisons between the model and experiments indicate that also indirect energy transfers, such as via intermediary free radicals or other secondary reaction products, may play a role in carcinogenesis.
3. For radiation carcinogenesis the model leads to a single but sufficiently flexible dose-response relationship without, but in some

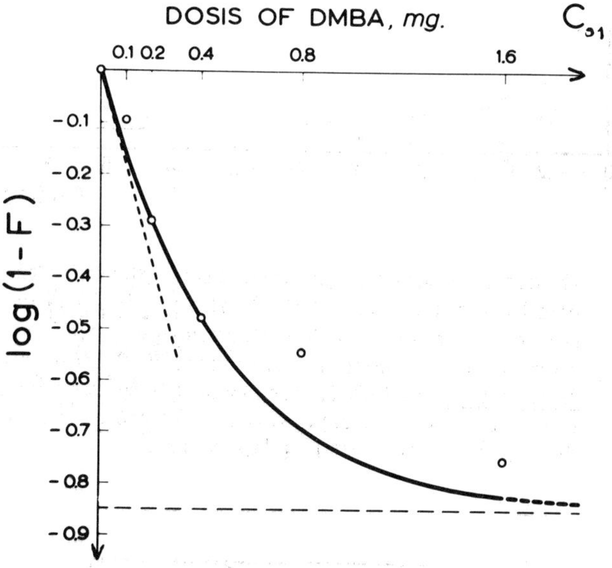

Figure 22. Theoretical final relative incidence plotted as log (1-F) versus the applied concentration of the first and for fixed concentration of the second of two successively applied chemical agents. Experimental points from Niskanen and Arley, Nature 199, 83 (1963) for DMBA given once orally to mice, followed by repeated local treatments with Tween 40. (Arley and Eker [3] figure 12).

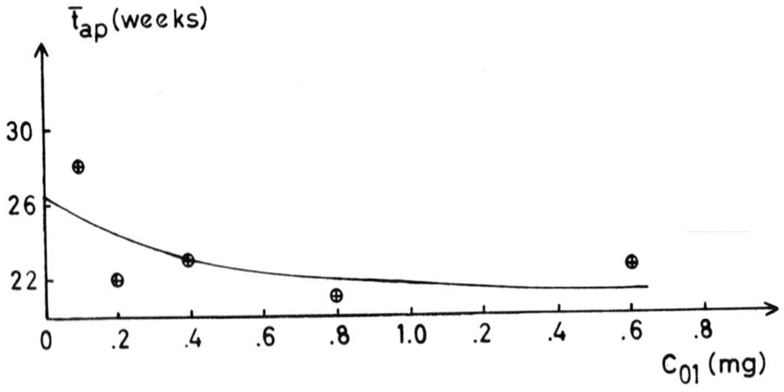

Figure 23. Theoretical average induction time plotted versus the applied concentration of the first and for fixed concentration of the second of two successively applied chemical agents. Experimental points from Niskanen and Arley Nature 199, 83 (1963) for DMBA given once orally to mice, followed by repeated local treatments with Tween 40. (Arley and Eker [3] figure 13).

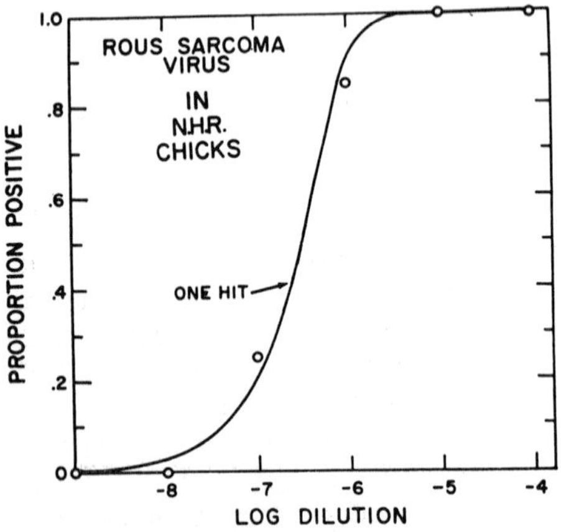

Figure 24. Theoretical final relative incidence plotted versus the logarithm of the applied concentration of a carcinogenic virus. Experimental points from Bryan 1956 for Rous sarcoma virus inoculated once to chickens. (Arley and Eker [3] figure 14).

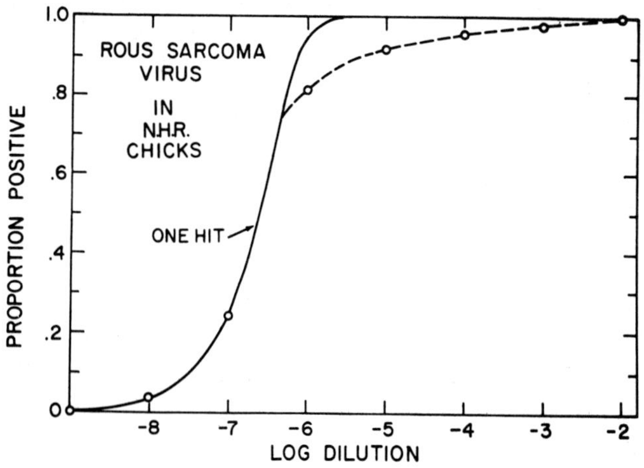

Figure 25. Theoretical final relative incidence as in figure 24 but for different chickens of the same flock. The broken line is the theoretical curve for genetically heterogeneous chickens with a two-point susceptibility distribution. (Arley and Eker [3] figure 15).

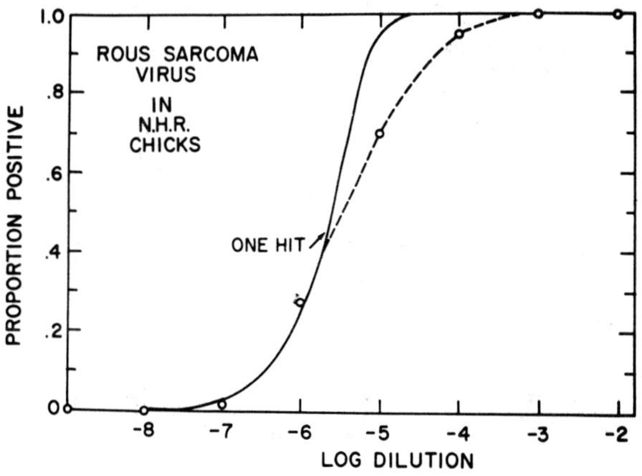

Figure 26. Theoretical final relative incidence as in figure 24 but for a different strain of the same virus (Bryan, Calnan, and Moloney 1955). Broken line as in figure 25. (Arley and Eker [3] figure 16).

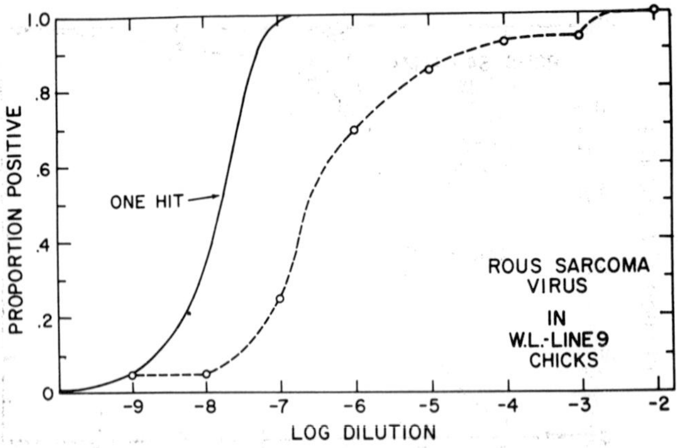

Figure 27. Theoretical final relative incidence as in figure 24 but for a different strain of chickens with a line inbred for highly increased susceptibility (Burmester, Fontes, Waters, Bryan, and Groupé 1960). Broken line as in figure 25, corresponding to a large fraction of chickens being assumed highly susceptible, a small fraction being assumed relatively resistant. (Arley and Eker [3] figure 17).

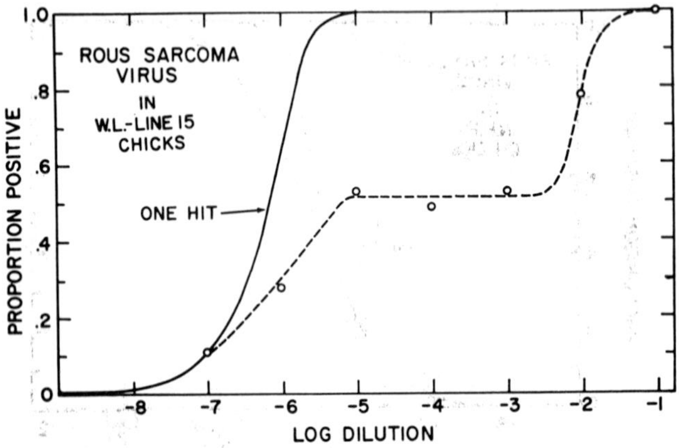

Figure 28. Theoretical final relative incidence as in figure 24, but for a different line of chickens inbred for less increased susceptibility as in figure 27 (Burmester, Fontes, Waters, Bryan, and Groupé 1960). Broken line as in figure 25, corresponding to one-half of the chickens being assumed highly susceptible, the other half being assumed relatively resistant. (Arley and Eker [3] figure 18).

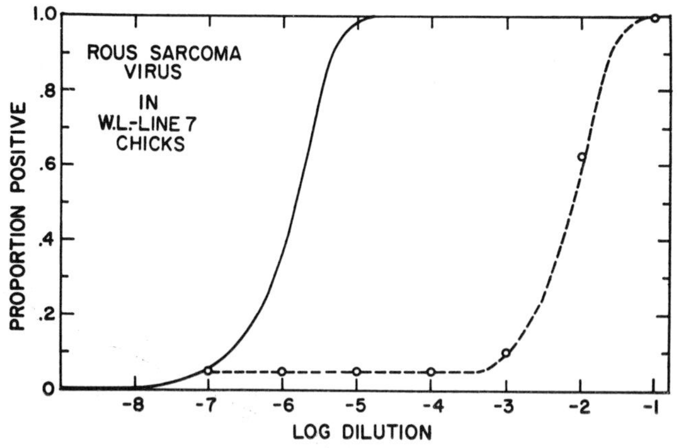

Figure 29. Theoretical final relative incidence as in figure 24, but for a different line of chickens inbred for decreased susceptibility (Burmester, Fontes, Waters, Bryan, and Groupé 1960). Broken line as in figure 25, corresponding to a large fraction of chickens being assumed relatively resistant and a small fraction being assumed highly susceptible. (Arley and Eker [3] figure 19).

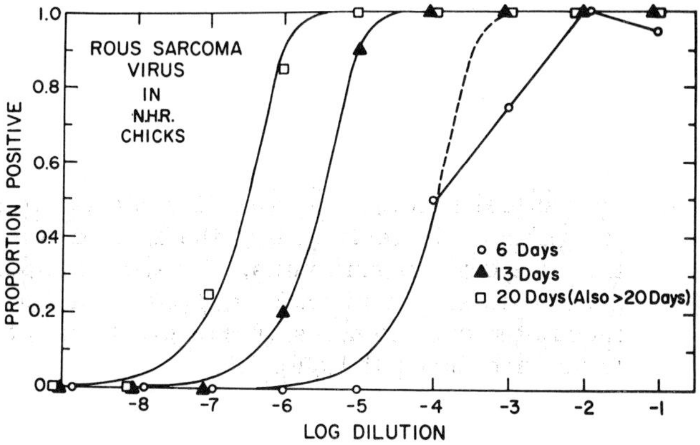

Figure 30. Theoretical relative incidences as in figure 24 but at fixed successive times from the same data as in figure 24. For the curve for 6 days the solid line above the -4 abscissa consists of just straight lines connecting the experimental points. (Arley and Eker [3] figure 20).

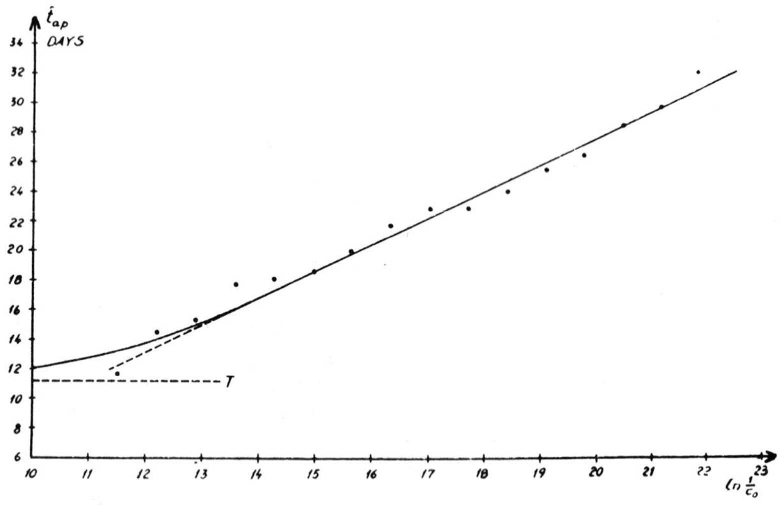

Figure 31. Theoretical average induction time plotted versus the logarithm of the reciprocal of the applied concentration of a carcinogenic virus. Experimental points from Bryan and Beard 1939 for Shope's papilloma virus inoculated once to areas of scarificed skin of rabbits. (Arley and Eker [3] figure 21).

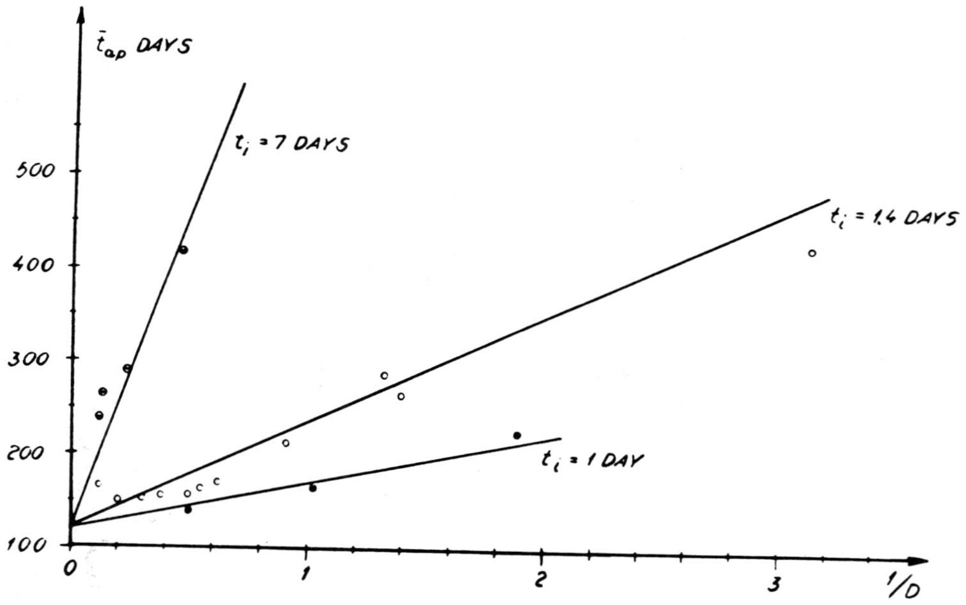

Figure 32. Theoretical average induction time plotted versus the reciprocal of the applied dose of ultraviolet radiation for various fixed values of the time interval between successive irradiations. Experimental points from Blum 1950 for mice. (Arley and Eker [3] figure 22).

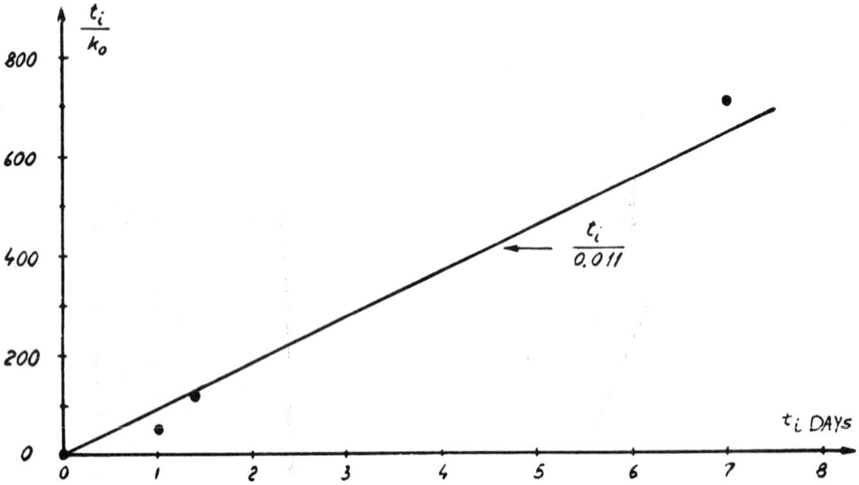

Figure 33. The slopes of the theoretical lines in figure 32 plotted versus the time interval between successive irradiations. (Arley and Eker [3] figure 23).

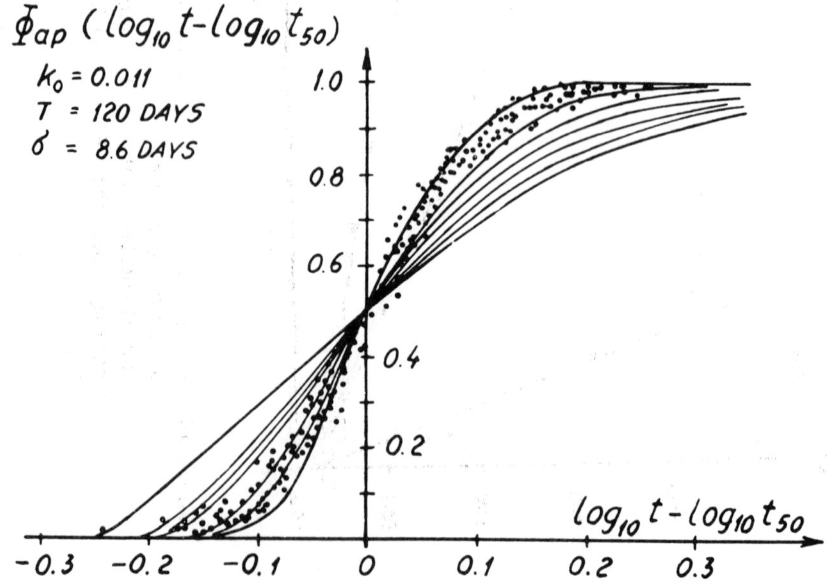

Figure 34. Theoretical relative incidences plotted versus the logarithm of the induction time for various fixed values of the dose of ultraviolet radiation and the time interval between successive irradiations. Experimental points from Blum 1950 for mice. (Arley and Eker [3] figure 24).

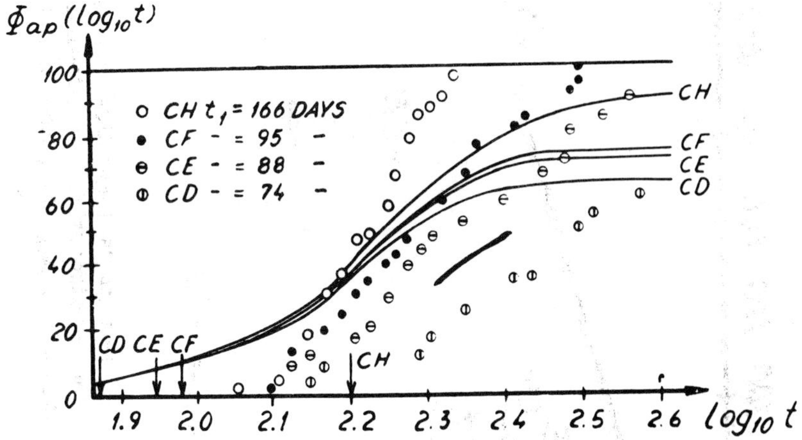

Figure 35. Theoretical relative incidences plotted versus the logarithm of the induction time for one fixed value of the dose of ultraviolet radiation, one fixed value of the time interval between successive irradiations, and various times of discontinuing the irradiations. Experimental points from Blum 1950 for mice. (Arley and Eker [3] figure 25).

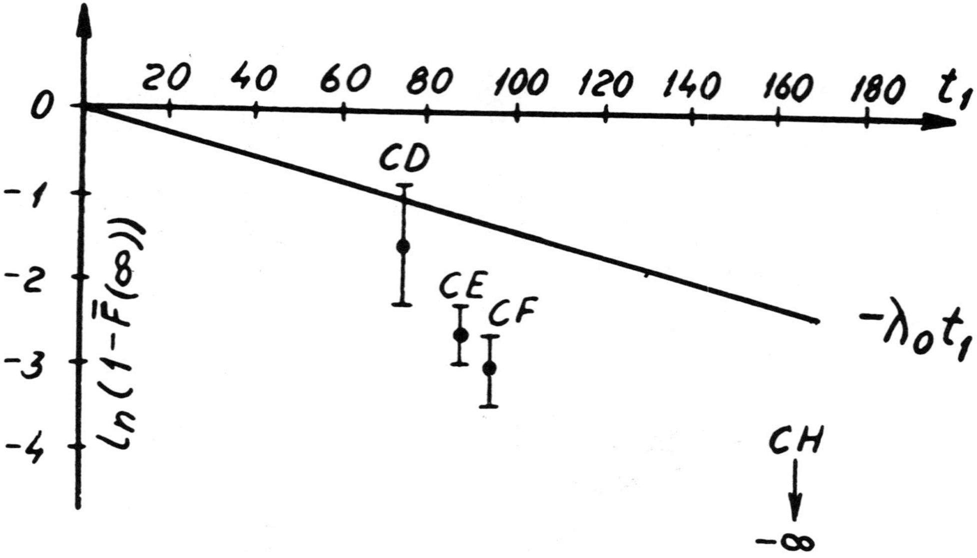

$$\ln(1-\bar{F}(\infty)) = -\lambda_0 t_1$$

Figure 36. Theoretical final relative incidence for the theoretical curves in figure 35 plotted versus the time of discontinuing the irradiations. Experimental points determined from figure 35. (Arley and Eker [3] figure 26).

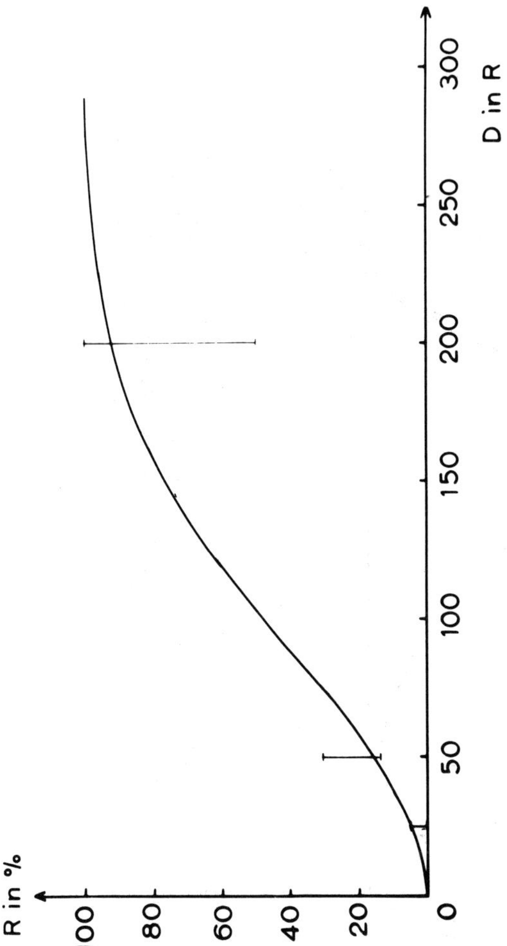

Figure 37. Theoretical final relative incidence plotted versus the dose of a single irradiation with X-rays from an external source. Experimental points from Deringer, Lorenz, and Uphoff 1955 for local irradiation of the ovarian region of mice. (Arley and Eker [3] figure 28).

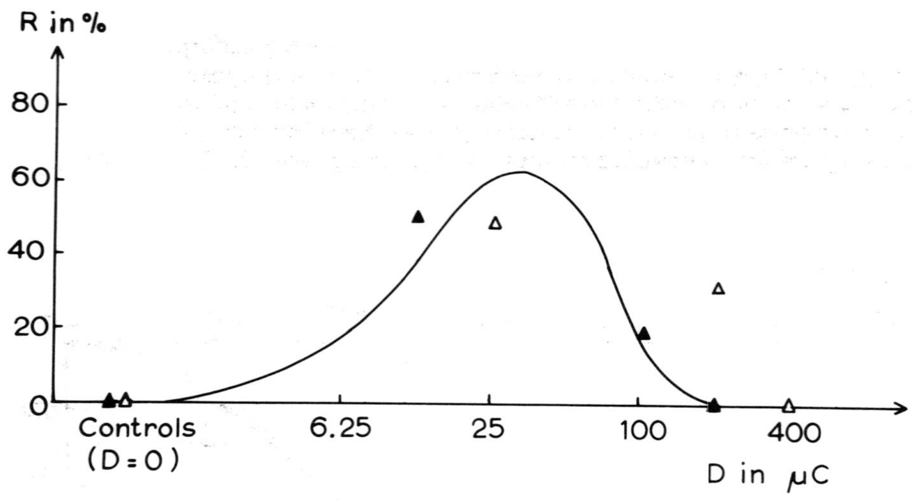

Figure 38. Theoretical final relative incidence plotted versus the logarithm of the dose of a single injection of a radioisotope. Experimental points from Lindsay, Potter, and Chaikoff 1957 for iodine-131 and thyroid adenomatas in rats. (Arley and Eker [3] figure 29).

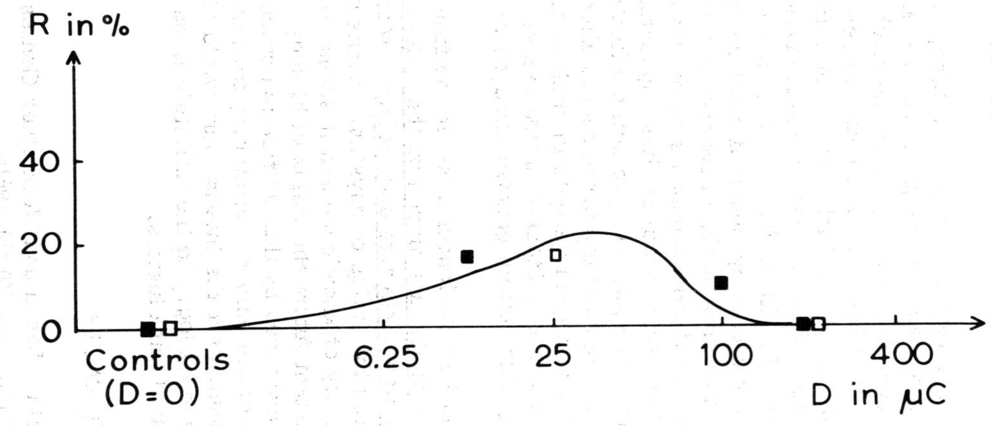

Figure 39. Theoretical final relative incidence plotted versus the logarithm of the dose of a single injection of a radioisotope. Similar experimental points as in figure 38 but for a different type of tumor, thyroid carcinomas (Lindsay, Potter, and Chaikoff 1957). (Arley and Eker [3] figure 30).

cases simulating, a threshold dose, which can be fitted with good agreement to experimental data showing a linear form, a sigmoid form, and a form with a maximum. The form of the relationship given by the model varies from case to case depending on the experimental conditions and on the relative importance of certain special factors in each special case.

In conclusion I wish again to stress that it is, of course, ultimately only possible by direct laboratory experimentation to analyze for each type of carcinogenic agent the finer details of the mechanisms of carcinogenesis. However, I hope that such work as reported very briefly here may be a helpful guide for further experimentation. Actually you will find that a number of further experimental investigations are suggested in the paper [3]. Thus, for example, in my institute we hope that studies of free radicals by means of electron spin resonance techniques will also sometime in the future turn out to be fruitful for elucidating the problems of carcinogenesis as discussed in the paper [3]. Other important experimental studies suggested in the paper [3] are investigations of the possible protective effects of cysteamine and similar substances against the carcinogenic effects of ionizing radiations and other carcinogenic agents in analogy to the recent findings of Lüning and his group in Stockholm that cysteamine does have a protective effect against certain genetic damages by ionizing radiations [11].

Let me finish by stating that I am no longer alone in the firm conviction that all the basic secrets of life are hidden on the molecular level in the borderland between atomic physics and biology. Modern quantum theory has already united the fields of physics, chemistry, and astronomy to one grand entirety of knowledge and it seems to me not unlikely that in a not too distant future the fields of biology, including medicine, will also be embraced by this unification process thus giving us a unified picture of the universe stretching from the infinitely small world of the atoms, over the intermediary world of everyday physics, chemistry, and biology, to the infinitely large expanding world of the galaxies and their clusters.

REFERENCES

1. Seelig, C., "Albert Einstein. Leben und Werk eines Genies unserer Zeit", p. 397. Europa Verlag, Zürich 1960.

2. Einstein, A., and Infeld, L., "The Evolution of Physics" 1938.

3. Arley, N., and Eker, R., "Mechanisms of Carcinogenesis", Adv. Biol. Med. Phys. 8, 375 (1962). (With an extensive bibliography).

4. Sciama, D. W., "The Unity of the Universe". Faber and Faber, London 1959.

5. Heitler, W., "Der Menscn und die naturwissenschaftliche Erkenntnis". Vieweg, Braunschweig, 1961.

6. Löwdin, P. -O., "Quantum Genetics and the aperiodic Solid. Some Aspects on the biological Problems of Heredity, Mutations, Ageing, and Tumors in View of the Quantum Theory of the DNA Molecule". Preprint No. 85, Quantum Chemistry Group, Uppsala University, Uppsala, Sweden, 1962.

7. Levan, A., "Relation of Chromosome Status to the Origin and Progression of Tumors: The Evidence of Chromosome Numbers", in "Genetics and Cancer", p. 151. Owen, London 1961.

8. Levan, A., "The Role of Chromosomes in Carcinogenesis". Proceedings 1st Scandinavian Symposium on Carcinogenesis, Oslo, Norway, 1961. (Not published but filed with The World Health Organization's head office in Geneva and its European regional office in Copenhagen, Denmark, where the papers are publicly available. Cf. Arley, N., and Setälä, K., "First Scandinavian Symposium on Carcinogenesis", Nature 194, 436 (1962.)

9. Andreasen, E., and Borum, Kirstine, "A Method for in vivo Determination of the Size of Papillomas in epidermal Carcinogenesis", Acta Path. Microbiol. Scand. 41, 483 (1957).

10. Borum, Kirstine, "Growth of chemically induced epidermal Tumours in Mice", Acta Path. Microbiol. Scand. 44, 179 (1958).

11. Lüning, K. G., Frölén, H., and Nelson, A., "The protective Effect of Cysteamine against genetic Damages by X-Rays in Spermatozoa from Mice", Rad. Res. 14, 813 (1961).

12. Levan, A., "The Cancer Problem from the Point of View of Chromosome Research", Statens Naturvetenskapliga Forskningsråds Årsbok 12, 212 (1959) (In Swedish).

DISCUSSION PARTICIPANT

Professor Charles Heidelberger
130 McArdle Memorial Laboratory, University of Wisconsin, Madison, Wisconsin

DISCUSSION

Charles Heidelberger. One important contribution that the experimentalist can make to the theoretician is to act in a critical fashion to protect him from pitfalls in the experimental literature. For example it is well known that in mice bearing papillomas, that are really warts, these are nibbled off by other mice or rubbed off against the cages.

The mechanism of carcinogenesis is a mirror into which every man looks and sees himself. Professor Levan is interested in chromosomes and sees a chromosomal mechanism. The virus people see a viral mechanism, and I as a biochemist see a biochemical mechanism. The new trinity of DNA, RNA, and protein, whose dogma is promulgated by its various high priests, makes it most simple to regard carcinogenesis as a consequence of the direct interaction of the carcinogen, be it physical or chemical, with the DNA -- the genetic material. However, recently some of the exquisitely sensitive control mechanisms that enable cells to respond to environmental changes are beginning to be understood. Professor Pitot and I have written a theoretical paper (not yet published) which can explain the carcinogenic change and its perpetuation in daughter cells on the basis of cytoplasmic interruptions or alterations in control mechanisms without the interaction of the chemical with DNA itself. One consequence of this idea (which I will not dignify by calling a theory) is that it may be possible by suitable manipulation of the metabolic control circuitry to restore a tumor cell to normal, provided that secondary chromosomal changes have not yet occurred. It will be interesting to see whether this rather unorthodox prediction can be verified experimentally.

Niels Arley. Regarding Professor Heidelberger's first point I wish to say that Dr. Borum has informed me that the test animals were not isolated from each other and that the neoplasiae were not protected against biting, licking, or scratching, neither in her experiments on DMBA-initiated tumors, which I have described in my paper, nor in any other experiments in the Fibiger laboratory. What is done in other similar laboratories I cannot tell. Actually both licking off and scratching off with the paws, especially by the animal itself, does occur in Dr. Borum's experiments and this fact you can see directly in her growth curves. The mice were very carefully inspected and scratching and biting off of a papilloma, wholly or partly, was in each case registered. As you will see such an example is in fact shown in Dr. Borum's material reproduced in figure 10 in my paper and indicated there in the legend by (b) . Dr. Borum's growth curves in figure 10 correspond to her casts reproduced in figure 9 in my paper. From these casts it cannot be seen directly that parts of the papilloma in question has been bitten off, but this fact is evident from her corresponding growth curves in figure 10.

Dr. Borum thinks that it is an open question which can be discussed, whether her and the Fibiger laboratory's experimental conditions, or experimental conditions in which each test animal is isolated from the other test animals and each tumor is protected one way or the other, give the more correct picture of tumor growth. Dr. Borum deliberately planned her experiments so that the mice and their DMBA-initiated tumors are exposed to exactly the same conditions as are all the other mice in her laboratory, in which also i. a. such phenomena as regression was registered. Dr. Borum thinks that in her experiments the tumors developed under the most "natural" conditions when the animals were allowed to scratch since she feels that scratching and the ulceration it leads to is an important factor for the transformation of a benign into a malignant tumor.

Charles Heidelberger. I am glad that Dr. Borum's experiments were carried out under conditions that are comparable to carcinogenesis, but my point remains that the mice chew off these papillomas and that no correlation should be drawn between these changes in papillomas, which may only correspond to the appetites of the mice, and the mechanism of carcinogenesis.

Niels Arley. I quite agree with Professor Heidelberger's remark. I have here only reported Dr. Borum's own views, and I hope Professor Heidelberger, Dr. Borum and others will get an opportunity to discuss directly how best to carry out well controlled experiments and comparisons. Personally I have in the review article I am reporting in my paper (especially pp. 395-396) expressed the view that elucidation of the problem of how tumors develop once they have been initiated will presumably not give us much new knowledge about the primary problem of how tumors arise. However, what Dr. Borum's and others growth studies do show, and this is why I have mentioned them in my paper, is the fact that tumor growth is most probably of a complicated multistage type being governed by continued genotype variation, adaptation, and selection within the genetic mosaic of cell clones constituting a tumor as shown by the chromosome findings I have mentioned. Since with present experimental techniques we cannot observe a tumor until it has been growing for some time, this randomness of its growth has, unfortunately, still today to be taken into account in any theoretical model of carcinogenesis, but as discussed in the review article I am reporting in my paper the consequences of the model with regard to the basic mechanisms of tumor initiation will presumably not depend critically on the way this randomness of the growth is taken into account quantitatively.

Regarding Professor Heidelberger's second point I wish to say, first, that I think it is a most striking illustration of the general introductory remarks about our ignorance of Nature's fundamental secrets, which I made in my paper: today we even do not know whether the key steps in carcinogenesis are to be sought in the cell nuclei or in the cell cytoplasms. To elucidate this most fundamental question I have suggested in the review article I am reporting in my paper that one should try to develop experimental microsurgical methods for exchanging the nuclei between normal and tumor cells, thereby producing chimeras of normal cell cytoplasms and tumor cell nuclei and vice versa, as well as daughter cells of such chimeras.

Next, I wish to say that a chromosome mechanism, a viral mechanism, and a biochemical mechanism need not be mutually exclusive possibilities. As discussed in the review article I am reporting in my paper, most probably all three mechanisms are used by Nature, and if so they are presumably intimately interrelated. However, what is the essential lesson we have been taught during the last decade or so is that most probably all the basic cell processes take place at the macromolecule level. It is this essential fact which on the one hand is the reason why it has turned out experimentally to be so difficult to fill all the gaps in our knowledge, and on the other hand has made it possible to work out quantitative theoretical models of carcinogenesis by utilizing the methods of quantum theory and stochastic processes. Unfortunately such work cannot, so far as I can see, elucidate the question raised by Professor Heidelberger, whether the key steps in carcinogenesis take place in the cell nuclei or in the cell cytoplasms, since the same models are equally applicable in both cases and therefore cannot distinguish between them.

Professor Heidelberger has kindly let me read his draft of the paper he mentions in his question, and I fully agree that his cytoplasmic hypothesis is a fruitful possibility that should be tested experimentally as much as possible. However, I wish to mention that there is also the possibility that Nature may combine a cytoplasmic mechanism, such as that one suggested by Professor Heidelberger, with a DNA mechanism, which latter I personally feel that the total experimental evidence favors at present, as discussed in more detail in the review article I have reported in my paper. There is the possibility that Professor Heidelberger's cytoplasmic mechanism, or any other cytoplasmic mechanism, comes into play only in such cells the genetic information content of which, as coded in the DNA molecules, has been first changed in a suitable way, e. g. spontaneously by the quantum mechanical tunnel effect I referred to in my paper, so that these, and only these, cells become susceptible to the further cytoplasmic interruption or alteration which transforms them into neoplastic cells. I think we are here again reminded of Einstein's modest remarks about our ignorance, which I quoted at the beginning of my paper. Finally, I wish also to point out that the possibility mentioned by Professor Heidelberger of restoring a tumor cell to a normal cell by suitable manipulations may also exist in other mechanisms as discussed at some detail in the review article I am reporting in my paper, especially in connection with the possibility, indicated by the theoretical studies mentioned, that free radicals or other intermediary reaction products may play an important role in carcinogenesis. Consequently, it is a most difficult problem to plan crucial experimental tests.

I hope that there will be more opportunities in the future to discuss directly the most promising experimental methods of how best to plan well controlled experiments to elucidate these fundamental problems of carcinogenesis. In conclusion I wish to take this opportunity to thank most heartily the Mathematics Research Center US Army and the University of Wisconsin, which plays such a central role in basic cancer research, for taking the initiative to organize this very fruitful symposium which I am sure will be a great inspiration and stimulus in our further studies of the secrets of Nature and especially of the secrets of Life.

J. NEYMAN and ELIZABETH L. SCOTT

A Stochastic Model of Epidemics

SUMMARY

The purpose of the paper is to propose a statistical model of epidemics taking explicitly into account two elements of the real phenomenon of epidemics that are most usually neglected in earlier models. One of these elements is that the number $\nu(u)$ (treated as a random variable) of susceptibles infected by an infectious individual depends on the location u of the latter in the habitat. The other element is that an individual infected at one point, say u, of the habitat does not usually remain at that point through his incubation period (assumed fixed) but moves away and becomes infectious himself at a different point X, which we treat as a random variable. Thus, the datum of the problem regarding an epidemic must include a family Φ of probability generating functions $g(t|u) = E[t^{\nu(u)}]$ and another family Ψ of conditional probability densities $f(x|u)$ of X given u, called dispersal functions. With this general setup the proposed model appears as an extension of the classical branching process (new elements being Φ and Ψ) and many theorems relating to the latter are almost bodily transferred to the theory of epidemics. Formulas are deduced for the joint p. g. f.'s of the numbers of new cases in arbitrary disjoint regions in the habitat, all these cases belonging to the nth generation of an epidemic. Similarly, formulas are given characterizing an epidemic continuously nurtured by mutation of bacteria that occur at random within the population. Other formulas refer to the total size of an epidemic started by a single individual. Specific examples illustrate the fact that, with a given spread of infectiousness, that is, with a given family Φ of p. g. f.'s $g(t|u)$, the development of an epidemic depends strikingly on the dispersal functions $f(x|u)$. Several results obtained appear unexpected. One is that, under rather broad conditions, the probability of an epidemic in a small community getting out of hand coincides with the probability of the epidemic in the whole habitat becoming explosive. Another is that, under the assumption of homogeneity with regard to the distribution of $\nu(u)$, the immunization of a randomly selected group of susceptibles, representing a proportion θ of the total, will reduce the expected size of the total epidemic to a level below a calculable limit of $(1-\theta)/\theta$. An important element of real epidemics ignored by the present model (along with quite a few other models!) is that each new case diminishes the number of susceptibles who remain under risk of being infected.

1. Introduction.

The present paper is inspired by the perusal of the very interesting book [1] by Norman T. J. Bailey, "The Mathematical Theory of Epidemics." This book summarizes the many contributions, by a number of research workers, to the study of propagation of communicable diseases. The account begins with the pioneer investigations of McKendrick of 1926 and proceeds to the more recent works of the author himself and of Bartlett, D. G. Kendall, Whittle, and others. Of the many difficulties in treating mathematically the tremendously complex phenomenon of epidemics, Bailey repeatedly stresses the outstanding problem of a mathematical machinery capable of handling the lack of uniformity of conditions prevailing in a population affected by an epidemic, particularly the lack of spatial uniformity. One of the basic assumptions involved in most of the epidemics models described by Bailey is that, given a population including S susceptibles, the appearance of a single infectious individual creates a probability of contracting the disease that is the same for each of the S susceptibles. As Bailey repeatedly points out, this assumption may well be satisfied in cases where the population considered represents a single household or even a boarding school, but with reference to the population of a city it is plainly untenable. Bailey describes two models advanced to deal with populations of this category, a deterministic model due to D. G. Kendall and a stochastic model due to Bartlett, both continuous time infection models and both of great complexity.

The purpose of the present paper is to propose a stochastic model of epidemics in which the space distribution of susceptibles and of infectious is taken into account explicitly, as well as their motions over the habitat. The probability that a given susceptible will be infected by a given infectious is taken to coincide with the probability that these two individuals will be in close contact. The model advanced was obtained by combining selected hypotheses involved in the various epidemic models, discussed in Bailey's book, with several new hypotheses, borrowed from the study of the stochastic process of clustering that we found fruitful in several domains of research. Since the happenings in the successive "generations" of infected is an essential part of any theory of epidemics, the start with the process of clustering brought us to an extensive use of the theory of branching processes due to Everett and Ulam [5], Harris [6], [7] and to Otter [8]. The results of these authors will be referred to as classical theory and the present model of epidemics may be considered as a modification or as a slight extension of that theory.

It seems to us that, with reference to epidemics, the combination of hypotheses adopted here offers some gains in realism and in manageability. However, these are achieved at a price: We had to assume, as in the chain-binomial model, discrete generations of infected, with the period of infectiousness reduced to zero, and a fixed "serial" period.

2. Basic assumptions.

The biological assumptions adopted here are those of Lowell J. Reed and Wade Hampton Frost relating to the chain-binomial model as described by Bailey. If at time $t = 0$ a susceptible individual is infected, then for a certain period of time T, the same for all individuals, this infection is "latent." Thereafter, for a moment, the individual becomes "infectious" and, on a sufficiently close contact, may communicate the infection to others.

The probabilistic assumptions adopted are as follows.

(i) Number of infected by one infectious. Consider an infinite plane H described as the habitat. We assume that to every point $u = (u_1, u_2)$ in H there corresponds a random variable $\nu(u)$ representing the number of susceptible individuals who would be infected at point u if at that point there is a member of the population undergoing his period of infectiousness. The probability generating function of $\nu(u)$ will be denoted by

$$g(t|u) = E[t^{\nu(u)}] \quad . \tag{1}$$

After a fixed period of time T all those infected at u will become infectious. We assume that the random variables $\nu(u)$ are mutually independent and independent from all other variables in the system and that their distributions remain unchanged in time. In the general discussion no special assumptions are made regarding the function $g(t|u)$, except that it is Lebesgue measurable in u, and that $g(0|u) = P\{\nu(u) = 0\} < 1$.

Remark 1. The motivation for assumption (i) is as follows. We visualize a disease that is spread perhaps by coughing. If an infectious individual coughs and expectorates droplets containing virulent bacteria, the result is likely to depend on the location of the individual. If he coughs in an isolated place and assuming that the bacteria released die within a short period of time, then no one will become infected. On the other hand, if the coughing occurs, say in a crowded subway train, then quite a few fellow passengers may become infected. Thus, it appears realistic to assume that $g(t|u)$ depends on the location u where an infected individual becomes infectious.

Remark 2. Assumption (i) implies the independence of $g(t|u$ from time, or from the generation, of the epidemic. This is equivale to assuming that the earlier removals of susceptibles do not change materially the number of susceptibles still exposed to the risk of infection. Similar assumptions are adopted in a number of epidemic models discussed by Bailey, some of them relating to small communities. It seems to us that this assumption with reference to a big city is even more acceptable.

Remark 3. The present remark is occasioned by a question put to us by Professor William G. Cochran as to the possibility of using the present model in order to evaluate the expected decrease in the total size of an epidemic as a result of immunization of a sizeable fraction, say θ, of the population. Clearly, in order to answer questions of this kind, it is necessary to assume a change in the distribution of each random variable $\nu(u)$. However, such a change will not be a temporal change. In other words, the study of the possible effect of an immunization campaign will, within the framework of the present model, reduce to the study of epidemics developing under two different systems of probability generating functions $g(t|u)$ one corresponding to the situation before the immunization campaign and the other to the situation after this campaign. Naturally, the results will depend very much not only on the number of persons immunized, but also on how the immunized individuals are distributed within the various strata of the population.

(ii) Dispersal of infected. It is assumed that during the latent period T all the individuals infected at u travel independently from each other. Furthermore, it is assumed that to each point u of the habitat plane there corresponds a function $f(x|u)$, where for brevity $x = (x_1, x_2)$, representing the probability density of the location of the individual at the time he himself becomes infectious, given that he was infected at u . Thus, given any region R in the habitat, the probability that an individual infected at u will become infectious somewhere in R is given by the integral, say,

$$p(R|u) = \int_R f(x|u)\, dx_1\, dx_2 \quad . \tag{2}$$

No special assumptions are made regarding the family of functions $f(x|u)$, except that they are Lebesgue measurable with respect to u. These functions will be described as dispersal functions.

Remark 1. If the infection of an individual takes place, say in a neighborhood grocery, it is likely that at the time this individual (frequently a housewife) becomes infectious himself he will be at not too great a distance from the store. On the other hand, an infection contracted in a subway train may be expected to be carried to great distances. This explains the assumption that the dispersal function depends upon the location u where the infection takes place.

Remark 2. We are grateful to Professor Agnes Berger for calling our attention to the fact that, while there is considerable freedom of specific assumptions regarding the functions $g(t|u)$ and $f(x|u)$, these functions cannot be selected arbitrarily. It is clear that the expectation of $\nu(u)$, say $\nu_1(u) = g'(1|u)$, must be strongly correlated with the density of population at u. In order that a given distribution of population density could be maintained, it is necessary that the family of dispersal functions $f(x|u)$ possess a regularity property, whereby the individuals departing from any point u are replaced by others. The nature of the limitations to be imposed on the family of functions $f(x|u)$ to insure stability of the population is a very interesting problem to which we hope to return in due course. However, in the present paper we concentrate on the model of epidemics in which the functions $g(t|u)$ and $f(x|u)$ are supposed to be included in the datum.

(iii) Immigration. The term immigration will be used to describe real infected immigrants to the population considered and also the possible spontaneous birth of infection, perhaps through a mutation occurring in some of the bacteria carried by the particular individuals. A priori, it seems likely that cases of infectiousness occurring from such sources will be extremely rare and also that their density over the habitat will not be uniform. For example, if the "immigrant" infection is due to mutant bacteria, then it is likely to occur more frequently in the more densely populated areas of the city than in those with sparse population. For the above reason we postulate the existence of an immigration density function $\lambda(u) \geqq 0$ defined for all $u = (u_1, u_2)$ and Lebesgue measurable. Further, it is assumed that, whatever be the region R of the habitat, the number $\alpha(R)$ of cases of immigrant infectiousness occurring in R during a unit of time is a Poisson random variable with probability generating function

$$(3) \qquad G_{\alpha(R)}(t) = \exp\{-(1-t)\int_R \lambda(u)\,du\} .$$

Lastly, it is assumed that $\alpha(R_1)$ and $\alpha(R_2)$ corresponding to any two disjoint regions are mutually independent and that they are independent of all other random variables of the system. For definitiveness, it will be assumed that all the "immigrant" cases of infection occur at the beginning of each serial period T. At the beginning of the next period these cases will become infectious.

The three basic assumptions (i), (ii), (iii) complete the description of the chance mechanism suggested as a model of epidemics. It will be seen that it is a modification of the mechanism of clustering studied by us in earlier papers [2], [3]. Also, with reference to the study of successive generations of an epidemic and of its total size, the present model is an extension of the branching process. Here the new elements are the explicitly introduced dispersal functions $f(x|u)$ and the p.g.f. $g(t|u)$, both depending on u, the location of the infectious. Mathematically the present model reduces to the general branching process studied by Everett and Ulam if one assumes that the habitat H is composed of a finite number of points $u_1, u_2, \ldots, u_N$.

In accordance with the assumptions adopted, the development of the epidemic will be considered at discrete periods of time, $0, T, 2T, \ldots, nT, \ldots$. Namely, for every n and for every system of disjoint regions (really Borel sets) $R_1, R_2, \ldots, R_s$, we shall consider the random variables representing the numbers of individuals who at the beginning of the nth serial period were in R_i and became infectious there. Thus, each such variable is what is usually called the number of new cases occurring in R_i during the nth serial period.

3. Formula on conditional expectations.

In the following we shall repeatedly apply the classical formula connecting the conditional and the unconditional expectations of a random variable. Let X be a random variable and Y another random variable having a well-defined conditional distribution for any given value x of X, with its first moment $E(Y|x)$. Then $E(Y|X)$ denotes a random variable defined to be equal to $E(Y|x)$ whenever $X = x$. With this notation, the unconditional expectation of Y, if it exists, is

$$E(Y) = E[E(Y|X)] \quad (4)$$

4. Number of infectious all simultaneously infected at a point u.

Let there be an infectious at an arbitrary point u. He will infect a random number $\nu(u)$ of susceptibles surrounding him. Let $R_1, R_2, \ldots, R_s$ be arbitrary disjoint regions and let $N_{1i}(u)$ stand for the number of those individuals, originally infected at u, who at the beginning of the next serial period become infectious in R_i, for $i = 1, 2, \ldots, s$. Repeating the argument used by us in other connections, we find the probability generating function of the vector

$\underset{\sim}{N}_1(u) = (N_{11}(u), N_{12}(u), \ldots, N_{1s}(u))$ as follows, say,

$$G_1(\underset{\sim}{t}|u) = E\left\{\prod_{i=1}^{s} t_i^{N_{1i}(u)}\right\}$$

(5)

$$= E\left\{E\left[\prod_{i=1}^{s} t_i^{N_{1i}(u)} \Big| \nu(u)\right]\right\} .$$

However, for any given value of $\nu(u)$, say $\nu(u) = n$, the distribution of the numbers $N_{1i}(u)$ is multinomial with

(6) $$E\left[\prod_{i=1}^{s} t_i^{N_{1i}(u)} \Big| \nu(u) = n\right] = \left[1 - \sum_{i=1}^{s} (1-t_i)\, p(R_i|u)\right]^n ,$$

where $p(R_i|u)$ is the probability that an individual infected at u will become infectious in R_i, as in (2) .

In order to obtain (5) it is sufficient to multiply (6) by the probability that $\nu(u)$ will be equal to n and to sum for n . Obviously, the result of this operation is

(7) $$G_1(\underset{\sim}{t}|u) = g\left[1 - \sum_{i=1}^{s} (1-t_i)\, p(R_i|u) \Big| u\right] .$$

The vector $\underset{\sim}{N}_1(u)$ with probability generating function given by (7), will be described as the first generation in the regions $R_1, R_2, \ldots, R_s$ of an epidemic started by a single infectious at u . Further below we shall adopt a similar definition relating to the nth generation of the same epidemic. At this moment, notice the special case where $s = 1$ and where R_1 coincides with the whole habitat H . Then $p(H|u) \equiv 1$ and formula (7) coincides with $g(t|u)$.

5. Number of infectious all infected by a single individual who himself became infected at u .

Consider again an individual A who at time $t = 0$ became infectious at an arbitrary point u . Assume that this individual infected several susceptibles and consider one of the latter, say B . After the latent period T this individual will be located at a random point $X = (X_1, X_2)$ and will become infectious himself. Let $M_{11}(u), M_{12}(u), \ldots, M_{1s}(u)$ stand for the numbers of persons, all infected by B at time T, who at time 2T will become infectious, respectively, in regions $R_1, R_2, \ldots, R_s$. Denote by $h_1(t|u)$ the p.g.f. of the vector $\underset{\sim}{M}_1(u) = (M_{11}(u), M_{12}(u), \ldots, M_{1s}(u))$. This vector will be described as the first generation in the regions $R_1, R_2, \ldots, R_s$ of an epidemic started by a single individual who himself has been infected at u.

Obviously

$$(8) \qquad h_1(\underset{\sim}{t}|u) = \int_H G_1(\underset{\sim}{t}|x) f(x|u)\, dx .$$

6. Numbers of infectious forming the nth generation of an epidemic started at u.

Generalizing the definitions given in the two preceding sections we now define two vectors $\underset{\sim}{N}_n(u) = (N_{n1}(u), N_{n2}(u), \ldots, N_{ns}(u))$ and $\underset{\sim}{M}_n(u) = (M_{n1}(u), M_{n2}(u), \ldots, M_{ns}(u))$ described, respectively, as the nth generation in $R_1, R_2, \ldots, R_s$ of an epidemic started by a single infectious at u and as the nth generation in the same regions of an epidemic started by a single individual who himself became infected at u.

The definition is recursive. We assume that vectors $\underset{\sim}{N}_n(u)$, and $M_n(u)$ have been defined for some $n \geqq 1$ and denote by $G_n(\underset{\sim}{t}|u)$ and $h_n(\underset{\sim}{t}|u)$, the corresponding probability generating functions. Consider a single individual A who at time zero is infectious at u. He will infect $\nu(u)$ individuals, say $B_1, B_2, \ldots, B_{\nu(u)}$. At time T each of them will be located at a random point somewhere in H and will start there a subepidemic, the nth generation of which in $R_1, R_2, \ldots, R_s$ will be a vector $\underset{\sim}{M}_n(u)$ assumed to be already defined. Let $\underset{\sim}{M}_n^{(i)}(u)$ stand for this vector referring to B_i. Then the (n+1)st generation in $R_1, R_2, \ldots, R_s$ of an epidemic started by a single infectious at u is defined as a vector $\underset{\sim}{N}_{n+1}(u)$ with components

$$(9) \qquad N_{n+1,j}(u) = \sum_{i=0}^{\nu(u)} M_{nj}^{(i)}(u) .$$

Because the vectors $\underset{\sim}{M}_n^{(i)}(u)$ are independent and identically distributed, reasoning similar to that employed in section 4 yields

$$(10) \qquad G_{n+1}(\underset{\sim}{t}|u) = g[h_n(\underset{\sim}{t}|u)\,|u] .$$

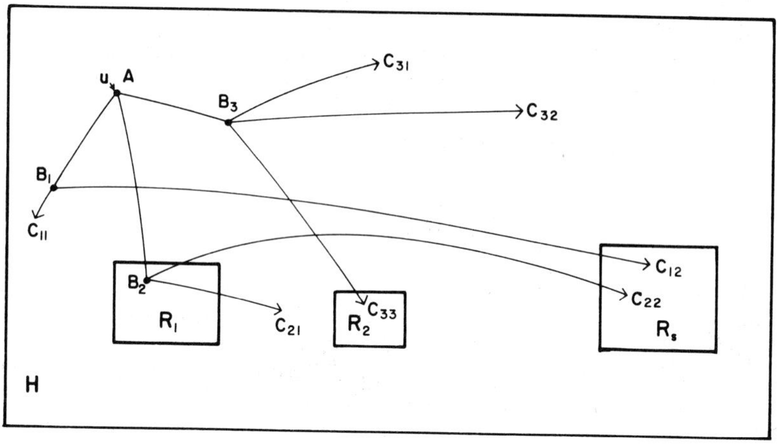

Figure 1

Diagrammatic representation of the first two generations of an epidemic started by a single infectious at u .

In order to define $\underset{\sim}{M}_{n+1}(u)$ consider one of the individuals B infected at u . At time T this individual will become infectious himself, being located at a random point X . In due course he will produce the (n+1) st generation of the subepidemic started by himself with the already defined vector $\underset{\sim}{N}_{n+1}(X)$, where the distribution of X is governed by the probability density $f(x|u)$. Given that $X = x$, the random vector $M_{n+1}(u)$ is conditionally defined as being equal to $\underset{\sim}{N}_{n+1}(x)$. It follows that the unconditional p. g. f. of $\underset{\sim}{M}_{n+1}(\underset{\sim}{t}|u)$ is given by

$$h_{n+1}(\underset{\sim}{t}|u) = \int_H G_{n+1}(\underset{\sim}{t}|x)\, f(x|u)\, dx \; . \tag{11}$$

Figure 1 illustrates the definitions of the random vectors $\underset{\sim}{N}_n$ and $\underset{\sim}{M}_n$. The large rectangle represents the habitat H . The three small rectangles mark the regions R_1, R_2 and R_s . The letter A at point u marks the single infectious individual originating the epidemic. Its first total generation is composed of say $N_1 = 3$ individuals and the letters B_1, B_2, B_3 mark the positions where they become infectious. Of the three only one, namely B_2 is located in one of the three regions R_i, so that $N_{11} = N_{13} = 0$ and $N_{12} = 1$. Letters C_{ij} for $i = 1, 2, 3$ mark the positions where the individuals infected by members of the first generation (B_1, B_2, B_3) become infectious. It is seen that the second generation in $R_1, R_2, \ldots, R_s$ of an epidemic started by a single infectious at u is represented by the vector

$$N_{21} = 0,\ N_{22} = 1,\ \ldots,\ N_{2s} = 2\ . \tag{12}$$

Since the total first generation is composed of $\nu(u) = 3$ we have in the diagram three subepidemics started by individuals infected at u . Two of these subepidemics, those generated by B_1 and B_2 yield the same vector $M_{11}(u) = M_{12}(u) = 0$, $M_{1s}(u) = 1$. The third, generated by B_3, yields $M_{11}(u) = M_{13}(u) = 0$ and $M_{12}(u) = 1$.

Formulas (10) and (11), combined with (7) and (8), yield in turn

$$\begin{aligned} G_1(\underset{\sim}{t}|u) &= g\left[1 - \sum_{i=1}^{s}(1-t_i)\,p(R_i|u)\,\Big|\,u\right], \quad h_1(\underset{\sim}{t}|u) = \int G_1(\underset{\sim}{t}|x)\, f(x|u)\, d \\ G_2(\underset{\sim}{t}|u) &= g\left\{\int g\left[1 - \sum_{i=1}^{s}(1-t_i)\,p(R_i|x)\,\Big|\,x\right] f(x|u)\,dx\,\Big|\,u\right\}, \end{aligned} \tag{13}$$

$$h_2(\underset{\sim}{t}|u) = \int G_2(\underset{\sim}{t}|x)\, f(x|u)\,dx\ ,$$

etc. These formulas are easy generalizations of those in the classical theory of branching processes. In order to obtain the latter in their simplest form, it is sufficient to assume $s = 1$, $R_1 = H$, and $g(t|u) \equiv g(t)$, independent of u . Then $G_1(t|u) = g(t)$ and $G_{n+1}(t|u) = g[G_n(t)]$ for all u .

The formulas deduced can be used to obtain expressions for the moments of the variables $\underset{\sim}{N}_n(u)$ and $\underset{\sim}{M}_n(u)$. Generally let $\xi_{ni}(u)$ and $\eta_{ni}(u)$ stand for the expectations of $N_{ni}(u)$ and $M_{ni}(u)$, respectively. Differentiating the first part of (13) with respect to t_i, substituting $t_1 = t_2 = \ldots t_s = 1$ and denoting the expectation of $\nu(u)$ by $\nu_1(u)$, whether it is finite or infinite, we obtain

$$\xi_{1i}(u) = \nu_1(u)\,p(R_i|u)\ , \quad \eta_{1i}(u) = \int_H \nu_1(x)\,p(R_i|x)\,f(x|u)\,dx \tag{14}$$

and then, operating similarly on (10) and (11),

$$\xi_{n+1,i}(u) = \nu_1(u)\eta_{ni}(u), \quad \eta_{ni}(u) = \int_H \xi_{ni}(x) f(x|u)\,dx \quad . \tag{15}$$

Higher moments are obtained in a similar manner. It is interesting that, in general, the finiteness of $\nu_i(u)$ for all u does not insure that $\xi_{2i}(u)$ will be finite.

The same formulas (10) and (11) can be used to study the correlations between the numbers of new cases in the several regions of the habitat.

7. Some specializations and the problem of ultimate extinction.

Formulas (10) and (11) are the tools for the study of the development of an epidemic started by one infectious at a point u. It will be seen that this study must concern two families of functions. First is the family, say Φ of probability generating functions $g(t|u)$, of the number infected by a single infectious located at an arbitrary point u. Second is the family, say Ψ of dispersal functions $f(x|u)$. For each $u \in H$ the dispersal function $f(x|u)$ corresponds to an individual supposed to have been infected at u and represents the probability density of his location at the time when he himself becomes infectious. More or less specific assumptions concerning the two families of functions Φ and Ψ and also regarding the regions $R_1, R_2, \ldots, R_s$ will lead to conclusions of varying generality regarding the development of the epidemic in these regions. Here many theorems of the classical theory of branching processes can be bodily transferred to the present model. Certain results, relating to the frequently treated question of the eventual extinction of the epidemic, are immediate.

Theorem 1. If for every $u \in H$, the expectation $\nu_1(u) = E[\nu(u)]$ does not exceed a number ν_1 less than unity, then, whatever be the family Ψ of dispersal functions and whatever be the starting point of the epidemic, the probability of there being no new cases in the nth generation tends to unity as $n \to \infty$.

In order to describe the phenomenon asserted in Theorem 1 it will be convenient to use the expression: "epidemic is heading to extinction."

This theorem refers to the total number of new cases, wherever they may occur in the habitat. Thus, in this case $s = 1$, $R_1 = H$, and $p(H|u_0) = 1$.

We begin by noticing that if $\varphi(t)$ is a probability generating function of a random variable Z with a finite expectation z, then, for every t between zero and unity,

$$(16) \qquad 1 - \varphi(t) = \varphi(1) - \varphi(t) = (1-t)\varphi'(t^*) \leqq (1-t)z \ .$$

In particular, this applies to $t = 0$, so that

$$(17) \qquad 1 - \varphi(0) = 1 - P\{Z=0\} \leqq z \ .$$

If follows that, in order to prove the theorem, it is sufficient to prove that, as $n \to \infty$, the expected value of $N_n(u)$, the total number of infectious in the nth generation, tends to zero. Using formulas (14) and dropping the subscript i, we obtain in turn

$$(18) \qquad \xi_1(u) = E(N_1|u) = \nu_1(u) < \nu_1, \quad \eta_1(u) < \nu_1 \ .$$

Formulas (15) imply that, if for any n and all x, the expectation $\xi_n(x) < \nu_1^n$, then $\eta_n(u) < \nu_1^n$ and

$$(19) \qquad \xi_{n+1}(u) = \nu_1(u)\,\eta_n(u) < \nu_1^{n+1} \ .$$

Under the conditions of Theorem 1, the bound $\nu_1 < 1$ and formula (17) imply that $\xi_n(u) \to 0$ as $n \to \infty$ for all u. Thus, no matter what the starting point u of the epidemic, it will be heading for extinction, irrespective of the family of dispersal functions.

It will be seen that while the conditions of Theorem 1 insure eventual extinction of the epidemic no matter what the dispersal functions are, eventual extinction may be certain even in those cases where for some starting points $u \in H$ the expectations $\nu_1(u)$ are arbitrarily large, provided the dispersal functions $f(x|u)$ are, in a sense, favorable.

Theorem 2. If the expectations $\nu_1(u) < +\infty$ and the dispersal functions $f(x|u)$ are such that, for all $u \in H$,

$$(20) \qquad \eta_1(u) = \int_H \nu_1(x) f(x|u)\,dx < \eta_0 < 1 \ ,$$

then, no matter what the starting point u of the epidemic may be, this epidemic will be heading for extinction.

Using formulas (15) we see that, under the conditions of Theorem 2,

$$(21) \qquad \xi_2(u) = \nu_1(u)\,\eta_1(u) < \nu_1(u)\,\eta_0 \ ,$$

$$(22) \qquad \eta_2(u) = \int_H \xi_2(x) f(x|u)\,dx < \eta_0 \int_H \nu_1(x) f(x|u)\,dx = \eta_0 \eta_1(u) < \eta_0^2 \ .$$

By induction we find $\eta_n(u) < \eta_0^n$ for any u, and this implies $\xi_n(u) \to 0$ as $n \to \infty$. But then, as in Theorem 1, $P\{N_n(u) = 0\} \to 1$ and the epidemic started by a single infectious at u must be heading for extinction.

It will be seen that the conditions of Theorem 2 will be satisfied even if the habitat H contains some "dangerous areas," say HD, where the expected number of infected by a single infectious, that is $\nu_1(x)$, are large. For this to be possible, the dispersal functions $f(x|u)$ must insure, roughly speaking, small probabilities that an individual infected at any point u will become infectious at some point $x \in HD$.

In the above connection it appears interesting to inquire whether habitat conditions, specified by families Φ and Ψ, are possible such that epidemics started in some areas will head for extinction and those started in some other areas, will not.

Theorem 3. *If for every point u in the habitat, the probability that a single infectious at u will infect some individuals is greater than zero so that $P\{\nu(u) > 0\} > 0$, and if the dispersal functions $f(x|u) > 0$ for all x and u, then an epidemic started by a single infectious at u will head for extinction either for all $u \in H$ or for none.*

Operationally, the first of the hypotheses of the theorem means that the habitat does not include "deserts" where there are no people to infect. The second hypothesis means that, no matter where an infectious is located, the individuals infected by him may become infectious in any part of the habitat.

Theorem 3 may be considered as lending support to the usual policy of a well-organized public health service tending to insure satisfactory sanitary conditions in all parts of the country: a serious neglect at any single point will open the possibility of an epidemic getting out of hand.

First we consider the situation where, except perhaps for a set of locations u in the habitat of measure zero, $P\{\nu(u) = 0\} = g(0|u) = 0$. In this case

$$h_1(0|u) = \int_H g(0|x)\, f(x|u)\, dx = 0 \tag{23}$$

for all $u \in H$. But then

$$\begin{aligned} P\{N_2(u) = 0\} &= G_2(0|u) = g[h_1(u)|u] \\ &= g(0|u) = P\{\nu(u) = 0\} \end{aligned} \tag{24}$$

and easy induction based on (10) and (11) yields

$$P\{N_n(u) = 0\} = P\{\nu(u) = 0\} < 1 \tag{25}$$

for all u. Thus, in this case, no matter where the epidemic is started, it will not head for extinction.

Consider now the case where there exists a set of points u having positive measure, such that

$$0 < P\{\nu(u) = 0\} = g(0|u) < 1 \ . \tag{26}$$

Then, under the second condition of the theorem

$$h_1(0|u) = \int_H g(0|x)\, f(x|u)\, dx$$

is a positive number less than unity and, since $g(t|u)$ is a strictly increasing function of its argument t,

$$\begin{aligned} P\{N_2(u) = 0\} &= G_2(0|u) \\ &= g[h_1(0|u)\,|u] > g(0|u) = P\{N_1(u) = 0\} \ . \end{aligned} \tag{28}$$

Using again (10) and (11), easy induction reasoning yields

$$P\{N_{n+1}(u) = 0\} = G_{n+1}(0|u) > G_n(0|u) = P\{N_n(u) = 0\} \tag{29}$$

for all $u \in H$. Thus, the sequence of probabilities of no new cases in the nth generation is strictly increasing and must tend to a limit which we denote by $G_\infty(0|u)$. Correspondingly

$$\begin{aligned} \lim_{n \to \infty} h_n(0|u) &= h_\infty(0|u) = \int_H G_\infty(0|x)\, f(x|u)\, dx \ , \\ G_\infty(0|u) &= g[h_\infty(0|u)\,|u] \ , \end{aligned} \tag{30}$$

for all $u \in H$.

Formulas (30) are basic for the proof. Suppose that for a particular u_0 we have $G_\infty(0|u) = 1$, so that an epidemic started at u_0 must be heading for extinction. Since for $0 \leqq t \leqq 1$ the function $g(t|u_0)$ is equal to zero only at $t = 1$, it follows from the second part of (30) that $h_\infty(0|u) = 1$. The first part, with $u = u_0$, implies then that $G_\infty(0|x)$ must be equal to unity with the possible exception of a set of measure zero of points x. But then $h_\infty(0|u) = 1$ for all $u \in H$, which implies $G_\infty(0|u) = 1$ for all $u \in H$.

Thus, if an epidemic started by a single infectious at u_0 must head for extinction, the same will be true for an epidemic started at any other point of the habitat. Conversely, if the epidemic started by a single infectious at an arbitrary point u_0 does not head for extinction, the same will be true for epidemics started at any other point.

Theorem 3 deals with an aspect of sameness in the development of total epidemic started anywhere in the habitat. Specifically, $N_n(u)$ stands for the total number of new infectious cases of the nth generation occurring anywhere in the habitat as a result of a single infectious at u that occurred n generations in the past. The following theorem is concerned with the subepidemic developing in an arbitrary limited region R in the habitat. Namely, it answers the natural question whether the subepidemic developing in R can be heading for extinction, while the total epidemic in the infinite habitat does not.

Consider an epidemic started by a single infectious at u and denote by $N_{Hn}(u)$ and $N_{Rn}(u)$ the total number of individuals of the nth generation becoming infectious, respectively, anywhere in the habitat H and anywhere in a region R.

Theorem 4. If there exists a positive number α such that, for all $u \in H$, the probability of an infected at u becoming infectious in R is at least equal to α, so that

$$p(R|u) = \int_H f(x|u)\,dx \geqq \alpha > 0 \quad , \tag{31}$$

then, in order that for any particular starting point $u \in H$ of an epidemic

$$\lim_{n \to \infty} P\{N_{Rn}(u) = 0\} = 1 \quad , \tag{32}$$

it is necessary and sufficient that

$$\lim_{n \to \infty} P\{N_{Hn}(u) = 0\} = 1 \quad . \tag{33}$$

The number α mentioned in the conditions of the theorem may be just as small as desired and all that is required is that the probability $p(R|u)$ is at least equal to α for all u. In practice the condition will be met by every substantial subdivision of a country. However, R may also stand for a tiny community such, however, that whatever point u in the country, the probability that an individual starting from u at time zero will land in R at time T, exceeds a fixed limit α, say one in a million. In practice then, it appears that the conditions of the theorem will be met by any community in a country with normal circulation of at least a part of the population. Then the conclusion is that for a subepidemic in the community R to head for extinction it is both necessary and sufficient that the total epidemic in the whole country head for extinction.

Since $N_{Rn}(u) \leqq N_{Hn}(u)$ for all n, the sufficiency of condition (33) is obvious. In order to prove the necessity we assume that a region R satisfies both conditions (31) and (32). Our purpose is to show that (33) must hold. This is done by establishing that, for all n, and for all $u \in H$

$$(34) \qquad P\{N_{Rn}(u) = 0\} \leqq G_n(1-\alpha|u) \quad ,$$

where $G_n(t|u)$ stands for the p.g.f. of $N_{Hn}(u)$. We begin with formula (7) with $s = 1$ and R_1 identified with the region R. For $n = 1$

$$(35) \qquad P\{N_{R1}(u) = 0\} = g[1 - p(R|u)|u]$$

and, because $1 - p(R|u) < 1 - \alpha$,

$$(36) \qquad P\{N_{R1}(u) = 0\} < g[1 - \alpha|u] = G_1(1-\alpha|u) \quad .$$

Now, assume that (34) has been established for some n. The combination of formulas (10) and (11) yields then

$$(37) \qquad \begin{aligned} P\{N_{R,n+1}(u) = 0\} &= g\left[\int P\{N_{R,n}(x) = 0\} f(x|u)\,dx \,\middle|\, u\right] \\ &\leqq g\left[\int G_n(1-\alpha|x)\, f(x|u)\,dx \,\middle|\, u\right] \quad , \end{aligned}$$

where the expression on the right is $G_{n+1}(1-\alpha|u)$, which completes the induction. Now, the hypothesis (32) implies that

$$(38) \qquad \lim_{n\to\infty} (G_n(1-\alpha|u_0) = 1 \quad .$$

However, for any probability generating function $\varphi(t)$ and for $0 \leqq t \leqq 1$ we have

$$(39) \qquad \varphi(t) \leqq \varphi(0) + (1-\varphi(0))t$$

or

(40) $$1 - \varphi(t) \geqq (1-\varphi(0))(1-t) .$$

Applying (40) to $G_n(1-\alpha|u)$ and remembering that $G_n(0|u) = P\{N_{Hn}(u) = 0\}$, we obtain

(41) $$1 - G_n(1-\alpha|u) \geqq [1 - P\{N_{Hn}(u) = 0\}]\alpha \geqq 0$$

and the convergence of $\{G_n(1-\alpha|u)\}$ to unity implies (32) .

One of the interesting theorems proved by Everett and Ulam, reworded in the present terms of epidemics, etc., asserts that, if the habitat H can be divided into a finite number of components, say $C_1, C_2, \ldots, C_m$, such that for all $u \epsilon C_i$ the p.g.f. $g(t|u)$ is the same, say $g_i(t)$, and if for any $u \epsilon H$ the probability $p(C_i|u) > 0$, then

(42) $$\lim_{n\to\infty} G_n(t|u) = G_\infty(0|u) = \lim_{n\to\infty} G_n(0|u)$$

for all positive $t < 1$. The proof of the same assertion based on somewhat less restrictive assumptions is soon to be published in a joint paper by Robert Bartoszynski, Jerzy Łoś and Maria Łoś . This theorem implies that the limiting distribution of $N_{Hn}(u)$ has a probability generating function with a graph represented by a horizontal line. If $G_\infty(0|u) = 1$, this means the probability of ultimate extinction of the epidemic equal to unity. Otherwise, if $G_\infty(0|u) < 1$, the theorem asserts that, whatever the number m,

(43) $$P\{0 < N_{Hn}(u) < m\} \to 0$$

as $n \to \infty$ or, in other words, that the probability of $N_{Hn}(u)$ being positive but finite tends to zero. Speaking a little loosely, still in other terms, in the same conditions the limiting probability of $N_{Hn}(u) = 0$ is $G_\infty(0|u) < 1$ and the limiting probability of $N_{Hn}(u)$ being infinite is $1 - G_\infty(0|u) > 0$. In the third part of the paper Everett and Ulam give a rigorous justification for this kind of description of the pnenomenon.

The combination of the theorem of Everett and Ulam, as extended by Bartoszynski and J. and M. Łoś with the above Theorem 4 leads to the following interesting conclusion that, at first sight, appears paradoxical.

Consider an epidemic started at u satisfying the conditions of Theorems 3 and 4 and of the Everett-Ulam theorem. More specifically, consider the total number $N_{Hn}(u)$ of members of the nth generation becoming infectious anywhere in the habitat and the number $N_{Rn}(u)$

of those that became infectious in a limited community R . As mentioned earlier $N_{Rn}(u) \leqq N_{Hn}(u)$. Therefore, and because of (34)

$$P\{N_{Hn}(u) = 0\} \leqq P\{N_{Rn}(u) = 0\} \leqq G_n(1-\alpha|u) \quad . \tag{44}$$

However, because of the Everett-Ulam theorem, as $n \to \infty$ the extreme right part of (44) tends to the same limit as that of the extreme left. It follows that

$$\lim_{n\to\infty} P\{N_{Rn}(u) = 0\} = \lim_{n\to\infty} P\{N_{Hn}(u) = 0\} \quad . \tag{45}$$

In other words, under the conditions stated, the probability of ultimate extinction of an epidemic started, say in a village in Mississippi and developing in the whole of the United States, is exactly the same as the probability of ultimate extinction of the subepidemic developing say in Berkeley, California ! The intuitive explanation is, of course, that (i) if the whole epidemic becomes extinct, so must its part developing in Berkeley and (ii) if the whole epidemic does not become extinct and, as time goes on, the number of infectious grows indefinitely, Berkeley cannot escape being afflicted by the same epidemic.

8. Epidemics continuously generated by immigrants.

In this section we deduce a formula characterizing the development of hypothetical epidemics continuously nurtured by mutations of bacteria (or by immigrations) occurring at rates constant in time. Here we refer to the hypotheses of "immigrants" described in Section 2. Specifically, we use the assumption that there exists a function $\lambda(x)$ defined, nonnegative and continuous at almost all points x in the habitat H such that, whatever may be the region R, the number of new cases of the disease considered occurring in R at the beginning of any given serial period, due to mutated bacteria or to real immigrants, is a Poisson variable $\alpha(R)$ with expectation

$$E[\alpha(R)] = \int_R \lambda(x)\,dx \quad . \tag{46}$$

It is reasonable to assume that $\lambda(x)$ so defined must be proportional to the local density of the population and that, therefore, it must depend upon the particular epoch considered. However, in the present paper we leave this possibility out of consideration and assume that $\lambda(x)$ remains constant in time. Also, we assume that as time goes on, the dispersal functions and the distributions of the numbers $\nu(u)$ infected by a single infectious at point u remain unchanged.

As before, let $R_1, R_2, \ldots, R_s$ be arbitrary disjoint regions in the habitat H and let X_i denote the number of new cases of the disease considered occurring at the beginning of a serial period that we shall describe as the present, or $t = 0$. Our problem is to find an expression for the joint probability generating function of $X_1, X_2, \ldots, X_s$.

We begin by noting that any one of these variables, say X_i, can be considered as a sum of an infinity of mutually independent components. The first of these components is $\alpha(R_i) = \alpha_i$ (say), the number of cases occurring at time $t = 0$ within R_i, due to fresh immigrations or mutations. The next component, that we shall denote by $\beta_1(R_i) = \beta_{1i}$ (say), is the number of new cases in R_i resulting from mutants at time $t = -T$ occurring anywhere in H. Similarly β_{ni} will stand for the number of new cases at time $t = 0$ in R_i that result from mutants that occurred anywhere in H at time $t = -nT$. It follows that

$$X_i = \alpha_i + \sum_{n=1}^{\infty} \beta_{ni} \quad . \tag{47}$$

The assumptions of independence adopted at the outset imply that all the components of the sum in (47) are mutually independent. However, β_{ni} is not independent of β_{nj}. It follows that the probability generating function of $X_1, X_2, \ldots, X_s$ is an infinite product, say,

$$\begin{aligned} G_{\underset{\sim}{X}}(\underset{\sim}{t}) &= G_{X_1, X_2, \ldots, X_s}(t_1, t_2, \ldots, t_s) \\ &= \left(\exp\left\{ - \sum_{i=1}^{s} (1-t_i) \int_{R_i} \lambda(x)\,dx \right\} \right) \prod_{n=1}^{\infty} G_{\underset{\sim}{\beta}_n}(\underset{\sim}{t}) \end{aligned} \tag{48}$$

where, for brevity,

$$G_{\underset{\sim}{\beta}_n}(\underset{\sim}{t}) = G_{\beta_{n1}, \beta_{n2}, \ldots, \beta_{ns}}(t_1, t_2, \ldots, t_s) \quad . \tag{49}$$

It follows that, in order to obtain the formula for $G_{\underset{\sim}{X}}(\underset{\sim}{t})$ it is sufficient to obtain $G_{\underset{\sim}{\beta}}(\underset{\sim}{t})$. This can be evaluated by an easy application of the formula on conditional expectations. Omitting the details, we give the final result

$$G_{\underset{\sim}{\beta}_n}(\underset{\sim}{t}) = \exp\left\{ - \int_H [1 - G_n(t_1, t_2, \ldots, t_s | x]\lambda(x)\,dx \right\} , \tag{50}$$

where $G_n(t_1, t_2, \ldots, t_s | x)$ is the probability generating function of the nth generation of an epidemic in $R_1, R_2, \ldots, R_s$ started by a single infectious at x, see Section 6.

Using (48) and (50) we obtain

$$G_{\underset{\sim}{X}}(\underset{\sim}{t}) = \exp\left\{-\sum_{i=1}^{s}(1-t_i)\int_{R_i}\lambda(x)\,dx\right\} G^*_{\underset{\sim}{X}}(\underset{\sim}{t}) , \tag{51}$$

where

$$G^*_{\underset{\sim}{X}}(\underset{\sim}{t}) = \exp\left\{-\int_H \lambda(x)\sum_{n=1}^{\infty}\left[1 - G_n(t_1, t_2, \ldots, t_s | x)\right] dx\right\} \tag{52}$$

represents the p. g. f. of the numbers of new cases in the s regions considered, generated by mutations occurring some time in the past. It is formula (52) that is of particular interest.

One of the problems repeatedly referred to by Bailey is that of a chance mechanism implying the observed quasi-periodic recurrence of epidemics. In the present framework of ideas the study of this and of similar problems reduces to the study of the integral in the exponent in (52). One theorem concerned with this situation is immediate.

Theorem 5. (i) If

$$\int_H \lambda(x)\,dx = \lambda < +\infty , \tag{53}$$

(ii) If the least upper bound ν_1 of the expectation $E[\nu(u)] = \lambda_1(u)$ for $u \in H$ is less than unity and

(iii) the least upper bound, say ρ, of $P\{\nu(u) = 0\}$ is also less than unity.

Then, whatever be the dispersal functions $f(x|u)$, the p. g. f. of the total number, say X^*, of new cases originating from earlier mutations anywhere in the habitat H, is contained between the limits

$$\exp\left\{-\lambda\frac{\nu_1}{1-\nu_1}(1-t)\right\} \leqq \exp\left\{-\lambda\frac{1-\rho}{\rho}(1-t)\right\} . \tag{54}$$

It will be seen that the two extreme expressions in (54) are themselves p.g.f.'s, namely of Poisson variables. Also, (54) implies that the expectation of X^* is bounded by

$$\lambda\frac{1-\rho}{\rho} \leqq E(X^*) \leqq \lambda\frac{\nu_1}{1-\nu_1} . \tag{55}$$

The proof is based on a double inequality valid for any probability generating function $h(t)$ with finite expectation h_1, namely

$$1 - (1-t)h_1 \leqq h(t) \leqq t + h(0)(1-t) \quad . \tag{56}$$

This double inequality, applied to each $g(t|u)$, implies that, if ν_1 and ρ are the least upper bounds of $E[\nu(u)]$ and of $P\{\nu(u) = 0\}$, respectively, then

$$1 - \rho \leqq \nu_1 \quad , \tag{57}$$

which insures the consistency of formulas (54) and (55). Furthermore, if $\nu_1 = 1 - \rho$, then this implies that for every $u \in H$

$$g(t|u) = 1 - \nu_1(1-t) \quad . \tag{58}$$

In this case each infectious individual would have the probability ν_1 of infecting just one susceptible and could not infect any more. This circumstance makes it intuitively clear why, in this case, the two bounds in (54) coincide and the random variable X^* must have a Poisson distribution.

Turning to the proof of Theorem 5 we begin by noticing that, if we are concerned with only $s = 1$ region and if this region represents the whole habitat H, then

$$\begin{aligned} G_1(t|u) &= g(t|u) \quad , \\ G_2(t|u) &= g\left[\int_H G_1(t|x)\, f(x|u)\, dx \,\Big|\, u\right] \quad , \end{aligned} \tag{59}$$

and, generally,

$$G_{n+1}(t|u) = g\left[\int_H G_n(t|x)\, f(x|u)\, dx \,\Big|\, u\right] \quad . \tag{60}$$

Applying (56) to $G_1(t|u)$ we obtain

$$1 - \nu_1(u)(1-t) \leqq G_1(t|u) \leqq t + (1-t)\, P\{\nu(u) = 0\} \quad , \tag{61}$$

and it is obvious that

$$1 - \nu_1(1-t) \leqq G_1(t|u) \leqq t + (1-t)\rho = 1 - (1-\rho)(1-t) \quad . \tag{62}$$

Again, applying (56) to $G_2(t|u)$ as in (59) we write

$$1 - \nu_1 \left[1 - \int_H G_1(t|x) f(x|u)\, dx\right] \leq G_2(t|u) \leq 1 - (1-\rho) \left[1 - \int_H G_1(t|x) f(x|u)\, dx\right] . \tag{63}$$

Taking (62) into account, inequality (63) is replaced by

$$1 - \nu_1^2 (1-t) \leq G_2(t|u) \leq 1 - (1-\rho)^2 (1-t) , \tag{64}$$

where the two extreme expressions do not depend upon u. Formulas (62) and (64) suggest that, in general, that is, for all $n = 1, 2, \ldots,$

$$1 - \nu_1^n (1-t) \leq G_n(t|u) \leq 1 - (1-\rho)^n (1-t) . \tag{65}$$

Using (60) this formula (65) is, in fact, easily established by induction. It implies that

$$\lambda(1-\rho)^n (1-t) \leq \int_H [1 - G_n(t|x)]\, \lambda(x)\, dx \leq \lambda \nu_1^n (1-t) \tag{66}$$

and that, therefore,

$$\lambda \frac{1-\rho}{\rho} (1-t) \leq - \log G_X^* (t) \leq \lambda \frac{\nu_1}{1-\nu_1} (1-t) , \tag{67}$$

which establishes Theorem 5.

It will be seen that, while the conditions of Theorem 5 are sufficient for the nondegeneracy of X^*, they can hardly be expected to be necessary. Furthermore, these conditions are so restrictive that the conclusion of the theorem is true for all possible families of dispersal functions. Thus, contemplating Theorem 5, one might perhaps obtain the idea that in the problems considered the role of the dispersal functions is not significant. The discussion of a specific example given in the next section indicates that such an idea is definitely false.

9. Example indicating that $\beta_1(R)$, corresponding to a bounded region R, may be nondegenerate or equal to infinity with probability one depending upon the dispersal functions.

In this section we consider a somewhat paradoxical example of a random variable $\beta_1(R) = \beta_1$ (say) representing the number of new cases in a finite region R originating from mutants occurring a unit time ago anywhere in the habitat. Let R be a unit square about the origin of coordinates, say $|x_i| \leqq a = 0.5$, for $i = 1, 2$. We shall assume a uniform distribution of mutations over the habitat, so that $\lambda(x) \equiv \lambda$. Also, we shall assume an apparently innocent distribution of $\nu(u)$, which is the number infected by a single infectious at $u = (u_1, u_2)$. In fact we shall assume that this distribution is independent of u and that it is given by

$$(68) \qquad \begin{aligned} &P\{\nu = 0\} = P\{\nu = 1\} = \gamma , \\ &P\{\nu = n\} = \frac{1-2\gamma}{n(n-1)}, \qquad \text{for } n = 2, 3, \ldots . \end{aligned}$$

Here γ must be less than 0.5 but may be just as close to 0.5 as desired. With γ close to 0.5, assumption (68) implies that each new infective will have an almost 50-50 chance of infecting no one or just one person but that, in exceptional cases, the probability of which is $1 - 2\gamma$ or almost zero, he may infect more, 2, 3, ... The p. g. f. of ν is then

$$(69) \qquad g(t) = \gamma(1+t) + (1-2\gamma)\, g_0(t) ,$$

with

$$(70) \qquad g_0(t) = t + (1-t)\log(1-t)$$

representing a probability generating function with $P\{X = n\} = 1/n(n-1)$ for $n = 2, 3, \ldots$.

In the example discussed it is this p. g. f. $g_0(t)$ that plays the decisive role. Figure 2 shows the graph of the distribution corresponding to $g_0(t)$ and it is easy to visualize the general appearance of the distribution that corresponds to $g(t)$, with any selected value of γ: the first two possible values of ν, that is, 0 and 1, will have substantial probabilities γ and all other values will be very improbable. If anything, one would probably judge that the p. g. f. has been selected "conservatively."

The point of the example is that, notwithstanding this "conservatism," the distributions $g(t)$ and $g_0(t)$ have infinite expectations. As a result, the left bound in the double inequality (56) has no meaning and can be replaced by zero.

In order to make our example entirely specific, we must make some assumption regarding the dispersal functions $f(x|u)$. For the moment we shall assume only that, for each $u = (u_1, u_2)$

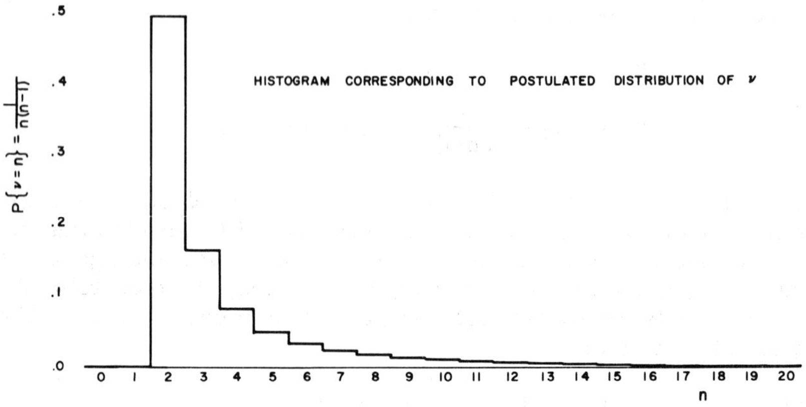

Figure 2

Graph of the distribution corresponding to $g_0(t)$, postulated for the number ν .

$$f(x|u) = \varphi(x_1-u_1)\ \varphi(x_2-u_2) \tag{71}$$

where the function φ is a one-dimensional probability density. Later we shall make several specific assumptions regarding φ.

For the single unit square region R the p.g.f. of β_1 is

$$G_{\beta_1}(t) = \exp\left\{-\lambda \int_H \{1-g[1-(1-t)\,p(u)]\}\,du\right\}. \tag{72}$$

We shall examine this p.g.f. taking $\gamma = 0$ so that g is replaced by g_0. Returning to (70), replacing t by $[1-(1-t)\,p(u)]$ and substituting the result in (72) we obtain

$$G_{\beta_1}(t) = \exp\left\{-\lambda(1-t)[1-\log(1-t)]\int_H p(u)\,du - \lambda(1-t)\int_H p(u)\,|\log p(u)|\,du\right\}. \tag{73}$$

Using (71) we have

$$\begin{aligned} p(u) &= \int f(x|u)\,dx = \int_{-a}^{+a}\varphi(x_1-u_1)\,dx_1 \int_{-a}^{+a}\varphi(x_2-u_2)\,dx_2 \\ &= \pi(u_1)\,\pi(u_2) \quad (\text{say}) \end{aligned} \tag{74}$$

and it follows that

$$\int_H p(u)\,du = \int_{-\infty}^{+\infty}\pi(u_1)\,du_1 \int_{-\infty}^{+\infty}\pi(u_2)\,du_2 . \tag{75}$$

Easy calculations show that each of the integrals in the right side of (75) is equal to unity, irrespective of the function φ. Thus, the value of (75) is unity. Simple algebra shows that the second integral in the right side of (73) has the value

$$\int_H p(u)\,|\log p(u)|\,du = 2\int_{-\infty}^{+\infty}\pi(u)\,|\log \pi(u)|\,du = I \quad (\text{say}) \tag{76}$$

and that it does depend on the nature of φ. It follows that the p.g.f.

$$G_{\beta_1}(t) = h_1(t)\,h_2(t|\varphi) , \tag{77}$$

where both functions $h_1(t)$ and $h_2(t)$ happen to be probability generating functions. The first is independent of the dispersal function and has the form

$$h_1(t) = e^{-\lambda(1-t)[1-\log(1-t)]} . \tag{78}$$

The random variable having this p. g. f. (78) will be denoted by N_1. The other function $h_2(t|\varphi)$ has the form

$$h_2(t|\varphi) = e^{-\lambda I(1-t)} . \tag{79}$$

Provided the integral I is convergent, the random variable corresponding to $h_2(t|\varphi)$, say N_2, is the familiar Poisson variable with expectation

$$E(N_2) = \lambda I . \tag{80}$$

On the other hand, if I is divergent, then $h_2 \equiv 0$ and $N_2 = +\infty$ with probability one. It follows from (56) that

$$\beta_1 = N_1 + N_2 , \tag{81}$$

where N_1 and N_2 are mutually independent. As mentioned, the distribution of N_1 is independent of the dispersal function. Simple calculations show that all the moments of N_1 are infinite.

The probabilities that N_1, N_2, and their sum β_1 will have specified values can be calculated recursively. Using the familiar procedure, we notice that the first derivative of the relevant p. g. f. is equal to the product of this same function by the derivative of its logarithm. Differentiating this product n times, substituting $t = 0$ and replacing the kth derivative of the p. g. f. by k! times the probability that the relevant variable will assume the value k, for $k = 0, 1, \ldots,$ we obtain a formula representing the probability of the value $n+1$ as a linear combination of probabilities as smaller values of the same variable. This method applied to (78) yields

$$\begin{aligned} &P\{N_1 = 0\} = e^{-\lambda} \\ &P\{N_1 = 1\} = 0 \\ &P\{N_1 = k\} = \frac{\lambda}{k} \sum_{i=0}^{k-2} \frac{1}{k-i-1} P\{N_1 = i\}, \quad \text{for } k = 2, 3, \ldots . \end{aligned} \tag{82}$$

Figure 3 shows the distribution of N_1 for selected values of λ. As the value of λ increases, the distribution becomes very flat. However, the irregularities for small values of N_1 persist, as can still be seen in the ten-fold enlargement in the lower panel of the figure.

Since N_2 is a Poisson variable, we have immediately from (79),

$$(83) \qquad P\{N_2 = k\} = e^{-\lambda I} \frac{(\lambda I)^k}{k!} \quad \text{for } k = 0, 1, \ldots .$$

In the computations shown in Figure 4, the function φ appearing in the dispersal function $f(x|u)$ is taken to be the familiar Normal density with varying values of the variance equal to T. This is motivated as follows.

Up to the present, the length T of the incubation period of the disease in question did not play any role. However, just as soon as we begin to take into account the mobility of the individuals forming the population, the length of the incubation period becomes important. The assumption underlying the Normal density taken for φ results from the presumption that the individuals forming the population studied move about more or less like particles in a Brownian motion. In this case each of the coordinates of an individual at time T is a normal variable with a variance proportional to T or, with an appropriate adjustment of units, with a variance equal to T. Thus the calculations performed taking different values for T correspond to varying assumptions regarding the length of the incubation period.

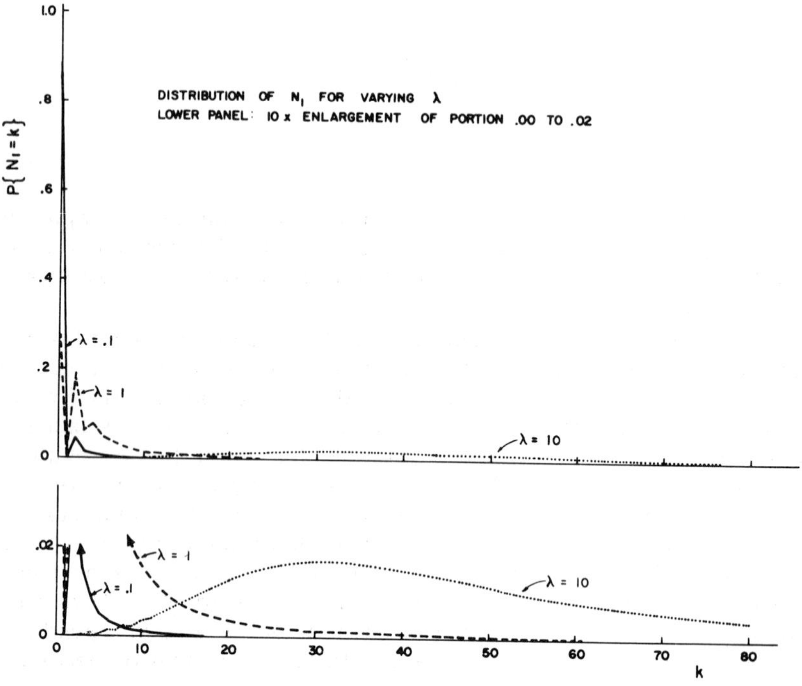

Figure 3

The distribution of N_1 for selected values of λ .

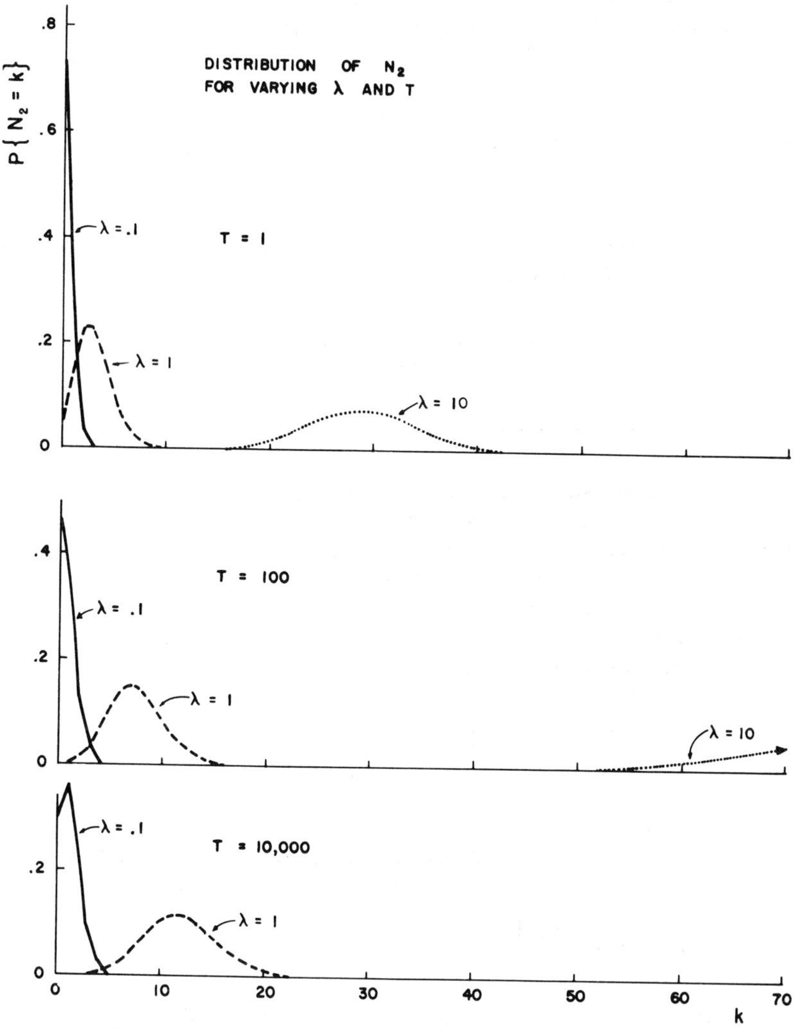

Figure 4

The distribution of N_2 for selected values of λ and of T .

Under this assumption that the dispersal function (71) is the product of Normal densities each with variance T, the integral I needed to compute the probabilities (83) for N_2 must be calculated numerically. This was done using the definition (76) of I with

$$(84) \qquad \pi(u) = \frac{1}{\sqrt{2\pi}} \int_{(-u-0.5)/\sqrt{T}}^{(-u+0.5)/\sqrt{T}} e^{-z^2/2}\, dz$$

from (74). The resulting values of I depending upon T are as follows, for selected values of T.

T	1	100	10,000
I	2.9	7.4	12.0

Easy calculations show that, as $T \to \infty$, the integral I tends to infinity. The probability distribution of N_2 is shown in Figure 4 for varying λ and varying T. The distribution becomes flatter and shifts to higher k when either λ or T increases. When both increase the effect is very striking.

The variable of practical interest is $N_1 + N_2 = \beta_1$, the number of new cases in an arbitrary unit square of the habitat. We have, from (81),

$$(85) \qquad P\{\beta_1 = k\} = \sum_{r=0}^{k} P\{N_1 = r\}\, P\{N_2 = k - r\}$$

or we can compute the probability distribution recursively from the p.g.f. (73) with (75) and (76),

$$(86) \qquad P\{\beta_1 = 0\} = e^{-\lambda(1+I)}$$

$$(87) \qquad P\{\beta_1 = k\} = \frac{\lambda}{k}\left[I\, P\{\beta_1 = k-1\} + \sum_{i=0}^{k-2} \frac{1}{k-i-1} P\{\beta_1 = i\}\right], \quad \text{for } k = 1, 2, \ldots .$$

The resulting distribution is shown in Figure 5 for varying λ and varying T. The distribution of β_1 is noticeably flatter and more shifted to the right than either of its components N_1 and N_2.

The figure illustrates a paradoxical result. Given a specified density λ of mutations, given the distribution of the number ν of

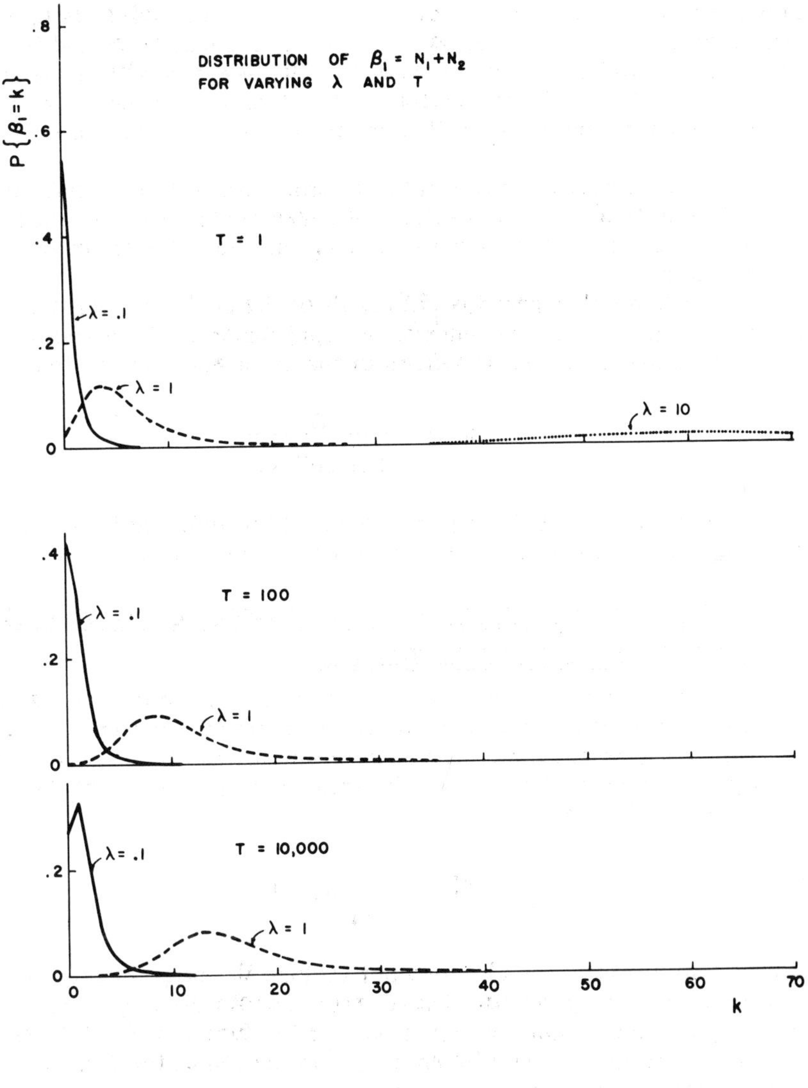

Figure 5

The distribution of $\beta_1 = N_1 + N_2$, the number of new cases.

individuals infected by a single infectious, and given that the dispersal of infected proceeds as in Brownian motion, the probability that an arbitrary unit square R in the habitat will have more than any specified number of new cases, say 100 new cases, depends upon the length of the incubation period T . If this incubation period is short then the probability of having more than 100 new cases in R is tiny. However, if the incubation period is long then this probability is large; the probability increases as T increases and can be shown to tend to unity.

The computations shown in the figures were ably performed on the IBM 7090 by Mrs. J. L. Lovasich, who was assisted in the checking by Mr. Pal Bhasin. We want to express our appreciation for their excellent help.

There is another paradoxical result of the same kind as that illustrated in Figure 5. If the function φ, appearing in the dispersal function, behaves for large values of the argument $|x|$ so that

$$\pi(x) = \frac{C}{|x|\log^2|x|}, \tag{88}$$

then the integral I is divergent. Thus, if the infected have this kind of mobility, the probability that $\beta_1 = +\infty$ is equal to unity.

10. Total size of an epidemic started by a single infectious and the effect of an immunization campaign.

Returning to the general setup of Sections 4, 5 and 6, we shall consider the total number, say $N(u)$ of infected anywhere in the habitat during an epidemic started by a single infectious at u . Denoting, as formerly, by $N_n(u)$ the total nth generation of the same epidemic we shall have

$$N(u) = \sum_{n=1}^{\infty} N_n(u) . \tag{89}$$

Notice that the total $N(u)$ does not include the original infectious at u who starts the epidemic. Let $G(t|u)$ denote the p.g.f. of $N(u)$. Our purpose is to obtain an equation that the function $G(t|u)$ must satisfy. This is achieved by an easy application of the formula on conditional expectations. We have:

$$G(t|u) = E[t^{N(u)}] = E\{E[t^{N(u)} \mid N_1(u)]\} \tag{90}$$

or, remembering (88),

(91) $$G(t|u) = E\left\{ t^{N_1(u)} E\left[t^{\sum_2^\infty N_n(u)} \middle| N_1(u) \right] \right\}.$$

Now, suppose that $N_1(u) = k > 0$. On this assumption, $\sum_2^\infty N_n(u)$ is the sum of k independent components, each representing the total epidemic $N(x)$ started by a single infectious of the first generation, where x stands for the location of this infectious. This location is random with the probability density $f(x|u)$. Thus, the unconditional p. g. f. the total epidemic started by one individual who himself became infected at u is

(92) $$\int_H G(t|x)\, f(x|u)\, dx = h(t|u),$$

say, and

(93) $$E\left[t^{\sum_2^\infty N_n(u)} \middle| N_1(u) = k \right] = \{h(t|u)\}^k .$$

Since the p. g. f. of $N_1(u)$ is $g(t|u)$, it follows

(94) $$G(t|u) = g[th(t|u)|u],$$

which is the equation sought. Substituting in it x for u, multiplying by $f(x|u)$ and integrating, we obtain

(95) $$h(t|u) = \int_H g[th(t|x)|x]\, f(x|u)\, dx .$$

Thus far very little is known about the general equations (94) and (95). Because of the definition (89) of the random variable $N(u)$ it is clear that

(96) $$P\{N(u) = 0\} = P\{\nu(u) = 0\},$$

which means that, for every u, the p. g. f. $G(0|u) = g(0|u)$. Another obvious property of $N(u)$ is that it may well have infinite values. Thus we must be prepared to find that, in some circumstances,

(97) $$P\{N(u) < +\infty\} = G(1|u) < 1 \ .$$

Then $P\{N(u) = +\infty\} = 1 - G(1|u) > 0$. The general conditions expressed in terms of the p.g.f.'s $g(t|u)$ and of the dispersal functions $f(x|u)$ implying the explosive character of the epidemic, as in (97), are an interesting subject for further studies. In a preliminary manner we notice the following circumstances. We assume that $g(0|u) = P\{\nu(u) = 0\} < 1$.

Because of equation (94) and because $g(t|u)$ is equal to unity only for $t = 1$, in order that $G(1|u) < 1$ for a particular u, it is necessary and sufficient that $h(1|u) < 1$. Equation (95) implies then that $h(1|x) < 1$ for a set of points x the measure of which is greater than zero. Under the extra assumption that $f(x|u) > 0$ for all x and u in H, equation (95) implies then that $h(1|0) < 1$ for all u and that, therefore, $G(1|u) < 1$ for all $u \in H$. Thus, we have proved the following theorem.

Theorem 6. *If $P\{\nu(u) = 0\} < 1$ and $f(x|u) > 0$ for all x and u, and if there exists in the habitat a point u_0 such that the total size of an epidemic started at u_0 by a single infectious has a positive probability of being infinite, then the same will be true for all points $u \in H$.*

This theorem has an obvious connection with Theorem 3. However, Theorem 3 does not necessarily imply Theorem 6 because the random variable $N(u)$ may well assume an infinite value without any of the components in the right side of (89) being infinite.

A special case investigated by Otter corresponds to the situation where $g(t|u) = g(t)$ is independent of u. Then equations (94) and (95) yield

(98) $$G(t) = h(t) = g[tG(t)] \ .$$

Otter found an elegant explicit solution for $G(t)$ when ν is a Poisson variable. In general, a graph can easily be found corresponding to $G(t)$ of (98) providing a graph for $g(t)$ is known. The construction is as follows. Fix a value of t and let $tG(t) = \tau$. Then equation (98) gives $G(t) = g(\tau)$ where

(99) $$t = \tau/g(\tau) \ .$$

Hence, if the value of g is known for every τ, in order to obtain a graph of $G(t)$ it is sufficient to plot $g(\tau)$ against $t = \tau/g(\tau)$. The situation is illustrated in Figure 6. Since t must not exceed unity, the construction applies to the values of $\tau \leqq \lambda$ where $\lambda \leqq 1$ is the root of the equation $\lambda = g(\lambda)$. In all cases, $G(1) = \lambda$ which

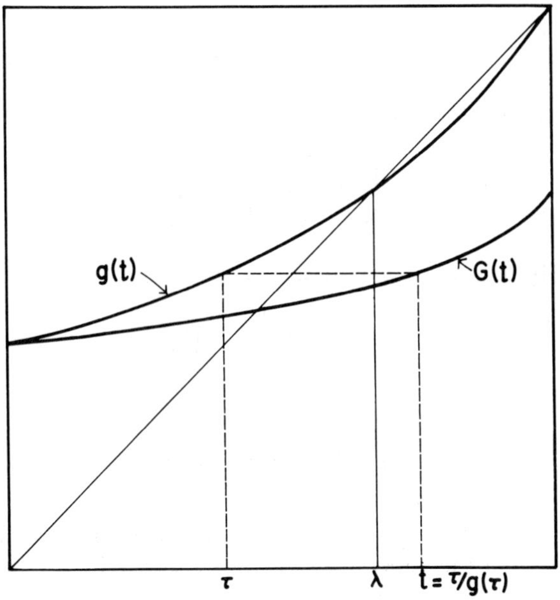

Figure 6

Graph of $G(t)$ constructed from that of $g(t)$.

is the probability that the total epidemic will have a finite value. Also $P\{N = \infty\} = 1 - \lambda$. An explicit formula for $G(t)$ can be obtained provided one can obtain an explicit solution for τ of the equation

(100) $$\tau = tg(\tau) \quad .$$

In particular, this solution is available when

(101) $$g(t) = [1 + \vartheta - \vartheta t]^{-1} \quad ,$$

that is, when the distribution of ν is geometric,

(102) $$P\{\nu = n\} = \frac{1}{1+\vartheta}\left(\frac{\vartheta}{1+\vartheta}\right)^n , \qquad \vartheta > 0 \quad .$$

In this case equation (100) reduces to a quadratic

$$\vartheta\tau^2 - (1+\vartheta)\tau + t = 0 \tag{103}$$

and easy calculations yield, for $0 \leqq t \leqq 1$,

$$G(t) = \frac{1+\vartheta}{2\vartheta t}\left\{1 - \left[1 - \frac{4\vartheta t}{(1+\vartheta)^2}\right]^{1/2}\right\}, \tag{104}$$

which is easily expanded in powers of t. At $t = 0$

$$G(0) = g(0) = \frac{1}{1+\vartheta} . \tag{105}$$

Also

$$G(1) = \frac{2}{1 + \vartheta + |1-\vartheta|} . \tag{106}$$

If $0<\vartheta\leqq 1$ this yields $G(1) = 1$. On the other hand, if $\vartheta > 1$, then $G(1) = 1/\vartheta < 1$ and the total size of the epidemic has a positive probability, namely $(\vartheta-1)/\vartheta$, of becoming infinite.

As mentioned in Section 1, Professor Cochran inquired about the possibility of using the present model of epidemics in order to evaluate the effect that an immunization campaign may have on the expected size of the total epidemic.

The variable $\nu(u)$ that plays a basic role in the present model, represents the number of individuals that would be infected (and eventually would become infectious themselves) if at point u there is a person undergoing his brief period of infectiousness. In the present instance, this would be the susceptible individuals prior to the immunization campaign. If such a campaign immunizes a sizeable proportion of the population, then, at least at some points u in the habitat, the distribution of $\nu(u)$ will be altered. Let $g(t|u)$ and $g^*(t|u)$ represent the p. g. f. 's of $\nu(u)$ prior to and after the immunization campaign. The effect of the campaign can be investigated by studying equations (94) and (95) corresponding to the same system of dispersal functions but to two different systems of p. g. f. 's, $g(t|u)$ and $g^*(t|u)$. At the outset, it is obvious that the effect of immunization must depend on the details of the campaign. Ordinarily, the individuals immunized will not be randomly selected from the total population but will be members of specific categories, such as school children, soldiers, etc. This would mean that for some $u \in H$ the difference between $g(t|u)$ and $g^*(t|u)$ will be very substantial, while in other points it may be nil.

Let $\xi(u)$ represent $E[N|u]$. Limiting ourselves to the case where $G(1|u) \equiv 1$ for all u, it is easy to find that $\xi(u)$ is a solution of the Fredholm type integral equation

$$\xi(u) = \nu_1(u) \left[1 + \int_H \xi(x) f(x|u)\, dx \right] . \tag{107}$$

This equation can be conveniently transformed putting $\xi(u) = \nu_1(u)\rho(u)$. Then $\rho(u)$ satisfies the equation

$$\rho(u) = 1 + \int_H \rho(x) k(x,u)\, dx \tag{108}$$

where the kernel $k(x,u) = \nu_1(x) f(x|u)$. A solution of (108) can be obtained by the familiar method of successive approximations. Multiplying this solution by $\nu_1(u)$ one obtains $\xi(u)$.

For the particular case where $g(t|u)$ and $g^*(t|u)$ do not depend upon u, the effect of immunization is characterized by an elegant formula. Let ξ and ξ^* represent the expected size of the total epidemic without and with immunization, respectively. Similarly let ν_1 and ν_1^* be the expectation of ν in the same conditions. Let $\nu_1^* = \nu_1(1-\theta)$ so that θ stands for the fraction of the susceptible population that becomes immunized. Then, differentiating (98) and setting $t = 1$, we obtain

$$\begin{aligned} \xi &= \nu_1(1+\xi) \\ \xi^* &= (1-\theta)\, \nu_1(1+\xi^*) \end{aligned} \tag{109}$$

and it follows that

$$\xi^* = \frac{(1-\theta)\xi}{1+\theta\xi} < \frac{1-\theta}{\theta} . \tag{110}$$

For example, then, if one immunizes one-half of the total susceptible population, the expected size of the whole epidemic resulting from one infectious will be less than unity. Again, if only 10 per cent of the susceptibles are immunized, the expected total size of the epidemic will be less than 9 .

While this evaluation may appear paradoxically optimistic, it will be remembered that it is based on the assumption that both before and after the immunization campaign, the probability that an infectious individual will infect any specified number k of susceptibles is exactly the same as for any other infectious individual, irrespective of where they are located in the habitat. However, even though this particular assumption is unrealistic, formula (110) does suggest that, in general, a properly conducted immunization campaign must have a very strong effect on the development of an epidemic.

We are grateful to Professor Cochran for calling our attention to the paper by Serfling [9], giving empirical data that appear to corroborate the above qualitative conclusion.

11. Concluding remarks.

Each attempt to treat mathematically a complicated category of phenomena must rely on idealizations of certain factors deemed of predominant importance and must ignore innumerable other factors. The model of epidemics introduced in this paper puts into the foreground two elements of the phenomenon that appear to us of prime importance, namely the mobility over the habitat of individuals who contracted infection and the number of persons that each of them can infect. The proposed idealization of these two factors, through the dispersal functions $f(x|u)$ and through the random number $\nu(u)$ of those infected by a single infective individual at $u = (u_1, u_2)$, respectively, are completely general. The example of Section 9 indicates that, in order to bring the model into conformity with actual facts, certain limitations on this generality will have to be adopted. The exact nature of these necessary limitations may be determined through a further study of the properties of the model.

While dealing explicitly with the geographical distribution of new cases induced by the explicitly treated mobility and infectiveness of those who contracted the disease, the model ignores a number of elements in the development of an epidemic. Whether as a whole this model is close enough to the actual phenomenon to be useful for practical purposes, for example for predictions, can be established only through comparison with the data. However, even if the model proves totally inadequate, it is our hope that the mere process of establishing the model's inadequacy will contribute to a better understanding of the fascinating phenomenon.

REFERENCES

1. Bailey, N. T. J., The Mathematical Theory of Epidemics. Charles Griffin, London (1957).

2. Neyman, J. and Scott, E. L., A theory of the spatial distribution of galaxies, Astrophys. J. Vol. 116 (1952), pp. 144-163.

3. Neyman, J., Sur la théorie probabiliste des amas de galaxies, Ann. Inst. H. Poincaré, Vol. 14 (1955), pp. 201-244.

4. Neyman, J. and Scott, E. L., Stochastic models of population dynamics, Science, Vol. 130 (1959), pp. 303-308.

5. Everett, C. J. and Ulam, S., Multiplicative systems in several variables, I, II, III, Los Alamos Scientific Laboratory Declassified Documents LADC-534 (AECD-2164), LADC-533 (AECD-2165), LA-707, 1948.

6. Harris, T. E., Branching processes, Ann. Math. Stat., Vol. 19 (1948), pp. 474-494.

7. __________, Some mathematical models for branching processes, Proc. Second Berkeley Symp. on Math. Stat. and Prob., Univ. of Calif. Press, Berkeley (1951), pp. 305-328.

8. Otter, R., The multiplicative process, Ann. Math. Stat., Vol. 20 (1949), pp. 206-224.

9. Serfling, R. E. and Langmuir, A. D., A simple mathematical model of bias arising from effectiveness rates calculated from heterogeneous populations with some error in diagnosis (mimeographed paper presented at joint meeting Biometric Society (ENAR) and Institute of Mathematical Statistics, New York, N. Y.) April 21, 1960.

The work on this paper was started with the partial support of the National Science Foundation, Grant GP-10 and completed with the partial support of the National Institutes of Health, Grant GM-10525.

Due to unavoidable and unforseen circumstances Professor Neyman was unable to be present at the symposium. The preceding article, therefore, was not presented orally.

I. OPATOWSKI

Analysis of Degree of Dependence of Pathological Conditions in Two Different Organs: Sclerosis in Aorta and in Coronary Arteries

1. Object of the paper. The theory of atherosclerotic changes of arterial wall suggests that their causes are in general both local and systemic. The former are related to the local anatomy of the affected part and of adjacent tissues, to their mechanical stresses and their characteristics on cellular level, and to hydromechanical pattern of blood flow at the affected site. The latter, less known and to some extent uncertain whether they are causes or effects, or both at the same time, include hypertension and age in physiological sense. An interdependence between degrees of atherosclerosis in different arteries may be caused by systemic factors and by similarities in patterns of local factors; we will refer to all these as common factors. The present paper is an attempt to obtain some information on this interdependence in the more extensively investigated arteries: the thoracic and abdominal aorta, and the coronary arteries.

A handicap in analyzing quantitative data on the degree and extent of atherosclerosis is the presence of several random variables and the relatively limited size of the samples. Because of this, concepts are used which have a direct intuitive meaning, to make conclusions more easily comparable with general knowledge in the field.

2. Data used. The most common types of quantitative data on atherosclerosis use a set of numbers to characterize its degree, increasing numbers corresponding to higher severity or larger extension of sclerosis. Most of the authors have used a discrete scale consisting of few consecutive integers starting from 0, some others - more complex systems approaching a continuous scale. The data here used are those of S. Glagov et al. [1], whose grades 0, 1, ..., 5 for aorta, and 0, 1, ..., 4 for coronary arteries, are linearly transformed to make their maximum grades equal both to 5.5 and minimum to 0.5 and 0.7 respectively. Although the new grades require one digit after the decimal point, they express better the conditions at the lowest grade, which corresponds to a "trace" of atherosclerosis

(cf. [1]) and is more likely to be underestimated in coronary arteries than in aorta, because of the much smaller size of the former.

The data (cf. Figure 1 and Table I) refer to white males above 30 years of age: 54 normotensives (age range: 30-75, mean: 56 years) and 17 hypertensives (age range: 41-74, mean 57.8 years). Because of their small number, smoothing was not feasible for hypertensives, and no special analysis of this group was made beyond a few calculations of means.

3. Ratios of grades of atherosclerosis in different arteries of the same person and their common atherosclerotic factors. Figures 2, 3 and Table II are results of analysis of this ratio which is of interest not only in itself, but also because it offers some means of estimating the effects of common factors, even if the nature of the latter is unknown. In fact, assuming for a moment that no common atherosclerotic factors exist in two arteries of the same person, i.e., that their grades of atherosclerosis are statistically independent, the probability $P_i(r)$ that the ratio of these two grades be $\leq r$ can be calculated from the separate probabilities of the two grades, by elementary law of compound probability. The function $P_i(r)$ compared with a similar probability function obtained from direct observations of the two arteries, gives some idea on the effects of common factors.

Symbols A, T, C, will be used for grades of atherosclerosis in abdominal aorta, thoracic aorta and coronary arteries respectively; functions related to these grades will be indicated by subscripts A, T, C. The ratio $r = A/T$ (and similarly for A/C) will be analyzed by the following method: If $p_A(A)\, dA$ is the probability that an abdominal aorta have a grade between A and $A + dA$, and similarly $p_T(T)\, dT$ for the thoracic aorta, then:

$$P_i(r) = \iint p_A(A)\, p_T(T)\, dA dT \tag{1}$$

integrated over that part of the square $0 \leq A, T \leq 5.5$ which is below the straight line $A = rT$. This integral is easily transformed to:

$$P_i(r) = I(r;\, 1) \quad \text{for } r \leq 1,$$

$$P_i(r) = 1 - P^* + I(r;\, P^*) \quad \text{for } r \geq 1,$$

where

$$P^* = P_T\,(5.5/r),$$

$$I(r;\, M) = \int_{P_T=0}^{P_T=M} P_A(rT)\, dP_T(T)$$

and $\underline{P}_A(\underline{A}) = \int_0^{\underline{A}} \underline{p}_A(\underline{A})\, d\underline{A}$, $\underline{P}_T(\underline{T}) = \int_0^{\underline{T}} \underline{p}_T(\underline{T})\, d\underline{T}$ are the curves $\underline{P}$ of Figure 1. Calculations of $\underline{I}$ require elimination of $\underline{T}$ between the functions $\underline{P}_T(\underline{T})$ and $\underline{P}_A(\underline{A})$ when $\underline{A} = \underline{rT}$. This is done by plotting $\underline{P}_A(\underline{rT})$ against the corresponding values of $\underline{P}_T(\underline{T})$ for each constant $\underline{r}$ considered. The integration is then carried out by Simpson's rule. The method, although laborious, eliminates smoothing that a direct use of (1) would have required. Results of analysis are summarized in Figures 2, 3, (full lines) and Table II. Comparing the lines ($\underline{i}$) with ($\underline{d}$), and (0) with (Δ) of Table II, it is seen that the effects of common factors (other than hypertension) are of the same type as those of hypertension: reduction of the mean values of the ratios $\underline{A}/\underline{T}$ and $\underline{A}/\underline{C}$, of their range and of their deviations from the mean. Simple algebra shows that this reduction of the ratios can occur only when common factors increase the effects of other factors by an amount which, in the average, is smaller than would have been required by a direct proportionality relationship. This is confirmed by an inspection of the $\overline{\underline{G}}$ column in Table I which shows an increase of the three normotensive average grades of 2.96, 2.11, 1.85 by 44.9%, 47.9% and 88.1% respectively, as a consequence of hypertension.

4. Comparison with correlation analysis. If the grades of atherosclerosis in two arteries were statistically independent, the two fully drawn curves in Figure 2 (or Figure 3) would be identical; the correlation coefficient between the grades would be zero. These two facts form the basis for obtaining some idea about the interdependence of the two variables. Applied to the present data, both methods appear to be concordant only in a broad qualitative sense. The method based on probabilistic analysis of the ratio $\underline{r}$ of the two variables concludes with a comparison of two probability functions which have a direct intuitive meaning and are calculable in the whole range of $\underline{r}$ (cf. Figures 2, 3); the usual method of correlation formulates the results in a single quantitative statement: the magnitude of the correlation coefficient. The former method works with one random variable each time, and does not need to face the problem of smoothing multidimensional data.

Table III gives correlation coefficients for the data analyzed in previous sections, and also for a set of recent Swedish data [2]. Both show about the same correlation pattern, although the Swedish data refer to a somewhat different type of material (110 males, above 25 years of age, about 12 years older in average than in previous data), and use a somewhat different grading scale. The coefficients in Table III were found to be, in both sets of data, significant in 2nd and 3rd columns and probably significant in 4th column, by the conventional significance estimate method (cf. [2]).

The analysis of previous sections (Figures 2, 3, Table II) as well as the correlation coefficients indicate that there is an appreciable interdependence between atherosclerosis in the two parts of the same aorta, as well as between abdominal aorta and coronary arteries. The correlation coefficients indicate in addition, that there is more interdependence between the two parts of the aorta, than between abdominal aorta and coronary arteries; this is plausible by anatomical considerations. According to the last column of Table III (which has a lower statistical significance than the other columns) the degree of interdependence between atheroscleroses in thoracic aorta and in coronary arteries is small; no smooth diagram of the type of Figure 3 could be obtained for the ratio $\underline{T}/\underline{C}$. A partial explanation why the correlation coefficients ($\underline{T}, \underline{C}$) are smaller than ($\underline{A}, \underline{C}$) (cf. Table III) may be the fact that the abdominal aorta has a branching system of a more complex geometry than the thoracic aorta, and in this sense the coronary arteries have more characteristics in common with abdominal aorta than with thoracic aorta.

Figure 1

Probability $\underline{P}$ of a grade $\leq \underline{G}$ to occur in abdominal aorta ($\underline{A}$), thoracic aorta ($\underline{T}$) and coronary arteries ($\underline{C}$); details in text. The normotensives fit the full lines without smoothing. (The only cross + deviating from the $\underline{C}$-curve at $\underline{G} = 4.3$ is due to unusually few coronary arteries at this grade). Dotted lines are for hypertensives. All lines are extrapolated to $\underline{P} = 0$ below the lowest computed points. The statistically higher grades in hypertensives than in normotensives, and in abdominal than in thoracic aortas are apparent from the curves.

Figure 2

Probability that the ratio of the grade of atherosclerosis in abdominal aorta to the grade in thoracic part of the same aorta be $\leq \underline{A}/\underline{T}$. The points correspond to ratios actually observed, the line through crosses + is the hypothetical probability calculated from curves of Figure 1 under the assumption that both grades are statistically independent. 0 = normotensives, Δ = hypertensives. The differences between the ordinates of the two 0-curves have a regular pattern and are interpretable as due to factors (other than hypertension) common to the two arteries. These differences are quite large, mainly for higher values of $\underline{A}/\underline{T}$, indicating that local factors in one artery but not in the other are here very intense. For instance, if no atherosclerotic factors common to abdominal and thoracic aorta existed, 90% of the population of the sample would have had the ratio of grades in these two arteries ≤ 5.4; computations from observations give this ratio as ≤ 2.3. Apparently systemic (or common) factors reduce differences in atherosclerosis of arteries. At 50% level the estimated difference between the two values of the ratio $\underline{A}/\underline{T}$ is relatively small: about 1.4 against 1.2. The curves in the range $\underline{A}/\underline{T} < 1$ are not very accurate, and no reliably accurate calculations could be made in the range $\underline{A}/\underline{T} > 7$.

Figure 3

Probability that the ratio of the grade of atherosclerosis in abdominal aorta to the grade in its coronary arteries be $\leq \underline{A}/\underline{C}$. Details and interpretation as in Figure 2.

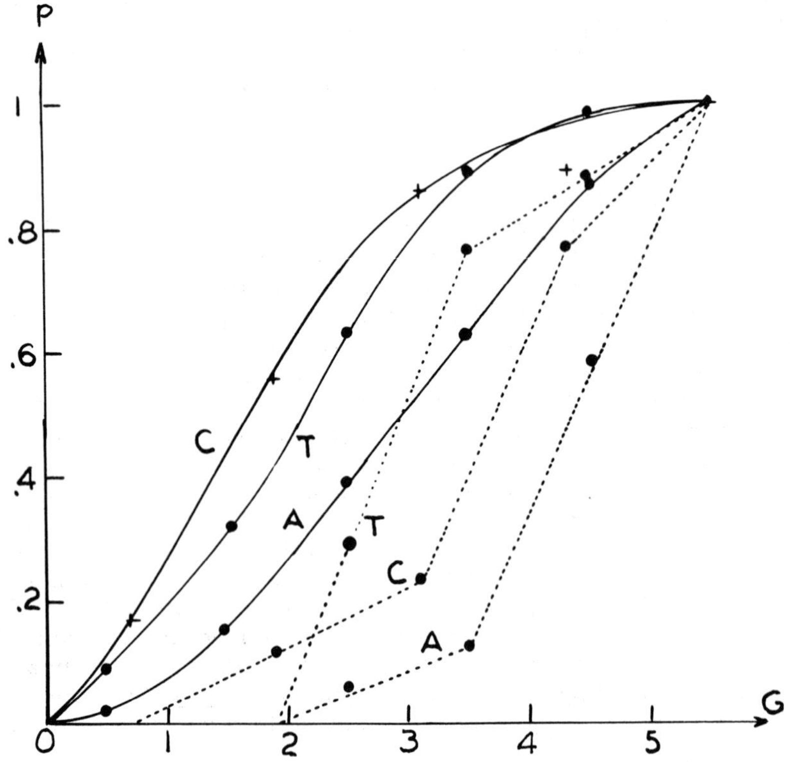

Figure 1

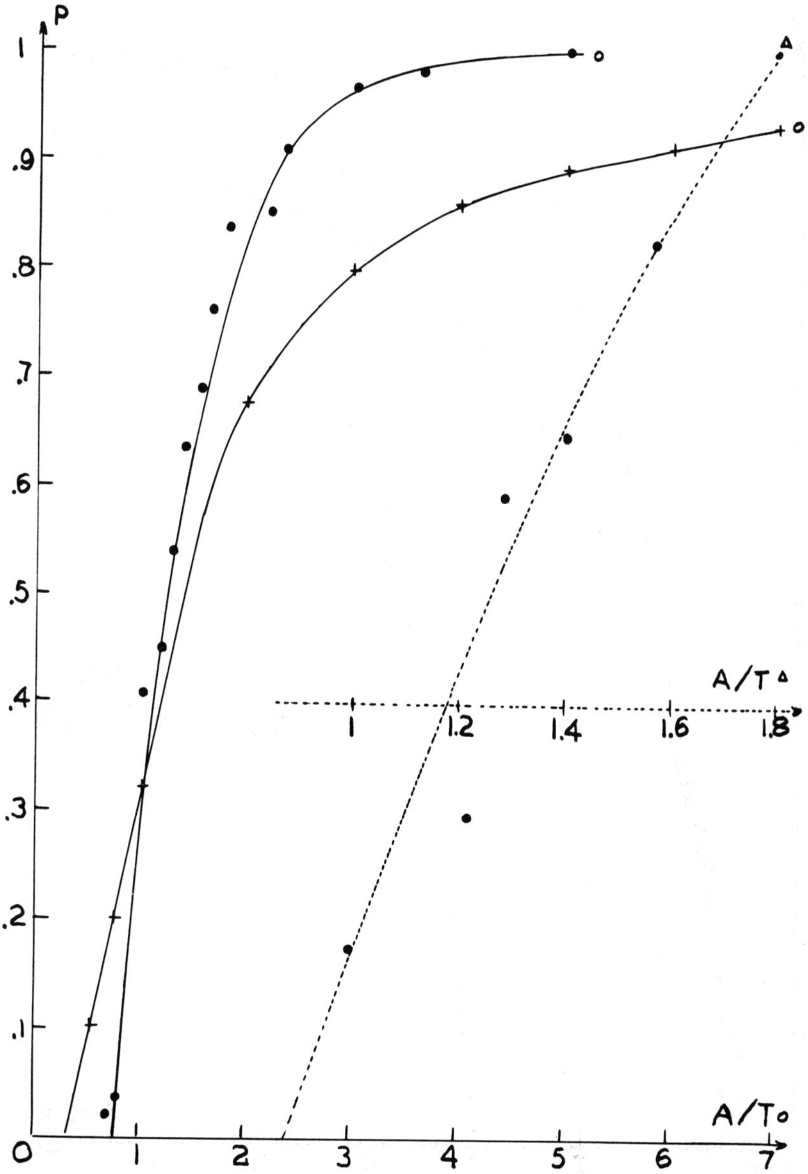

Figure 2

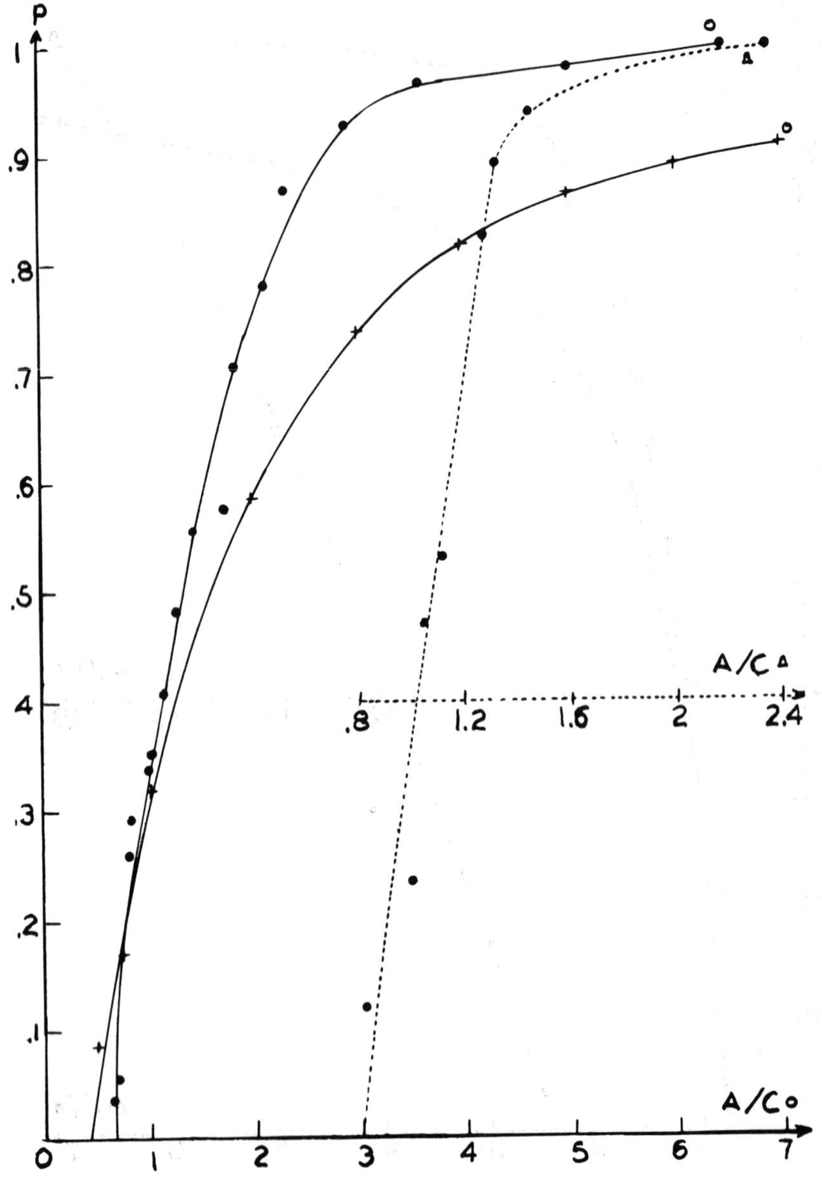

Figure 3

TABLE I
Characteristics of atherosclerosis gradings §

	Grade $\underline{G}$			Mean deviations of $\underline{G}$ from $\overline{\underline{G}}$	
	Range		Mean	to the left	to the right
	$\underline{G}_{min}$	$\underline{G}_{max}$	$\overline{\underline{G}}$	$\underline{\delta}_-$	$\underline{\delta}_+$
abdominal aorta (0)	0	5.5	2.96	1.09	1.09
" " (Δ)	1.9 ?	5.5	4.29	0.69	0.62
thoracic " (0)	0	5.5	2.11	0.96	0.90
" " (Δ)	1.9 ?	5.5	3.12	0.61	0.85
Coronary arteries (0)	0	5.5	1.85	0.83	0.98
" " (Δ)	0.7 ?	5.5	3.48	1.17	0.82

(0) normotensives; (Δ) hypertensives.

? Obtained by extrapolation without smoothing.

§ Computed by the following formulae to avoid calculation of differences:

$$\overline{\underline{G}} = \underline{G}_{max} - \underline{S} \; ; \quad \underline{\delta}_- = \underline{S}_- / \underline{P}(\overline{\underline{G}}) \; ; \quad \underline{\delta}_+ = \underline{S}_- / [1 - \underline{P}(\overline{\underline{G}})] \; ,$$

where $\underline{S}$ is the area under the curve $\underline{P}(\underline{G})$ (cf. Figure 1), and $\underline{S}_-$ the part of that area between $\underline{G} = \underline{G}_{min}$ and $\underline{G} = \overline{\underline{G}}$.

TABLE II

Ratios r of grades of atherosclerosis in abdominal part to thoracic part of the same aorta (A/T), and in abdominal aorta to its coronary arteries (A/C).

		Ratio r			Mean deviations of r from $\bar{r}$		
		Range		Mean	to the left	to the right	
		r_{min}	r_{max}	$\bar{r}$	δ_-	δ_+	
A/T	(0) (i) (*)	0.3	7	1.71	0.7	1.4	↓ Directions of decreasing means $\bar{r}$, of reduced range of r at its both ends, of smaller deviations from the mean
	(0) (d)	0.75	5	1.44	0.42	0.66	
	(Δ) (d)	0.87	1.8	1.28	0.20	0.23	
A/C	(0) (i) (*)	0.4	7	1.91	0.88	1.47	↓
	(0) (d)	0.65	6.45	1.58	0.57	0.91	
	(Δ) (d)	0.8	2.36	1.11	0.16	0.19	

(0) normotensives; (Δ) hypertensives.

(i) calculated under the assumption that no common atherosclerotic factors exist in the two arteries, i.e., that their grades are statistically independent.

(d) computed directly from observations.

(*) the range indicated is the one used in calculations. Following formulae were applied: $\bar{r} = r_{max} - (S/P_{max})$; $\delta_+ = S_-/(P_{max} - \bar{P})$, where $P_{max} = P(r_{max})$, $\bar{P} = P(\bar{r})$. They reduce to formulae § of Table I when $P(r_{max}) = 1$, and G is replaced by r. The range of the ratio based on grades observed separately in different arteries of the sample is:

A/T: 0.5/5.5 to 5.5/0.5 = 0.09 to 11

A/C: 0.7/5.5 to 5.5/0.7 = 0.13 to 7.86.

If the curves of Figures 2, 3 were extrapolated to these ranges, the mean $\bar{r}$ would be still larger than indicated in lines (i).

TABLE III

Correlation coefficients between grades of atherosclerosis in abdominal aorta (A), thoracic aorta (T) and coronary arteries (C) .

Source of material analyzed	Correlation coefficients		
	A, T	A, C	T, C
Chicago[1] (normotensives) *	0.69	0.43	0.30
Sweden[2] (normotensives + hypertensives)	0.65	0.44	0.21

---

*The sample appeared to be too small for smoothing of bivariate frequency functions and the correlation coefficients were calculated using directly the discrete set of observations. For aorta, the range of the grade (cf. Sec. 2) was divided in 5 equal intervals from 0.5 to 5.5, and one interval from 0 to 0.5 . Similarly for coronary arteries: 4 equal intervals from 0.7 to 5.5 and one interval from 0 to 0.7 . To take into account the approximate meaning of the grading system (see[1]) the average frequency in each interval (a, b) was taken as if the individuals in the higher degree b were uniformly distributed over the whole interval (a, b) . All integrals were calculated accordingly by rectangles or rectangular prisms. These calculations gave $\bar{A} = 2.95$, $\bar{T} = 2.12$, $\bar{C} = 1.99$ and for the standard deviations: $\sigma_A = 1.29$, $\sigma_T = 1.14$, $\sigma_C = 1.33$, against $\sigma_A = 1.29$, $\sigma_T = 1.18$, $\sigma_C = 1.10$ obtainable from the smooth curves of Figure 1 by the formula

$$\sigma^2 = G_{max}^{\;\;2} - \bar{G}^2 - 2 \int_{G_{min}}^{G_{max}} GP(G)\, dG \; .$$

The above numbers and those of Table I for $\bar{G}$ reveal differences between the two methods of analysis only for coronary arteries - due to the deviation of the data from the smooth curve C of Figure 1 at one point.

REFERENCES

1. Glagov, S., et al. Archives of Pathology, 72 (1961), 558-571.

2. Bjurulf, P., Acta Med. Scandinava, Suppl. 349. (1959).

DISCUSSION PARTICIPANTS

Dr. John Atkinson
Directorate of Medical Research, Edgewood Arsenal, Maryland

Dr. Joseph Berkson
Biometry & Medical Statistics, Mayo Clinic, Rochester, Minnesota

Dr. R. L. Evans
Physiology Department, University of Minnesota
Minneapolis, Minnesota

Dr. Anatol Rapoport
Mental Health Research Institute, The University of Michigan
Ann Arbor, Michigan

DISCUSSION

John Atkinson. Were any aortic pressures measured, or were they all assumed? University of Louisville Medical School feels that laws of hydraulics developed for non rigid pipe systems are misleading for a non rigid pulsing system as the vascular one.

Izaak Opatowski. The quoted paper by S. Glabov, et al. gives criteria on which the distinction between normotensives and hypertensives was based. I do not know what the pipe system you refer to is. Pulsatile motion of liquids in deformable tubes may have different properties depending on characteristics of the materials the tubes are made of.[1] Flow in arteries cannot be studied by disregarding the effects of surrounding tissues. This was clearly shown by the mathematical work of J. R. Womersley.[2]

Joseph Berkson. Dr. Opatowski, you seem to have related blood-pressure and particularly high blood-pressure to blood flow factors and sclerosis of the blood vessels. I believe that physicians think of hypertension as of two main types, one of which is not accompanied by excessive sclerosis of the vessels and in which, in fact, the vessel walls may be quite normal. Your basic model cannot apply to these cases, can it?

Izaak Opatowski. The sclerosis of a vessel decreases its elasticity and is often associated with a decrease of its lumen. Both increase the hydraulic resistance of the vessel, and consequently increase the blood pressure, unless appropriate compensations intervene, e.g., reduction of blood flow, increased use of blood reservoirs

1. cf. Abramson, D. I., 1962. Blood Vessels and Lymphatics, Chapter II.

   Rushmer, R. F., 1961. Cardiovascular Dynamics, Chapter 5.

2. See McDonald, D. A., 1960. Blood Flow in Arteries.

or others. This however may be only a secondary aspect of the relation between atherosclerosis and blood pressure; the predominant role of the latter as a cause rather than as an effect has been broadly discussed in recent literature.[1] The fact that hypertension is not always associated with atherosclerosis finds its expression in the lower part of the dotted lines of Figure 1 of the paper.

R. L. Evans. Please elaborate further on your sample selection to show whether it might have included such factors as Dr. Berkson just mentioned.

Izaak Opatowski. The sample is the same as described in the quoted paper by S. Glagov et al., except that more detailed data supplied by Dr. Glagov were used.

Anatol Rapoport. Do you assign the same function f as the modifying factor to both A_n and to T_n ? If so, is this not a specific assumption?

Izaak Opatowski. Your question uses symbols of slide which for brevity is not included in the paper; it concerns the last two sentences of its Sec. 3. The apparent comparative effect of hypertension, in relation to average normotensive grades, should not be assumed as valid beyond the sample and arteries analyzed.

1 See e.g. Steinmann, B. 1962. "Arteriosklerose" Schweiz. Med. Wochenschr. 92, 826-836.

ANTHONY F. BARTHOLOMAY

The General Catalytic Queue Process

1. Introduction

In this paper attention is called to certain processes in biochemistry and medicine which seem to be closely related mathematically. Since they have already been treated, in some cases, fairly extensively from the mathematical; and, in particular, the stochastic point of view, they are not new problems. But they are nevertheless problems worthy of further mathematical attention since they occupy important positions in their special, scientific contexts, and since they have been solved only partially due to the difficulties involved. One has the feeling that completely new mathematical approaches and insights are needed.

The biochemical phenomena discussed here have of course already been classified as catalytic processes; specifically, enzymatic catalytic processes. The medical processes have been studied along certain traditionally epidemiological lines. On the other hand their treatment and indeed their formulation have been compared by others [1] as well as myself to chemical catalytic processes. This is certainly apparent in the mathematical treatments, both deterministic and stochastic, as we shall see.

These widely dispersed catalytic phenomena may be formulated at once in terms of a single mathematical model suggested by the Theory of Queues. I have referred to this common feature as "The General Catalytic Queue Process" (for convenience abbreviated to "GCQP" in the sequel). It is conceivable that a large number of situations outside of the particularizations which generated this formulation may come under this same heading, among them economic and game-theoretic models, since the process described can be simplified to include the more direct applications of the theory of queues.

2. The General Catalytic Queue Process

Let it be assumed that initially there are a number n_0 of "customers"* each waiting to have a "service" performed by one of a much smaller number m_0 of "servers". Each server is capable of serving at least one customer at a time. It is thus allowed that in certain kinds of processes a given server may be capable of serving simultaneously more than one customer, i.e., of operating more than one "service counter" or area. In such cases, the number of customers served by a given server at the same time may be either a fixed constant or a random variable.

Random movements of customers and servers and their associated counters are allowed, so that, imposed on the driving force which brings together customer and server is a process which randomizes the arrival of customers at particular serving counters. The "service times" are values of a continuous random variable τ with probability distribution function $F(0 \leq \tau \leq t)$. Once the service mechanism is begun, there may be several outcomes: if a customer is dissatisfied, the service period ends with his re-joining the waiting line and he becomes mixed with the other waiting customers seeking service from the same or other servers; if satisfied, the service period ends by his departure from the service area; or in certain kinds of processes, he may himself become a server of other members of the waiting line. This would occur, e.g., in certain "auto-catalytic processes." Certain processes or service mechanisms may then be characterized by a priori probabilities p of "success" and $q=1-p$ of "failure."

Given the numbers of initial customers and servers and the probability distributions and factors in control of the process, the central problem is to determine the time dependent distribution of the queue size, i.e., the probability distribution of the number of waiting customers present at time t, and also the probable magnitude of T, the "duration time"; i.e., the time it takes for all customers to be satisfied.

Certain variants of this basic catalytic process in addition to the important class of autocatalytic processes mentioned above are also recognized. For example,

a. the server-attendant-customer process: the service mechanism requires the co-operation with the principal server of an assistant or a "co-factor".

---

* The terminology "customer" and "service" common to queueing theory is used is this description of the process. But these terms are thought of in a very general sense; e.g., they may be interacting particles or organisms (v.i.).

b. the competitive or server-customer-vs-customer process: each server is required to serve two different classes of customers; or to maintain two counters, each for a different service, so that both classes of customers are competing against each other for the attention of the server, who then must employ either one service mechanism or another depending on which customer reaches his counter first. In this case a "mixed waiting line" is involved and the calculation of the queue size involves the specification of the pair $(n_1, n_2,)$ where n_1 is the number of waiting customers of type 1; and n_2, the number of customers of type 2.

c. The server-customer-inhibitor process: in which a third class of individuals, called "inhibitors" is present, whose object it is to block the service mechanism either by occupying the counter or by interfering in some other way with the service mechanism or the server.

d. The competitive server-server-customer process: in which two different kinds of service represented by two different classes of servers are competing for the same customers who may be indifferent to the two types or have a particular preference or pronounced "specificity" or "selectivity" for one or the other.

Mixtures and obvious extensions of these variants may also be conceived, as well as very complicated situations arising from the ability of a server with multiple counters, say, to initiate and complete several different service mechanisms at once.

Certain important points of difference between better known queueing processes and this model should be emphasized. (1) An important intrinsic characteristic of this process is the random kinetic action of all classes of participants involved; i.e., arrivals at counters may result from random encounters between servers and customers. Thus, the onset of the service mechanism may be thought of in the same sense as the interruption of a "random walk" by an "absorbing barrier." The arrival at a given counter is a random event not only in time, but also in space. (2) Whereas in some realizations of the process the number m_0 of servers remains constant throughout the process; in other cases the number m of servers present at a given time $t>0$ may be a random variable $m>m_0$, the initial number present. This of course occurs in the turnabout, autocatalytic types of process in which customers become servers after successful completion of their service period. (3) The multiple service property of servers means that such processes are composed of as many subprocesses as there are counters present. Thus, in such cases where there is no interaction between different kinds of customers, then the catalytic queue process could be studied as the simple sum of the individual processes involved. In the more complex cases, of course, this could only be considered as a first approximation. (4) the subclass of catalytic queue processes which involve interaction

with or the cooperation of additional factors or "co-factors" such as attendants represents an extension of known queue processes to accommodate a number of natural "multimolecular" phenomena.
(5) It is permitted that the service period terminates either "successfully" or "unsuccessfully", so that each service period is in the nature of a "trial" or "random event" corresponding to a probability space consisting of two points with a priori probability weights. Thus the number of service periods indulged in by a given customer before the attainment of satisfactory service is an additional random variable of the process (which is associated, of course, with the random kinetic process giving the motions of customers and servers).

Clearly, the more common types of process investigated in the theory of queues may be considered as a special case of the GCQP. And in relation to the simpler processes, a catalytic queue process necessarily represents a multivariate extension. However, this is the usual situation in dealing with biological phenomena from which this generalization has been induced. (v.i.). As has been mentioned already, it is possible that such processes may be "factored" or "decomposed" in some cases to univariate queueing processes. But in any event the mathematical analyses required will be more extensive and more challenging. Certain methodological approaches may be suggested by a study of queues in series and in parallel (see Takacs (2) for example) but it appears that the analysis of particular processes of this kind calls for extensions of existing methods, mostly in the direction of multivariate analysis. However, as will be seen in later parts of this paper, earlier stochastic approaches to such phenomena do indicate ways of answering some of the simpler multivariate questions raised by the present formulation.

3. Deterministic Models for the Kinetics of Chemical and Biochemical Catalytic Phenomena

Originally, a catalyst was assumed to be a chemical substance which greatly accelerated the rate of a chemical reaction without actually participating in the reaction - i.e., without being a "reactant" itself. This assumption added to the fact that a "catalyzed reaction" referred to a reaction that would take place even in the absence of a catalyst, albeit at a very slow rate, did not call for modifying the mechanism of reaction in any profound way to accommodate the catalytic phenomenon. Thus, given the simple unimolecular chemical decomposition of substance A to substance B; symbolized by

(1) $$A \xrightarrow{k} B$$

(or in molecular set-theoretic [3] notation: T_1; $A \to B$) the deterministic model (in contrast to the stochastic model [4]-[6]) would consist of the following set of differential equations

$$
\frac{d\,x_1}{dt} = -\,kx_1 \tag{2}
$$

$$
\frac{d\,x_2}{dt} = kx_1
$$

where $x_1(t)$ and $x_2(t)$, the "concentration" values of A and B respectively at a given time t after initiation of reaction, are really assumed to be differentiable functions of time; and where, for $x_{10} = x_1(0) > 0$ and $x_{20} = x_2(0) = 0$ we have for any time t, $x_1 + x_2 = x_{10}$.

Now if this same reaction were known to be "catalyzed" by a substance C, where c = total concentration of catalyst used, then for example the first differential equation would be adjusted to

$$
\frac{dx_1}{dt} = -kcx_1 \tag{3}
$$

(The empirical justification in particular cases being that in linear plots of log $\left(\frac{x_1}{x_{10}}\right)$ vs t to check the intrinsic rate constant k, the slope of the straight line would seem to be multiplied by the factor c). However, later investigations of catalyzed reactions have shown the situation to be more complicated than this and have suggested the operation of alternate chemical mechanisms in the presence of catalyst, involving the formation of intermediate chemical species - implying specific interaction between reactant and catalyst. (see, e.g., Hinshelwood [7] and Weissberger [8]). An important preliminary step in promoting this newer point of view was the discovery that solid surfaces could act as catalysts; e.g., in gaseous reactions. It was thought that the surface exercised a retaining power on such reactants, holding them until they made the necessary contact with other interacting molecules. While originally this was thought of as a kind of physical adsorption process, as divorced from any chemical context, the work of Langmuir [9], [10] on the adsorption isotherm did much to erase the artificial distinction between physical adsorption and chemical adsorption (the term "chemisorption" came into use), so that even in these cases of catalysis by adsorption to solid surfaces, such as the glass walls of a reactant vessel, the catalyst came to be thought of as a kind of reactant which interacted with other reactant species.

Another step in the evolution of the chemical catalysis concept was the discovery of the phenomenon of "autocatalysis", in which a given reaction is catalyzed by its own products of reactions, so that imposed on the intrinsic rate of chemical reaction in a simple reaction say, such as (1) is a rate accelerating catalytic process resulting from the bimolecular interactions between the molecules of product species B and molecules of reactant species A . In terms of the mathematical model given above, one would therefore describe the resulting kinetics by the equation

$$\frac{dx_1}{dt} = -kx_1 x_2 = -k(x_{10} - x_1)\ (x_1) \ . \tag{4}$$

Integration of this equation results in the well known "logistic" or "autocatalytic" curve giving x_1 as a function of time (v. i.). Such reactions occur also in the presence of other catalysts as well. They occupy an important place in biological reactions; e. g., the conversion of the enzyme precursor trypsinogen into the active enzymatic species trypsin [11], [12] is auto catalyzed by the newly forming product trypsin itself; similarly the conversion of pepsinogen to the active enzyme pepsin [11], [13] is an autocatalytic reaction.

Trypsin and Pepsin are, of course, examples of a class of biochemical macromolecules called enzymes that are capable themselves of catalyzing other reactions which are presumed from in vitro studies to take place in living cells. They are, in fact, so called "proteolytic" protein splitting or "hydrolyzing" enzymes which play important roles in accelerating digestive processes, presumably. Originally, enzymes were thought to exert their catalytic action on reactions by acting as "physical adsorbants" (v. s.). More detailed subsequent biochemical studies explicated their action in characteristically, chemical mechanistic terms, pointing to the formation of actual chemical complexes between the individual reactant molecules, (the so-called "substrate" species) and the enzyme molecules, which catalyzed the transformation of the substrate into "product" species, the "reaction products". The complexes formed were referred to as "enzyme-substrate complexes" as the medium of direct transmission of reaction energy from enzyme molecule to substrate, sufficient to promote the transformation of substrate into the various product species. In a paper published in 1913, L. Michaelis and M. Menten [14] * hypothesized that the mechanisms of enzyme catalysis could be described by the "chemical equations":

---

* See also references [4] and [11] .

(5) $$E + S \underset{k_2}{\overset{k_1}{\rightleftarrows}} ES \overset{k_3}{\rightarrow} E + P \;;$$

or in molecular set-theoretic representation [3];

$\{T_1\colon ExS \rightarrow ES;\ T_2\colon ES \rightarrow ExS;\ T_3\colon ES \rightarrow ExP\}$ where E is the symbol for enzyme: S, substrate; ES, enzyme-substrate complex, and P, products of reaction. The constants k_i are the rate constants associated with each step of the mechanism. Thus, it was postulated that the enzyme actually interacts reversibly with the substrate to form the ES-complex (corresponding to bimolecular transformation T_1), which may then dissociate back into the original reactants (the unimolecular reverse or backward transformation T_2); or else decompose into the products of reaction (the unimolecular decomposition T_3) releasing "free" intact enzyme as well. Various simplifying assumptions were made in dealing with this suggested mechanism. Of particular importance was the assumption that the "equilibrium" between the original reactants and the ES-complex involved very rapid reactions compared to the decomposition step T_3; i.e. $k_1, k_2 \gg k_3$ so that the equilibrium would not be interrupted by the occasional decompositions. Reasoning in this way, but specifically in terms of the sucrose-hydrolysis reaction catalyzed by the enzyme invertase (or saccharese) a formula was developed* for expressing the initial rate v_0 of appearance of products P as a function of initial substrate concentration S_0; V, the maximum attainable rate (corresponding to complexation of all the enzyme molecules at once); and $K_m = k_2/k_1$ (later called "the Michaelis Constant"):

(6) $$v_0 = \frac{VS_0}{K_m + S_0}$$

This equation, the now classical "Michaelis-Menten Equation" came to be thought of as a general characteristic of enzymatic catalyses and forms the cornerstone of present-day enzyme kinetic theory.

More general treatments have superseded the original derivation. For example, the Briggs-Haldane derivation* lies closer to the more complete deterministic mathematical model corresponding to the enzymatic mechanism contained in equation (5). This model consists of the following set of ordinary differential equations:

---

* See Bartholomay [4] pp. 60-86 for an account of the details of reasoning here, also Haldane [15] as a further reference to the early work.

$$
(7) \quad \begin{cases} dx_1/dt = -k_1x_1x_2 + (k_2 + k_3)\,x_3 \\ dx_2/dt = -k_1x_1x_2 + k_2x_3 \\ dx_3/dt = k_1x_1x_2 - (k_2 + k_3)\,x_3 \\ dx_4/dt = k_3x_3 = v \text{ ("overall reaction rate")} \end{cases}
$$

where x_1 is the concentration of free enzyme; x_2, the substrate concentration; x_3 the enzyme-substrate concentration; x_4, the concentration of products. In relation to this model, the rate of overall reaction v for the so-called "steady state" is obtained by setting $dx_3/dt = 0$, replacing x_1 by $(x_{10} - x_3)$ (where x_{10} is the total concentration of enzyme), solving the resulting equation for x_3 and substituting this into the last equation. The result obtained is the more general form of the Michaelis-Menten equation:

$$
(8) \qquad v = \frac{V x_2}{K_m + x_2}
$$

where the maximum V of v equals the product $k_3 x_{10}$ corresponding to the case in which all of the enzyme (i.e. x_{10}) appears in complexed form; i.e. as a limiting value of x_3; and where K_m now equals $(k_2 + k_3)/k_1$, the "extended Michaelis Constant." The system (7) of first order, nonlinear differential equations has not been solved, although in most recent times approximate integral curves have been generated on analog and digital computers (see for example chapter 7 in reference [8]). While this model arose from particular studies, it has been accepted as a general explanation, though numerous exceptions have been uncovered; and, of course, the treatment has had to be extended to cover the case where more than the enzyme and single substrate species are present in the reaction mixture (v.i.). The central assumption in this account of the catalytic phenomenon is for formation of an actual chemical compound between the catalyst E and the substrate. Because of the rapidity of formation and dissociation of this complex, experimental identification did not occur until a quarter century after its postulation. It was finally accomplished spectrophotometrically in 1937 by Keilin and Mann [16] and kinetically by Chance [17] in 1943. It is now considered that in many cases the intermediate passes through a number of different forms (in the sense of a reversible chain reaction) before accomplishment of the final decomposition. (See equa. 9).

4. The Stochastic Approach to the Kinetics of Enzyme Catalysis

A fundamental point of difference between deterministic models for the kinetics of catalytic phenomena and stochastic models is the basic unit of transformation. It should be noted in the preceding deterministic treatment that while the catalytic processes involved are discussed mechanistically to some extent, in terms of individual molecular species and complexes, nevertheless the transformations are followed only in bulk, i.e., the interest in such models is in providing a mathematical framework for discussing changes in concentrations such as the number of moles /cc/sec. which in turn is treated mathematically as a continuous variable. Thus there is no particular emphasis in deterministic models on individual discrete events. Accordingly the method is not fine-structured enough to accommodate them. By the same token, the deterministic approach is not at all geared to random fluctuations which, according to molecular details would necessarily be predicted arguing physico-chemically [5], [6], (v.i.). It is misleading to postulate their origin on purely empirical grounds, in terms of the theory of random errors of methods and individual techniques.

It is clear even cursorily from the nature of the individual events involved in enzymatic catalysis that the "path" of a substrate molecule stepwisely through the chemical pathways described in the overall enzymatic catalytic Michaelis-Menten mechanism (equation 5) can be as unpredictable in length and in direction as is the actual path of a Brownian particle - particularly according to the most recent theories which postulate the passage of the intermediate complex through a number of forms. Thus, enlarging the simplest Michaelis-Menten mechanism to something which is schematized by:

$$(9) \qquad E + S \underset{k_2}{\overset{k_1}{\rightleftarrows}} (ES)_1 \rightleftarrows (ES)_2 \rightleftarrows \ldots \rightleftarrows (ES)_n \rightleftarrows ES \rightleftarrows E + P$$

we see that S may go all the way to $(ES)_j$, say, then return to $(ES)_{j-1}$, then proceed to $(ES)_{j+1}$, etc. before it returns either to its native form or to the produ[illegible] reaction. Thus, in all formulations of the enzymatic catalytic process, whether consisting of one intermediate form or more, probabilistic laws are involved which should find their way into the theoretical mathematical model for the kinetics. Clearly, the regularity of such a process has to be discussed in terms of statistical regularity - at least in theoretical treatments. This does not rule out the usefulness of deterministic formulations in dealing with empirical considerations. In fact, ideally the deterministic expectation of a smooth concentration - time course for kinetic data, represents the attainment of this regularity and should be thought of as the central tendency of a stochastic process. Thus, it would be expected that reactions involving high concentrations would give the appearance, kinetically, of a strong deterministic tendency with relatively small superimposed fluctuations - which could of course be charged to random error and uncontrolled environmental parameters. Dilute reactions would be expected to have more macroscopic fluctuations around the central tendency.

It was in order to provide a mathematical model sufficiently complete to account for random fluctuations and the differentiation between so-called "reproducible" (small fluctuations) and "irreproducible" (large scale fluctuations); and also to include quantum theoretic and modern physico-chemical rate theoretic principles that we have proposed [5], [6] stochastic models for chemical reactions and for enzymatic catalysis, in particular [18], [19] (see also Bharucha-Reid [20] for further remarks on stochastic models in biology and chemistry). Such models call for further investigations of th comparisons between predicted orders of magnitudes of "inherent fluctuation" (in the stochastic model) and extrinsic variations (due to experimental random error), though experiments for doing this may not be conceivable in the usual sense.

Stochastic models of course, provide a rationale for measuring inherent variation in terms of the variance of the stochastic process involved. Such measures have been obtained for the simplest reactions (see references [5], [6] and [20] and [21]). In the case of enzyme catalysis the variance function has not been derived, though the stochastic difference-differential equation of the process has been obtained, as well as the associated partial differential equation of the probability generating function (see Bartholomay [18] [19]).

In setting up the stochastic model, instead of treating the concentration variables of the various species as continuous functions of time, we have considered that the number of molecules of each species per total volume present at time t is a random variable, the total kinetics of the process being thus definable by a joint probability function of time; viz.

$p(n_1, n_2, n_3, n_4; \mu_1, \mu_2, \mu_3; t)$ where

n_1 = the number of enzyme molecules

n_2 = the number of substrate molecules

n_3 = the number of enzyme-substrate compounds

n_4 = the number of product molecules

and $\mu_1, \mu_2, \mu_3,$ are stochastic parameters* corresponding to the three types of component transformation steps. Taking advantage of the interrelationships between the variables: $n_1 = n_{10} - n_3$; $n_4 = n_{20} - (n_2 + n_3)$ the stochastic difference-differential equation obtained is:

$$\frac{\partial p(n_2, n_3; t)}{\partial t} = \mu_3 \gamma n_3+1)\ p(n_2, n_3+1; t) + \mu_2 (n_3+1)\ p(n_2-1, n_3+1; t)$$

(10) $$-n_1\mu_2(n_{10}-n_3)\ p(n_2, n_3; t) - (\mu_2+\mu_3)\ n_3 p(n_2, n_3; t)$$

$$+\mu_1(n_2+1)\ (n_{10}-n_3+1)\ p(n_2+1, n_3-1; t)$$

which leads to the following partial differential equation:

(11) $$\frac{\partial\phi}{\partial t} = (\mu_3+\mu_2 s_2-\mu_2 s_3-\mu_3 s_3)\frac{\partial\phi}{\partial s_3} + n_{10}\mu_1(s_3^2-s_2)\frac{\partial\phi}{\partial s_2} + \mu_1 s_3(s_2-s_3)\frac{\partial^2\phi}{\partial s_2 \partial s_3}$$

in which

(12) $$\phi(s_2, s_3; t) = \sum_{n_2=0}^{n_{20}} \sum_{n_3=0}^{n_{10}} p(n_2, n_3; t)\ s_2^{n_2} s_3^{n_3}$$

is the probability generating function of the process.

While this has not been solved, it has been noted [18], [19] that where $\bar{n}_i$ is the average value of $n_i(i=2, 3)$ and $\overline{n_1 n_2}$ the average value of the product $n_1 n_2$; i.e. $(n_{10}-n_3)(n_2)$, differentiation with respect to time leads to

(13) $$\begin{cases} \dfrac{d\bar{n}_2}{dt} = \mu_2\bar{n}_3-\mu_1\overline{n_1 n_2} \\ \\ \dfrac{d\bar{n}_3}{dt} = \mu_1\overline{n_1 n_2} - (\mu_1+\mu_3)\ \bar{n}_3 \end{cases}$$

---

* See the discussion in section 5 following the explication of these parameters and their physico-chemical bases, also references [18], [19].

In order to see the connection of these equations with the deterministic model, consider the two middle equations of the system of differential equations (7), which form an independent system:

$$\frac{dx_2}{dt} = k_2x_3 - k_1x_1x_2$$

(14)

$$\frac{dx_3}{dt} = k_1x_1x_2 - (k_2+k_3)\,x_3$$

Thus, the two forms are equivalent if we set up a correspondence between the "rate constants" k_1, k_2, k_3 and the probability parameters μ_1, μ_2, μ_3; and between the concentrations in molecules per volume x_1, x_2, x_3 (of enzyme, substrate and enzyme-substrate molecules, respectively) and the stochastic means of the corresponding random variables n_1, n_2, & n_3. The stochastic model is thus "consistent in the mean" with the deterministic model, (which is therefore deducible from the stochastic process). In this sense the stochastic model may be thought of as a stochastic extension of the deterministic process.

5. The Enzymatic Catalytic Process as a Realization of the GCQP

The study of enzyme catalysis from the stochastic point of view of individual discrete molecular-biological events embedded in a sample space leads quite naturally into a queue-theoretic interpretation of the process. There are in fact a number of characteristics of the enzymatic process that make it interpretable as a special queue process of the kind which has been described in section 1. Consider, for example, the action of the enzyme molecule itself. A given enzyme molecule, after catalyzing the transformation of one substrate molecule into the product or products P of reaction, is ready to serve another substrate molecule that happens to collide with it "effectively", and so on. That a given enzyme molecule is extremely busy is clear from the so-called "turnover number" of an enzyme species in a given reaction which corresponds, generally, to the transformations of thousands of substrate molecules per minute by a given enzyme molecule. It is for this reason that the concentration of enzyme in a given reaction is many orders of magnitude less than substrate concentration, in in vitro experiments. Another such characteristic derives from the random nature of the chemical mechanism itself which may be decomposed to random transitions of the ES molecule, governed by the laws of quantum mechanics from one quantum state to another until the appropriate state for decomposition is attained. (v. i.). Thus, the enzymatic mechanism suggests a complex "service mechanism". Finally, the primary purpose of stochastic models agrees with that of queue-theoretic models; viz., to provide means of estimating and predicting the time distribution of "queue size"; or, equivalently, the concentration of substrate or product present as a function of the time after initiation of reaction.

The enzymatic catalytic queue-like process begins by placing together in a reaction vessel a number n_0 of substrate molecules (the "customers") and a much smaller number $m_0 << n_0$ of enzyme molecules (the "servers"). In the simplest case each enzyme molecule of a given biochemical species has only one so-called "active site"; i.e. is capable of complexing ("serving") only one substrate molecule at a time. In other cases, an enzyme molecule may have a large number of active sites* ("serving counters"). No kinetic models have as yet been proposed for studying the details of the kinetics of multi-site enzyme systems, since, outside of the stochastic model mentioned in section 4, kinetic studies have not been aimed at the elucidation of individual chemical events. Our own studies of a purely theoretical nature can be extended to take these into account; but experimental kinetic methods cannot be geared to individual chemical events due not only to limitations of instrumentation but more basically to restrictions which are explicated in quantum theory. However, theoretical studies should make up for the deficiencies and natural limitations of experimental technique and observation and in this way actually strengthen experimental criteria.

Returning now to the single active site model corresponding to the catalytic mechanisms detailed by equation (5), we see that the component transformations: T_2: ExS→ES (dissociation), and T_3: ES→ExP (decomposition) are in competition with each other - so that from the point of view of general queueing theory, the catalytic process has the distinguishing characteristic that the service mechanism between customer and server can reach termination in one of two ways; either by "dissatisfaction", the ES-complex dissociating back into its native substances; or by "satisfaction", in which case

---

* Very early experiments on enzymes revealed that not the whole macromolecular surface is active; that there is only a very small area where presumably complexation could take place. A great deal of very detailed evidence is now accumulating on "active sites" and this constitutes a subject of intensive and ingenious, biochemical research (see, e.g. Laidler [11], Vallee, et al [22], [23] and Schoellmann and Shaw [24] made possible by new physicochemical methods and instrumentation for studying molecular morphology.

the substrate is decomposed into new substances; in both cases the enzyme is free to serve other substrate molecules. Of course, according to "the equilibrium theory" for such reactions, the probability that dissociation takes place would appear to be much greater than the probability that the reaction occurs since the steps, T_1, T_2 occur much more rapidly than T_3 (i.e. the corresponding rate constants k_1 and k_2 are much greater than k_3). Another distinguishing feature of our process is that the random motions, say of Brownian origin, of the customer and server molecules are an important intrinsic feature of the reaction mechanism: the enzyme and substrate molecules are constantly in random motion relative to each other, so that the Laws of chance control the arrival of customers at open serving counters. Thus, a new random variable of such a queue process would be the number of ineffective collisions for a given substrate molecule, before an "effective" collision leading to initiation of the service mechanism (i.e. the "complexation process") or enzyme-substrate association described by transformation T_1. Furthermore, it is clear from this that service is not rendered on a first-come-first-served basis - there may be many random encounters (leading to no complexation) before a serving counter is actually engaged in the catalytic action. Hence, the first part of setting up an enzyme catalytic queue model has to consist of an analysis of the random arrival mechanism. Of course, as we have already emphasized, on the basis of an ordinary macroscopic time scale, it would appear that in the presence of a very large concentration of substrate, compared to small enzyme concentration, a given enzyme molecule is kept busy continuously. But on the discrete event basis of our theoretical treatment, this would be only illusory.

Dealing with the population of enzyme and substrate molecules independently, a fundamental analysis of this aspect of the problem begins by considering each molecule (either substrate or enzyme) as a "free particle" in the Brownian motion-theoretical sense (see Chandrasekhar [25]). Accordingly, let it be assumed that the motion of the molecule is governed by a Langevin mixed stochastic differential equation:

$$\frac{d\vec{u}}{dt} = -\alpha \vec{u} + \vec{A}(t) \tag{15}$$

where $(x(t), y(t), z(t)$ gives the position of the molecule at time t and $\vec{u}$ is the velocity vector with components $(dx/dt, dy/dt, dz/dt)$ (or more conveniently $(\dot{x}, \dot{y}, \dot{z})$); $-\alpha\vec{u}$ is the systematic component of dynamical friction; and $\vec{A}(t)$, the random or fluctuating component characteristic of the Brownian motion. Also $\alpha = 6\pi a \eta/m$, where according to Stokes Law we are considering that each molecule is a spherical particle of radius a, mass m; and that η is the coefficient of viscosity of the surrounding fluid. By the solution of such an equation, in the classical random flight-theoretic treatment is understood the specification of a probability distribution $F(\vec{u}, t; \vec{u}_0)$ governing the probability of occurrence of velocity $\vec{u}$ at time t, given that $\vec{u}(0) = \vec{u}_0$. The usual physical circumstances of the problem require that $F(\vec{u}, t; \vec{u}_0)$ tends to a Maxwellian distribution for the temperature T of the surrounding medium, independently of initial velocity as $t \rightarrow \infty$:

$$\text{(16)} \qquad \lim_{t\rightarrow\infty} F(u, t; u_0) = \left(\frac{m}{2\pi kT}\right)^{3/2} \exp(-m|\vec{u}|^2/2kT) \;,$$

where k is Boltzmann's Constant. As in Chandrasekhar [25] (pp. 31-34) requirements can then be imposed on F that give this asymptotic behavior. They result in the solution:

$$\text{(17)} \qquad F(\vec{u}, t; \vec{u}_0) = \left(\frac{m}{2\pi kT(1-\exp\{-\{\alpha t\})}\right)^{3/2}$$

$$\exp\left\{-m\left|\vec{u} - \vec{u}_0 e^{-\alpha t}\right|^2 \Big/ 2kT\left(1-e^{-2\alpha t}\right)\right\}.$$

In practice, however, assumptions are usually made to the effect that the Maxwellian Distribution operates throughout the process. This assumption has been challenged, particularly in recent years in the development of "microscopic kinetics" [29], [30]; it is referred to as "the Equilibrium Hypothesis" and is invoked in its strongest form in "collision theory", into which context equations such as [16] and (17) fit. As is pointed out later, it is valid under certain circumstances, which may include a number of enzymatic catalytic processes (v. i.).

Assuming, then, the validity of the equilibrium hypothesis, the probability that an enzyme molecule of mass m_1 has a velocity in the range $(\vec{u}_1, \vec{u}_1 + d\vec{u}_1)$; or in Cartesian co-ordinates $(\dot{x}_1, \dot{x}_1 + d\dot{x}_1; \dot{y}_1, \dot{y}_1 + d\dot{y}_1; \dot{z}_1, \dot{z}_1 + d\dot{z}_1)$, is given by the expression:

$$\text{(18)} \qquad \left(\frac{m_1}{2\pi kT}\right)^{3/2} \exp\left\{\frac{-m_1}{2} \cdot \frac{\dot{x}_1^2 + \dot{y}_1^2 + \dot{z}_1^2}{kT}\right\} d\dot{x}_1\, d\dot{y}_1\, d\dot{z}_1$$

Similarly, the probability that a substrate molecule of mass m_2 has a velocity in the range $(\dot{x}_2, \dot{x}_2 + d\dot{x}_2; \dot{y}_2, \dot{y}_2 + d\dot{y}_2; \dot{z}_2, \dot{z}_2 + d\dot{z}_2)$ is:

$$\text{(19)} \qquad \left(\frac{m_2}{2\pi kT}\right)^{3/2} \exp\left\{\frac{-m_2}{2} \cdot \frac{\dot{x}_2^2 + \dot{y}_2^2 + \dot{z}_2^2}{kT}\right\} d\dot{x}_2\, d\dot{y}_2\, d\dot{z}_2 \;.$$

The results of equations (18) and (19) may be applied more conveniently to the catalytic process which involves large numbers of molecules of both types, by stripping the results of their probability context and imagining a large number of molecules in motion, starting under the same initial conditions and undergoing displacements without any mutual interference; and then interpreting (18), for example, as the fraction dn_1/n_1 of the n_1 molecules present at time t which lie in the velocity range $(\vec{u}_1, \vec{u}_1 + d\vec{u}_1)$. In this way, we arrive at the following expression for dn_{12}, the total number of pairs of molecules in the range $(\vec{u}_1, \vec{u}_1 + d\vec{u}_1; \vec{u}_2, \vec{u}_2 + d\vec{u}_2)$:

$$(20) \quad dn_{12} = dn_1\, dn_2 = n_1 n_2 \left(\frac{m_1 m_2}{4\pi^2 k^2 T^2} \right)^{3/2} \exp\left\{ - \frac{m_1 c_1^2 + m_2 c_2^2}{2\,k\,T} \right\} d\dot{x}_1 d\dot{x}_2 d\dot{y}_1 d\dot{y}_2 d\dot{z}_1 d\dot{z}_2$$

where

$$(21) \quad c_i^2 = \dot{x}_i^2 + \dot{y}_i^2 + \dot{z}_i^2 \quad (i = 1, 2)$$

On this basis, (as in Bartholomay [4] (pp. 27-29), particularly) the result is deduced that the number of random collisions or encounters between customers and servers taking place in time $(t, t + \Delta t)$ equals:

$$(22) \quad N_{12} \left(\frac{8\pi kT}{m_{12}} \right)^{1/2} d_{12}^2\, n_1 n_2\, \Delta t + o(\Delta t)$$

where

$$\begin{cases} d_{12} = \frac{1}{2}(d_1 + d_2) \quad \text{and} \\ d_1 = \text{average diameter of an enzyme molecule} \\ d_2 = \text{average diameter of a substrate molecule} \\ m_{12} = \dfrac{m_1 m_2}{m_1 + m_2} \end{cases}$$

and, of course, it is understood that N_{12} is taken to the nearest integer.

Suppose now that a given encounter taking place at any time t has a probability equal to $p = Pe^{-\epsilon/kt}$ of "success"; i.e. of leading to the formation of an enzyme-substrate complex (to initiation of the "service mechanism" between customer and server), where P is a characteristic parameter for the particular catalysis and ϵ, the so-called "critical activation energy". Then assuming that the collisions taking place in the infinitesimal interval $(t, t + \Delta t)$ satisfy independence conditions allowing them to be treated as a set of Bernoulli trials with probability p of success (i.e. complexation, or association), and probability $q = 1-p$ of failure (ineffective collision), the probability of formation of a single enzyme-substrate complex between any of the n_1 servers and n_2 customers present at time t can be deduced [4] as:

$$(23) \qquad Pe^{-\epsilon/kt}\left(\frac{8_{\pi}kT}{m_{12}}\right)^{1/2} d_{12}^{2}\, n_1 n_2\, \Delta t + o(\Delta t) \quad ,$$

whereas the probability of more than one such formation is negligible (a higher order infinitesimal $o(\Delta t)$) .

Setting (24) $$\mu_1 = Pe^{-\epsilon/kt}\left(\frac{8_{\pi}kT}{m_{12}}\right)^{1/2} d_{12}^{2}$$

allows us to write

$$(25) \qquad \mu_1 n_1 n_2\, \Delta t + o(\Delta t)$$

as the probability of a single effective customer-server pairing. Here the probability constant μ_1 corresponds to the deterministic rate constant k_1(v.s.).

Next, given a number n_3 of such customer-server combinations present at time t, it is necessary to derive for the catalytic queue process the component probability expressions for the mutually exclusive events that in the infinitesimal time interval $(t, t + \Delta t)$ a given complex will either dissociate, decompose, or remain in the same state. (i.e. with no termination of service) corresponding to the component transformations T_2 and T_3 of the process (v.s.). It can be seen that on the basis of these assumptions the probability of complexation followed by dissociation, by recomplexation, ..., etc. is negligible.

The Lindemann-Hinshelwood [26], [27] theoretical mechanism for the unimolecular transformation such as T_2 and T_3 may be invoked here in order to deduce on a collision-theoretic basis relations such as (25) corresponding to transformations T_2 and T_3 (see Bartholomay [18], [19]). In the earlier derivation [18], [19] leading to equations (10) and (11), the steps: T_2: ES→ExS and T_3: ES→ExP were treated in ways that mimic the traditional deterministic procedure* of analyzing a complex reaction into more elementary reactions

* See Bartholomay [4] for an exposition of this method.

(such as T_2 and T_3 in relation to the overall catalytic mechanism) and then obtaining the final resultant much as one combines forces using the independence of forces axiom of physical mechanics. * According to that axiom, the transformation T_2 is considered to exert a force on the n_3 complexes, independently of the force corresponding to competing transformation T_3, which is characterized by a probability $\mu_2 \Delta t + o(\Delta t)$ that a given one of these complexes will dissociate, and $1 - \mu_2 \Delta t + o(\Delta t)$, the probability that it will not in time $(t, t + \Delta t)$. And corresponding to T_3, independently of T_2, there is a probability $\mu_3 \Delta t + o(\Delta t)$ in favor of decomposition, and $1 - \mu_3 \Delta t + o(\Delta t)$ against decomposition.

A more precise formulation and line of reasoning seems called for in terms of the queue-theoretic analysis of discrete events. Thus, given an enzyme substrate complex (i.e. customer-service pair) where service is already initiated by time t, then in the subsequent infinitesimal interval of length Δt, three mutually exclusive events may occur: (1) the complex may dissociate according to the unimolecular T_2 process, in which case the service may be said to be <u>disrupted</u>, (2) it may decompose, according to the T_3 process, in which case the service may be said to be <u>satisfactorily completed</u>; or (3) it may <u>persist</u> in the complex state (service is continued). Now from earlier studies [5], [6] of unimolecular processes, it is reasonable to postulate that since in unimolecular decompositions the probability of reaction is independent of the time t at the beginning of the interval, but proportional to its length; then $p_2 = \mu_2 \Delta t + o(\Delta t)$ where μ_2 is a constant probability parameter corresponding to rate constant k_2, can be taken as the probability of a dissociation in this time; $P_3 = \mu_3 \Delta t + o(\Delta t)$, the probability of a decomposition of the same enzyme molecule; and $q = 1 - (\mu_2 + \mu_3) \Delta t + o(\Delta t) = 1 - (p_2 + p_3)$, the probability that it remains intact (though perhaps at a different quantum level). Both μ_2 and μ_3 may be analyzed into collision-theoretic components corresponding to the analysis of bimolecular μ_1, using the Lindemann-Hinshelwood scheme. Considering then that each of the n_3 ES molecules present at time t are undergoing independent trinomial trials, we have that the probability of r_2 dissociations each of probability p_2; r_3 decompositions each of probability p_3; and $r = n_3 - r_2 - r_3$ persistences each of probability of $q = 1 - (p_2 + p_3)$ is given according to the trinomial distribution by

$$\frac{n_3!}{r_2!\,r_3!\,r!}\, p_2^{r_2}\, p_3^{r_3}\, q^{r} \tag{26}$$

* See Bartholomay [4] for an exposition of this method.

Thus, for example, the probability of exactly 1 dissociation, no decompositions, and $(n_3 - 1)$ persistences is, according to (26) $n_3\mu_2 \Delta t + o(\Delta t)$ (where $n_3 > 1$) . Similarly, the probability of exactly one decomposition and no dissociation is $n_3\mu_3 \Delta t + o(\Delta t)$; and the probability of n_3 persistencies (no decomposition and no dissociation) is $1 - n_3(\mu_2 + \mu_3) \Delta t + o(\Delta t)$. On the other hand, the probability of more than one dissociation or decomposition or of one or more pairs of dissociations and decompositions is an infinitesimal of higher order; i.e., negligible in the limit. It can be seen that this alternative probability analysis leads to the same equations (10) and (11) for the stochastic model. For example on p. 228 of ref [19] event E_1 would be modified to consist of the joint occurrence of the following events: E_{11}, the presence of n_2 molecules of substrate and $n_3 + 1$ molecules of ES; E_{12} exactly one decomposition and no dissociation; and no additional complexation. According to the present interpretation, this has probability equal to

$$(27) \qquad p(n_2, n_3 + 1; t)\left[\mu_3(n_3+1)\,\Delta t + o(\Delta t)\right] \cdot \left[1 - (n_{10} - n_2 - 1)\,n_2\mu_1\Delta t + o(\Delta t)\right]$$

which equals $p(n_2, n_3+1; t)\,\mu_3(n_3 + 1)\,\Delta t + o(\Delta t)$ in agreement with equation (29) of that paper. Thus the distribution of the catalytic queue size n_2 (the number of waiting substrate molecules) is contained in the stochastic difference-differential equation of the process (equation (10) of section 4).

By no means is this a unique way of solving either the catalytic problem or its associated queue-theoretic model. It is perhaps the simplest approach and is commended mainly for its compatibility with the deterministic model of enzyme kinetics, so that wherever the latter applies, we would expect it to be contained in the suggested stochastic model. We have tried altering the basis probability assumption in ways which seemed reasonable, also, on theoretical grounds, and obtained different predictions [28]. One can go into much more detail and employ a much more complicated probability sample space, of course. For example, the random variable corresponding to "service time"; i.e. the time interval from the first moment of effective contact between enzyme and substrate to the eventual dissociation or decomposition, can be analyzed further. Such an analysis would be <u>intra</u>molecular relative to each molecule, and would rest on the random passage intramolecularly of the ES molecule from one quantum state to another, following the alterations in internal configurations of the molecules, which make up the details of the mechanism of transformation. This chemical situation has in fact been studied in a more general physico-chemical context [29]-[35] with particular emphasis on the simplest unimolecular reaction and more recently on the bimolecular case. And these studies can be used to explicate the probability parameters introduced here, the physico-chemical interpretation of which has so far in this paper bee confined simply to the earliest collision-theory, and within that context to the "equilibrium hypothesis".

The motivation, in fact, for these recent studies of Modern Absolute Rate Theory has been, essentially, the development of a micro scopic kinetics which does not rest on the controversial "equilibrium hypothesis" and which is advanced as a criterion for adjudging the validity in particular circumstances of that collision-theoretic Maxwellian hypothesis. The results support the view that there exists a critical value, call it C, for the ratio (ϵ/kt) such that the equilibrium hypothesis is tenable for any value of this ratio in excess of C . For values far below this value, it is necessary to invoke the microscopic kinetic models to obtain agreement with kinetic data. There are also some compromises with the very strong expression of the equilibrium hypothesis in collision theory. Thus in the more modern Absolute Rate Theory, begun by Eyring [36]-[38] a Maxwellian distribution of reactant molecules is assumed to be maintained in the "reactant valley" far removed from the "potential energy barrier" of the "potential energy surface", where passage over the barrier is a necessary event for reaction. Noteworthy investigations of this matter were carried out by Montroll and Shuler [29], [30], [40] * who employed probabilistic models for explicating and estimating departures from the equilibrium hypothesis.

Earlier work by Curtiss [31] Prigogine [32] and Takayanagi [39] considered the addition of energy to a system through heat of reactio and the removal of highly energetic molecules from the system of colliding reactant molecules as the causative factors in the perturbation of an initial Maxwellian velocity distribution. Their conclusion was that the critical value C = 5 .

The Zwolinski-Eyring [41] model schematically describes the reactants by one set of quantum states and the reactant products by another. These levels are schematic in that they are not really identified with translational energetic states or those of internal degrees of freedom, say; they are left unspecified and thus, perfectly general. The chemical reaction process is then described as the passage of molecules through a succession of reactant states (discrete jumps between states being under the control of transition probabilities) by collisions with other molecules, into the product state, signifying completion of the individual transformation. For unimolecular transformations, the gist of the mathematical model is seen in the linear rate equations of the form:

* See ref. 30 particularly, for comprehensive treatment of this point.

(28) $$dx_n/dt = \sum_{m \neq n} \left\{ W_{nm} x_m - W_{mn} x_n \right\}$$

which describe the rates of transition for the reactant species A between the various reactant and product quantum levels, where W_{nm} is the probability per unit time of transitions through collisions from states m to n and $x_n(t)$ is the portion of molecules in state n at time t . Here the W_{nm}, assumed to be calculable in principle from quantum-mechanical postulates, are not actually measurable in practice since they would require measurements of intermolecular forces which cannot be made. Approximating the factors W_{nm} for the case of a 4 level model, Zwolinski and Eyring [41] were able to show that such a model predicts rates whose maximum deviation from those predicted by the equilibrium theory could be of the order of 20%.

An extension of the Zwolinski-Eyring 4 level model to higher levels is discussed by Montroll and Shuler [30]. In this extension transition from reactant to product occurs by passage to the $(N+1)^{th}$ level, which is considered an "absorbing barrier". And the rate of reaction is given by the "mean first passage time"*, the average time required for a species to pass the Nth level and reach the absorbing barrier for the first time.

The idea for these approaches originated in the work of Kramers [43] who was the first to propose a Brownian motion model for chemical reaction. In his original work, which was not pursued directly by others apparently because of mathematical difficulties, reactant molecules were considered as becoming activated through collisions with other molecules of the surrounding medium which acts as a "constant temperature bath"; and after many collisional exchanges of energy some of the reactant molecules acquire sufficient energy of activation to cross a potential energy barrier. Even in the case of this model, as Montroll and Shuler have pointed out, the results are in agreement with the equilibrium hypothesis for C = 10, in a wide variety of reactions.

In the Montroll-Shuler quantum - mechanical analogue of the Kramers model, the intramolecular mechanism of reaction is described in stochastic terms as a 1-dimensional random walk with absorbing barrier, W_{mn} being the probability for unit time that a walker will take a step from level n to m . The time dependent distribution of reactant molecules among the energy levels n = 0, 1, 2, ..., N-1, N is given by the fraction $x_n(t)$ of walkers $(\sum' x_n(0) = 1)$ n levels from the origin at time t . "The rate of activation" is taken as inversely proportional to the mean first passage time (to the $(N+1)^{th}$ level, as before). The transition probabilities are as difficult to obtain as in other cases where they arise. Accordingly the assumption

* See also the related work S. Kim ref [42] on this approach.

was made that the reactant molecules be treated as simple "harmonic oscillators", permitting only weak interactions between oscillators and heat both molecules (as was first proposed by Landau and Teller [44] and improved by Kim [42]. In this way, simple expressions were obtained relating the W_{nm} factors to the transition probabilities per collision, the so-called P_{nm} factors. Incidentally, terms such as $\sum_{m}^{N} P_{N+1,m}$ in this model correspond to basic probability expressions such as $\mu n \Delta t + o(\Delta t)$ in the enzyme catalytic process being discussed.

Furthermore, while these results have been obtained mainly in studies of unimolecular reactions and hence, seem to elucidate the microscopic kinetics of transformation T_2 and T_3 in the enzymatic scheme, bimolecular studies are also proceeding which help elucidate the complexation mechanism intramolecularly; i.e. transformation T_1: $ExS \rightarrow ES$. For example, attention is called to the related work of Eliason and Hirschfelder [34] and Widom [35].

Thus, with reference to the GCQP process of this paper, various studies have been made which contribute to our understanding of the deeper aspects of the service mechanism and its component parts; which point the way to the development of a "microscopic enzyme kinetics" and one which has greater universality than those theoretical models which rest on the controversial equilibrium hypothesis. At the same time, the queue-theoretic formulation and special methodology of the enzymatic process discussed in this section, suggest an approach to other realizations of the general catalytic queue process as well. That a large number of physical phenomena can be treated in this way derives from the fact that many features of this stochastic approach, including the random flight and velocity distribution considerations, have been applied to a large number of phenomena to problems of stellar dynamics in astronomy, as has been so ably expounded in the classical physical paper on stochastic processes by Chandrasekhar [25].

That increased research on the queue-theoretic and general stochastic treatment of such problems is necessary is seen from the more complicated enzyme catalytic processes, which we shall have time only to mention. We have discussed here only the very simplest enzyme catalytic realization of the general catalytic queue process. The more complex queueing situations corresponding to the variants of the GCQP (v. s.) arise from complexities of structure and composition of biological systems and their resultant effects on such biological functions as catalytic activities.

There exist certain compounded enzymes which consist of a protein, referred to as the "apoenzyme", and an additional non-proteinacious moiety, called the "prosthetic group", the pair being called the "holoenzyme" - connoting that both are necessary for catalytic activity or function. In some cases where the prosthetic group is easily separated from the apoenzyme, it is called the "coenzyme". For example, the enzyme lactic dehydrogenase has for its cofactor, DPN, diphosphopyridine nucleotide. The co-factors are necessary for the enzyme activity to proceed; their removal leads to inactivation. Other kinds of catalytic activators exist also, such as metal ions. An enzyme with a prosthetic group that is firmly bound is catalase which has haematin for its prosthetic group. Certain coenzymes such as DPN and pyridoxal phosphate are required by a large number of enzymes. For example, the latter combined with an enzyme from pig heart [45] catalyzes a transamination reaction; in combination with an enzyme from E. Coli [46] it helps to catalyze the decarboxylation of glutamic acid; together with an enzyme from Neurospora sitophila [47] it helps catalyze the synthesis of triptophan.

While it may be that considerable fractions of most coenzymes are bound in vivo to certain enzymes, the concentrations of some coenzymes such as DPN are so high in relation to their enzymes that the coenzyme molecules must be in solution much of the time, perhaps acting as "carriers" of various groups involved in the corresponding transformations, possibly behaving kinetically like the corresponding substrates. Coenzymes such as DPN which can be oxidized and reduced, in turn, have the capability of serving as control mechanisms in the co-ordination of sequences of enzymatic reactions.

Enzyme-coenzyme-substrate systems in which it is necessary for the coenzyme to be present at the enzyme's "serving counter" in order for the service to the complexed substrate to be rendered is an example of the variant of the GCQP called the "server-attendant-customer" process. The unusual features of this as a queueing process would occur in cases where coenzyme is added with substrate to the enzyme system. In such a case the joint arrivals at a given enzyme of cofactor and substrate would be necessary. In fact, in cases of loosely bound coenzymes, additional complications would be introduced since initiation of the transformation of a waiting customer could not take place until the necessary enzyme-coenzyme complex formed.

Another known variant of the basic process involves the interesting catalytic mechanism, likely to occur in in vivo biochemistry where two or more species of substrates are competing for the active site on each enzyme molecule. In this case, one would have to consider the relative "specificities" of the different substrates for the enzyme. In any event the queueing problem here would consist of determining the multivariate distribution of the number of substrate molecules of different species waiting to be served at a given time. This process is an example of type b in section 2.

Particularly significant in terms of biological chemistry is anothe form of competitive queue process in which the action of the enzyme relative to a given substrate may be blocked by the presence of chemi cal species called "inhibitors". These latter substances can block enzymatic action in a number of different ways. Notable among these are so-called "competitive inhibitors" and "non-competitive" inhibitors. In the former case, presumably, the blocking effect of the service is performed by the tendency of the inhibitor to arrive at the active site and form a complex called the "enzyme-inhibitor complex" thereby preventing substrate customers from obtaining service. In the latter case, of "non competitive inhibition", the blocking action is indirect; the inhibitor exerts its action by interacting with the enzyme in such a way as to render the active site inactive, so to speak so that even if a substrate arrives there, no action is possible. Thes inhibition phenomena are realizations of variants (c) and (d) discussed in section 2. It may be inferred from in vitro studies that such catalytic mechanisms must play a fundamental role in the regula tion of living systems. In terms of in vitro studies per se, studies of inhibition have yielded valuable information on the structure and function of various enzymes.

Thus queue theoretic models are a natural extension of the stoch- astic models which have already been proposed [18], [19]. Further pursuit of this approach may yield a more powerful mathematical framework for analyzing and predicting biochemical and biological behavior. While the Michaelis-Menten approach has played a most important role in quantifying the study of biochemical phenomena, too many exceptions occur which are not explicable in terms of that theory. In proposing stochastic and queue theoretic formulations we are attempting to emphasize the statistical nature of such phenomena and their connections with intramolecular events that are explicable only in terms of stochastic elements; to provide a statistical framework for interpreting the regularities in such phenomena. Whereas a pure deterministic approach excludes fluctuations, the stochastic approach provides for both irregularities and regularities in the midst of irregularities - as can be seen from the consistency in the mean of the stochastic model relative to the deterministic equations. Such models are of more than theoretical interest since the appearance of random fluctuations in enzyme kinetic data are likely to lead to the wrong conclusions if one postulates only empirical origins for random- ness or irreproducibility.

6. Epidemiological Autocatalysis, Deterministic Models

We consider next, rather more briefly, a class of macroscopic biological phenomena which are in contrast to the microscopic or molecular catalytic processes just discussed; namely, "epidemics", i.e. "occurrences in a community or region of a group of illnesses of similar nature clearly in excess of normal expectancy and derived from a common or propagated source" (Gordon [52]). Mathematical models used in the elucidation of epidemiological kinetics are strikingly similar to those used in chemical kinetics, as we shall see. Furthermore, the description of the mechanics of the processes involved, when stripped of their biological context could just as well be reconstructed in meaningful chemical form. But the commonality of the suggested chemical and epidemiological phenomena is perhaps best captured in the form of the GCQP which, as we have already emphasized is therefore an abstraction of both of these widely dispersed classes of biological phenomena, as well as of other natural phenomena. In speaking of these as "widely dispersed" classes we are pointing up the restriction of our discussion of the epidemiology to the phenomenological level for we shall consider as our basic units whole organisms and interactions of organisms with organisms as opposed to molecular and submolecular interactions. The present obligation of medicine to relate disease to subcellular and molecular events is ignored in this, but it is understood that there may indeed be connections between these very processes at the biochemical level beyond the mathematical and phenomenological relationship. It should be emphasized at the outset that while the interpretation proposed for this class of processes may be original, our contributions to the stochastic models of biological phenomena of this type have been restricted to birth and death processes [48]. It is necessary for us to bring in some of the ideas presented in Bailey [49] and in references by other workers in this important field in order to show that the queue-theoretic approach in this case as well, is a kind of natural extension to the stochastic models which have already been introduced.

We begin by considering one of the simplest types of epidemics, "the Simple Epidemic with No Removal" in which it is assumed (1) that infection is spread by direct contact between different individuals in a given community and (2) there is no removal from circulation of the "infectives" either by death, removal, or isolation - so that ultimately all susceptibles might become infected. Thus, in terms of biomathematical transformation theory [2], [28], we may write

$$T:\ A \xrightarrow{k} B \tag{29}$$

where A is the population of "susceptibles" and B the population of "infectives". It may be assumed that the epidemic phenomenon begins by the introduction of one element of B into the community. Then, as in deterministic chemical kinetic models and deterministic biological growth processes [48]-[51] the mathematical assumption is made that the size of A subsequently (the "concentration") is a time dependent, differentiable function $x(t)$; and that of B, similarly a function $y(t)$, where of course x and y are permitted to have values on a continuum, overlooking their discrete realities. Furthermore, we have the initial conditions $x(0) = x_0$ and $y(0) = 1$.

This situation is formally equivalent to the case of auto-catalysis in chemistry in the sense that once the process is initiated, the transformation of further susceptibles into infectives is catalyzed by the presence of more and more individuals of class B. And the usual deterministic model employed for this case is exactly that which would be used for the auto-catalytic chemical transformation; viz.,

$$\frac{dx}{dt} = -k\,x\,y \tag{30}$$

where

$$\begin{cases} x(0) = x_0 > 0 \\ y(0) = 1 \\ x + y = x_0 + 1 \end{cases} \tag{31}$$

In this model, k is the "characteristic" rate constant of the process, reflecting the assumption underlying the differential equation (30) that the number of new infectives occurring in the time interval $(t, t + \Delta t)$ is $k\,x\,y\,\Delta t$. Integration of (30) then yields

$$x = \frac{x_0(x_0 + 1)}{x_0 + \exp\{(x_0 + 1)kt\}} \tag{32}$$

which is the expression for the well-known "autocatalytic" or "logistic curve."

Next let a more complicated epidemiological process be considered in which removal of infectives is allowed for. Here, in addition to transformation (29) an additional transformation is allowed: $T_2 : B \xrightarrow{k_2} C$ where B is the set of infectives in circulation; and C is the set of those which are removed. Thus, calling the first rate constant corresponding to (29) k_1, the following set of differential equations makes up the mathematical model in this case:

$$\begin{cases} \dfrac{dx}{dt} = -k_1\,x\,y \\ \dfrac{dy}{dt} = k_1 x\,y - k_2\,y \\ \dfrac{dz}{dt} = k_2\,y \end{cases} \tag{33}$$

where z(t) is the number of removals that have taken place by time t . Again it can be seen that this is the same model that would be used in analyzing the kinetics of the compounded chemical reaction $A \xrightarrow{k_1} B \xrightarrow{k_2} C$ with the added restriction that the presence of B acts as a catalyst on the reaction from A to B . Here of course, additional conditions would be specified, such as $x + y + z = n$ where n is the total size of the community; as well as arbitrarily set conditions such as $x(0) = x_0 > 0$, $y(0) = y_0 > 0$, $z(0) = 0$, so that $x_0 + y_0 = n$. Solutions to this system may be found in Bailey [49] on pages 22-29.

More complicated epidemiological situations involve the addition of a further intermediary species, the host or vector; where by "host" is meant the animal other than man that harbors the infectious agent pathogenic for man, and by "vector" is meant an arthropod or other invertebrate which transmits infection by innoculation into or through the skin or mucous membrane by biting, or by deposit of infective materials on the skin or on food or other objects. The vector may be infected itself or may act as a passive or mechanical carrier of the agent [52]. For example in malaria the parasitic agent is harbored in the anopheline mosquito.

Deterministic mathematical models for this case have concentrated largely on the special case of malaria epidemiology and all seem to refer back to the classical work of Sir Ronald Ross [53], in which the basic differential equations were set up. This work was followed up by Waite [54] and by Lotka [55], in particular, who gave a very extensive mathematical treatment of the malaria equations and their implications. Kermack and McKendrick published some work on the general case [56] in 1927, and this is discussed also by Bailey [49]. The paper by Kermack and McKendrick is noteworthy in one other respect; viz., in it is deduced the most important "Threshold Theorem", which in effect states that as infectious cases are introduced into a community of susceptibles, there is a critical number of susceptibles, above which an epidemic outbreak occurs which reduces the number of susceptibles (transforming them into infectives) to a number as far below the critical level as the original number exceeded this level. This theorem is a strong step in the direction of quantifying the whole concept of "epidemic" and is a result to which the mathematical method in biology should point with great emphasis as an example of the power of the method to contribute a basic parameter to biological phenomena. The interested reader is referred to the whole series of papers by these two authors [56]-[60] and to related work by later investigators who extended the result both deterministically and stochastically [61]-[64].

7. The Stochastic Approach to Epidemiological Catalysis

Thus, as in the case of chemical and biochemical kinetics all of the earliest work has been deterministic in character, little, if any attention being paid to random fluctuations and to the probabilistic context of discrete events composing the process. On the other hand, lessons learned from the theory of stochastic processes, which was not available to the earliest investigators, tell us that in epidemiology we find an excellent example of the principle that, particularly, for small numbers of interacting species, randomness is far from negligible. When the numbers are large, there is good agreement between stochastic and deterministic predictions. On the other hand, although for some processes (v. s.) the stochastic means are equal to the corresponding deterministic values, this is not generally true for epidemic processes and so it is all the more important to examine the stochastic approach intensively, in order to obtain further insight into important features of the epidemiological mechanism, which do not find their way into deterministic models at all. The appearance of data on epidemic curves (and kinetic data in general) may be misleading on this point (and is often used by opponents of stochastic methods as an argument against the necessity for introducing probabilistic reasoning), for the apparent smoothness of concentration - time data may be produced artificially by the method of reporting cases which may be obtained on a daily or per weekly basis; it may even represent a summation over several relatively independent epidemics occurring simultaneously in different subcommunities or subregions of a larger community or region. It is for example well-known that these smaller epidemics are generally not in phase and interact with each other [49].

On the other hand, there is no intent to discard the deterministic method. In fact, one sees a continuation of the old and the new in the work of those who are interested in mathematical kinetics and in mathematical epidemiology in general. Stochastic models may be regarded as complementary to deterministic models, methodologically speaking; where deterministic assumptions are approximately valid, the greater simplicity of such models necessarily commends them to us; and in passing to the stochastic models one can see fundamental deterministic principles or assumption recast into stochastic reformulation.

The transition from deterministic to stochastic models in epidemiology was accomplished gradually, an intermediary being "chains of binomial distributions", to represent successive sets of new cases. Work of this type was begun in the 1920's by L. Reed, W. Frost, and M. Greenwood, although as Bailey [49] points out they did not apparently publish anything on this (see Wilson and Burke [65];

Abbey [66]). Stochastic models for biological population kinetics* began to be introduced in the 1940's, so that the stochastic method was introduced into biology and in physics also (see Bharucha-Reid [20] and Chandrasekhar [25] as well as the various references: [48], [61], [73]) before it was used in chemical kinetics. The spread of the stochastic method between physics, chemistry, and biology is, in fact, an interesting and hopeful commentary on inter-disciplinary awareness.

According to Bailey [49], McKendrick [67] was probably the first to publish a stochastic treatment of the epidemic process (1926). In it he propounded a class of models which has come to be called "the continuous infection" type; it is continuous in that it assumes the infectiousness of an individual from the instant of infection until the moment he dies, recovers, or is isolated. And in it, much as in other catalytic and kinetic phenomena, the transfer of established deterministically stated principles to stochastic assumptions may be seen as follows: - Whereas in deterministic models the number of new cases in a short time interval $(t, t + \Delta t)$ is taken to be jointly and directly proportional to the numbers of infectives and susceptibles and to the length of interval, McKendrick began by assuming this same quantity to be proportional to the probability of a new case in that time. This passage from deterministic to stochastic epidemiological models is very similar to (1) the modification of the Law of Mass Action principle of chemistry for the construction of chemical kinetic stochastic models [4]-[6], [20] and [2] adaptations of the Malthusian axiom of Population Growth to stochastic models of birth and death processes.* McKendrick's work was not followed up until at least 20 years later, probably owing to mathematical difficulties. In fact, McKendrick and Kermack's enlightening research papers [57]-[60] following this isolated stochastic effort were deterministic.

An alternative stochastic treatment published by Greenwood [68] in 1931 however was followed up more closely. This was more along the lines of the Reed-Frost chain binomial treatments. In these models, in contrast to the continuous infection models, the assumption was made that the period of infectiousness was very short and that "latent" and "incubation" periods (v. i.) were short, so that, starting with a single case in a closed community, new cases would occur in a series of stages or generations, the cases occurring in each stage showing a binomial distribution dependent on the numbers of susceptibles and infectious individuals present at the previous stage (the "chain-binomial" concept.)

Many and important contributions to the stochastic theory of epidemics were made in the era following 1940 concomitant with the development of the theory of stochastic processes itself. No attempt

* See Bartholomay [48], Bharucha-Reid [20] Kendall [69], [70].

will be made here to even outline these later developments many of which are referred to in Bailey's book [49]. As background for our queue-theoretic interpretation of epidemiological catalysis, we shall cite briefly only two examples. The first is the stochastic analogue of the simple deterministic epidemic process mentioned in section 6 and is referred to as a "simple stochastic epidemic". It is of the continuous infection type.

a. The Simple Stochastic Epidemic. The random variables corresponding to the sizes of the two populations are, as in the enzymatic catalytic case, integral valued quantities: n, corresponding to the number of susceptibles present in the region at time t; and m, the number of infectives present at time t. Note that in the epidemiological case, because of its autocatalytic nature, the number m, unlike the total number of "free" or "bound" (occupied) enzyme molecules present at all times*, is not fixed; it is assumed that initially m has the value $m_0 = 1$. As susceptibles become infected, they are added to this number, so that the following relation exists between susceptibles and infectives at all times:

(34) $$m = n_0 - n + 1$$

Then the assumption that the probability of one new infective in the infinitesimal time interval $(t, t + \Delta t)$, independently of t, is $\mu\, n\, m\, \Delta t + o(\Delta t)$; i.e. $\mu\, n\,(n_0 - n + 1)\,\Delta t + o(\Delta t)$, where μ is the infectivity parameter, in conjunction with the usual methods in treating such Markovian processes allows us to obtain the stochastic difference-differential equations of the simple epidemiological process:

(35) $$\begin{cases} \dfrac{\partial p(n;t)}{\partial t} = (n+1)(n_0 - n)\mu p(n+1;t) - n(n_0 - n + 1)\,\mu p(n,t) \\ \qquad\qquad\qquad\qquad\qquad (n = 0, 1, \ldots n-1) \\ \dfrac{\partial p(n_0;t)}{\partial t} = -\mu n_0 p(n_0;t) \qquad (\text{initial condition } p(n_0;0) = 1) \end{cases}$$

The solution to this system, using Laplace transform methods, is discussed by Bailey [49], [72], who examines also ways of estimating the parameter corresponding to the infection rate. The expressions are very awkward mathematically; for $n_0 > 10$ mathematical difficulties grow rapidly, even in the case of this simple stochastic epidemic.

---

* Note that the number of "free" enzyme molecules (or, its complements, the number of "bound" molecules) however is a discrete valued random variable with values ranging from 0 to the initial number (v. s.).

b. The General Stochastic Epidemic Model. The order of mathematical difficulties increases, as we go to more realistic epidemic models. One of these is the so-called "general stochastic epidemic model" (see Bailey [49], [63]), corresponding to the second deterministic model discussed in the previous section, in which removal of infections from the community is permitted. The term "general" implies that the class of processes discussed goes beyond the simplest case of, say, mild infections in which infectives are not removed in any manner. However it is not the most comprehensive possible; such a model would have to include effects of migration, immunity loss, spatial distributions (as in the chemical catalytic models) etc.

Again letting n and m be the random variables corresponding to the numbers of susceptibles and infectives, respectively, present in the community, the problem is to determine the joint probability function of time; $p(n, m; t)$. The assumption that $\mu_1 n m \Delta t + o(\Delta t)$ is the probability of one new susceptible $\rightarrow$ infective conversion in time $(t, t + \Delta t)$ and $\mu_2 m \Delta t + o(\Delta t)$ the probability one removal in this time, leads [49], [63] to the equations:

$$(36)\quad \begin{cases} \dfrac{\partial p(n, m; t)}{\partial t} = (n+1)\,(m-1)\,p(n+1, m-1; t) \\ \qquad -m(n+\mu_2/\mu_1)\cdot p(n, m; t) + \mu_2/\mu_1 (m+1)\,p(n, m+1; t) \\ \dfrac{\partial p(n_0, m_0; t)}{\partial t} = -m_0 (n_0 + \mu_2/\mu_1)\,p(n_0, m_0; t) \end{cases}$$

whoro

$$(37)\quad \begin{cases} 0 < n + m < n_0 + m_0 \\ 0 \le n \le n_0 \\ 0 \le m \le n_0 + m_0 \end{cases}$$

which equations cannot be solved exactly except in the simplest cases. Of interest in this model is the information it contains concerning the distribution of the total size of epidemic; i.e., the value of $n_0 - n$ as $t \rightarrow \infty$. Such questions are discussed in Bailey [49], [63]. They are of great pertinence to the present discussion (v. i.) but time forbids our entering into them any further here. Instead we shall conclude by discussing the queue-theoretic characteristics of these epidemiological autocatlytic processes; i.e., by showing in what particular ways they may be regarded as realizations of the General Catalytic Queue Process.

8. Epidemiological Autocatalysis as a Realization of the GCQP

It is interesting to re-examine epidemiological processes from the point of view of the GCQP which, it will be seen, not only includes the important mathematical characteristics of the processes already studied but which calls for further elucidation of complex mechanisms of epidemiological catalysis along lines suggested by queueing theory. Again, as in enzymatic catalytic phenomena, the queue-theoretic approach flows out of the stochastic models for such phenomena and their connections with stochastic processes employe in classical queueing theory. Certainly Markovian methods are common to both.

Aside from assuming homogeneous mixing between susceptibles and infectives; i.e., "customers" and "servers", in a given restrict region or community, apparently little mathematical attention has been paid to the initial random events leading to "arrivals" of susceptibles at infective "service counters". Nevertheless there is a strong analogy here to biochemical catalysis where the random motions of the interacting species are in fact considered a part of the overall mechanism of the transformation. Thus, assuming that the epidemic process begins by the introduction of a single "server" into the community, a strong element of randomness must be in control of the contacts between that infective and a given susceptible or "waiting customer". On the other hand, it is impossible to characterize in any great mathematical detail random aspects of such arrivals which depend on so many human and large scale factors. Nevertheless, to encourage purely mathematical "in vitro" studies of single factors of this type, say, which are important for conceiving of measures of prevention and control, it might be useful to consider various random processes for describing random contacts between infectives and susceptibles and from these to attempt to deduce the basic probability statements from which the stochastic equations are constructed. For example, presently in all of these models, as we have seen, it is axiomatized that in time $(t, t + \Delta t)$ the probability of an effective contact resulting from "homogeneous mixing" would be $\mu\, n\, m\, \Delta t + o(\Delta t)$ where n and m are the numbers of "customers" and "servers", the factor μ being a basic probabilistic parameter. This of course corresponds to the basic stochastic enzymatic statement with enzyme and substrate substituted for a server and customer. But, as we have seen (v.s.), such a statement need not be taken as elementary, it being possible to deduce it from random laws in control of kinetic motions of the customer-server species. We have in mind here, a development of the stochastic equations which mimics the enzymatic catalytic treatment given in equations (15) to (25) of section 5, starting with the assumptions that the velocity distributions of an infective is, say, $p(\dot{x}_1, \dot{y}_1, \dot{z}_1)$ $d\dot{x}_1, d\dot{y}_1, d\dot{z}_1$ where $(x,y,z,)$ gives the location and $(\dot{x}_1, \dot{y}_1, \dot{z}_1)$ its associated velocity vector; that of a susceptible,

$$p_2(\dot{x}_2, \dot{y}_2, \dot{z}_2)\, d\dot{x}_2, d\dot{y}_2, d\dot{z}_2 \ .$$

These distributions may be used to characterize a stationary arrival process in the simplest case, corresponding to the enzymatic "equilibrium hypothesis".

Along more fundamental lines, this part of the problem may be treated according to methods which have been worked out in ecological studies of the random dispersal of logistic populations, for example (see references [74]-[79]). The invading population of servers "infectives" can thus be regarded as one which is diffusing into a given community and growing as it advances by adding new infectives according to the autocatalytic growth curve (see equation 32) or its stochastic counterpart. This approach might be set up by analogy with the treatment of the Langevin equation (equation (15)) discussed in section 5, modifying the partial differential equations cited in the references [74]-[79] as follows:

$$\frac{\partial u}{\partial t} - \beta^2 \frac{\partial^2 u}{\partial t^2} = \alpha\, u(1-u) + B(t) \tag{38}$$

where $u(x,y,z;t)$ is the population density function of infectives, β^2 is the "diffusion constant", α corresponds to the autocatalytic growth rate, and $B(t)$ is a random function of time.

While autocatalysis suggests the ordinary "many server queueing processes"*, there the usual situation considered assumes m servers at a given counter, where no server is idle if there is a waiting customer and where the customers arrive at the common counter at instants $t_0, t_1, \ldots t_n, \ldots$ such that the corresponding interarrival times are characterized as identically distributed, independent random variables with distribution function, say

$$P(t_{n+1} - t_n \leq x) = F(x) \ .$$

Because in the autocatalytic case, m itself is a random variable, and because each server has his own "counter" and is allowed to move relative to waiting customers, it is clear that new methods would be needed here.

A most important aspect of the queue analysis of the epidemic process is the service mechanism, in this case the mechanism of disease transfer from infective to susceptible; i.e. from "server" to

* See Takacs [2] pp. 147-158 and the bibliography given by him on pp. 157-8.

"customer". Essentially this refers to a time sequence of events involving the transfer of the causative organism or material from infective to susceptible; and in cases where a host or vector is involved, the transfer from infective to host to susceptible. This situation, incidentally, suggests the formation of a complex between enzyme and substrate; or in the host situation, between enzyme, coenzyme, and substrate - though of course in this case the susceptible-infective, or susceptible-host-infective complexes would be considered only abstractly. Epidemiological analysis of the sequence of events involved in this service mechanism is represented in the following diagram which lists also the terminology which has developed for identification of the distinct epidemiological epochs:

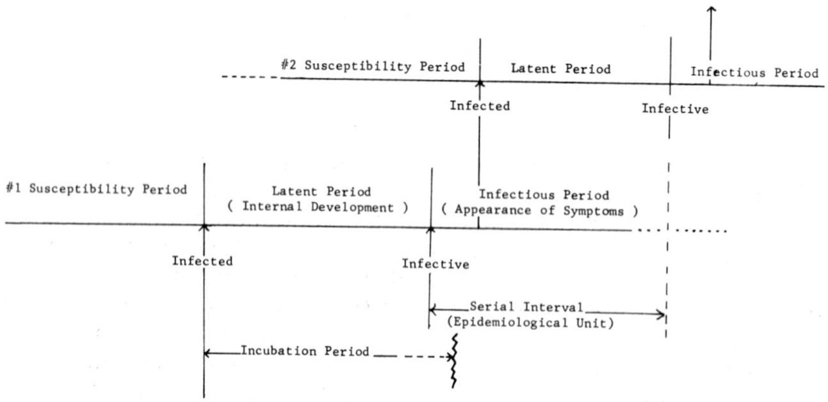

Figure I

Main Epidemiological Epochs

The analogue of the ordinary queue service period would be definable retrospectively as the time it takes the material to be discharged from the infective and received by the susceptible. In greater detail, there is a finite period during which the causative organisms or material may be discharged referred to as the "infectious period". This follows immediately the "latent period" during which there is purely internal development with no discharge of infectious material. The "incubation period" refers to the variable time elapsing between receipt of infection and the appearance of symptoms. Thus sometime during the infectious period symptoms occur which allow diagnosis of the disease and there is the first outward indication that a server has converted a susceptible into a potential infective. It is of course at this time, that preventive measures such as isolation may be installed to curtail the number of "servers". If symptoms occur just before the infectious period; i.e. at the interface between the latent and infectious period, then the most effective preventive measures may be taken. Thus connected with the queue-theoretic service mechanism are a number of significant intervals which are random intervals that correspond to such concepts of queueing theory as "interarrival times". However, the distribution functions of such random variables are not accurately determinable. It is the "serial interval", the time between the observation of symptoms in one case and the observation of symptoms in a second related case, that is considered the observable epidemiological unit of time. This interval reflects to some extent the life cycle of the parasitic organism.

As in general queueing theory an important measure of the overall epidemic process is the "total duration time, T"; i.e., the time from initiation of the process to the time when the epidemic dies out. In general, this will happen before all susceptibles are serviced. The current simplest stochastic models, of course, predict that the "mathematical" process is always completed sooner or later; e.g., in the first model discussed in section 7 it can be shown that $\lim_{t\to\infty} p(0, t) = 1$. Even in respect to the simplest epidemic process, general expressions for the distribution of the random variable T have not been obtained, though formulas for the cumulants have been deduced (Bailey [49] pp. 47-50).

In connection with the "general stochastic epidemic" an important queue-theoretic question relates to the distribution of the size of the "waiting line" as a function of time; viz; the distribution of n, the number of uninfected susceptibles present at time t. From the epidemiological point of view, the emphasis is on the complement of n; viz, $n_0 - n$, the number of susceptibles infected in time t, since $\lim_{t\to\infty} p(n_0 - n; t)$ characterizes probabilistically the "total size of epidemic". U - and J - shaped probability functions have been calculated for this quantity (see Bailey [49] pp. 58-61).

Equally difficult is the problem of determining the distribution function of the number m of servers present as a function of time. As we have already emphasized, this is one of the features, incorporated in the GCQP formulation and in epidemiological autocatalysis as an application, that represents an extension of the more common classes of queueing problems where the number of servers present is a constant throughout. In the general stochastic epidemic (b) which permits the retirement or "removal" of servers, it is known only that $0 \leq m \leq m_0 + (n_0 - n)$. However knowledge of the distribution of the size of the waiting line n can be made use of in the case of the simple epidemic (a) (which permits no removals) to obtain the probability distribution of m which in that case is always equal to $(m_0 + n_0) - n$.

A complete queue theoretic description of epidemiological autocatalysis would call for the determination of multivariate or joint distributions of the various significant successive time intervals involved; such as the incubation period, the serial interval, etc. However, the multivariate nature of the problem has been obscured by epidemiological analyses which, for mathematical and theoretical simplicity have reduced some of the time intervals involved either to a point or to non trivial but constant magnitudes. For example, in the chain-binomial models (v. s.) of Reed, Frost, and Greenwood, the infectious period is contracted to a point and the latent and incubation periods are regarded as approximately constant. In Bailey's modification* the latent period is given a roughly normal frequency distribution but the infectious period is considered to be of constant length. In the continuous infection model of McKendrick and Bartlett [73] a negative exponential distribution for the infectious period is assumed, but the latent period is assigned length zero.

In addition to certain analogies which have already been mentioned between the epidemiological autocatalysis and enzymatic catalysis there are several other likenesses which are noteworthy and which indicate variants of the basic General Catalytic Queue Process. For example, not all contacts between servers and customers are "successful." Various medical factors may contribute to "ineffective collisions": the susceptibles may be resistant in varying degrees to the infection depending on natural or acquired biological and biochemical defenses against the invading organisms. This means further that just as in the case of "susceptible" biochemical customer or substrate molecules, the implicit assumption of indistinguishability of different susceptibles represents a high degree of idealization which excludes intraspecies biological variation. In some cases complete resistance may have been acquired by previous exposure,

* See references [49], [63], [64], [71], [72].

so that the class of susceptibles is not necessarily the complement of the infectives in the community.

The concept of "inhibition" has meaning here also. For example, vaccines and other immunizing materials behave as "inhibitors" to the disease process - blocking passage to the "service counter" as in the enzymatic case of "competitive inhibition" - and indeed actual biochemical inhibition may be involved in certain processes. In contrast to this, biological factors of resistance may be thought of in the sense of the "non-competitive" enzymatic inhibition. By the same token, the presence of other disease or debilitating factors may be compared to co-operating "co-factors", or activators in the enzymatic case, thus calling for further variants such as (a) - (d) of the GCQP described in section 2.

There are also indications in epidemiological processes of complex queue-like processes involving the interactions of different diseases processes as well as those resulting from the case mentioned earlier in which the epidemic process under observation may actually be the resultant of several different "component" epidemics occurring in different subunits of the total region. Pertinent also to this point are multiple stage epidemic processes.

9. Summary and Conclusion

In this paper we have begun by defining the General Catalytic Queue Process (GCQP) which represents a crystallization of the common features of a number of chemical, biochemical and other biological and medical processes involving the servicing of a group of "customers" by a group of "servers". The latter group possesses the property, characteristic of "catalytic" agents, of being able to perform their service repeatedly without any apparent loss of power. Included in this process is also the generalized phenomenon of "autocatalysis" in which customers once served are capable of serving other waiting customers. Enzymatic catalysis was discussed as an example of the former refinement of the GCQP; and epidemic processes as an example of the latter. Catalysis conceived of in this way seems to us the mathematical statement of a rather general principle that cuts across the boundaries of various disciplines.

The similarity of these processes is not an artifact of the stochastic method; we have also discussed them at the simpler deterministic level as well, and in the language of biochemistry and of epidemiology phenomenologically. The correspondence between these processes seems to be an invariant of the context of discussion, pointing to the fact that the GCQP indeed has a broad foundation in natural occurring phenomena.

Particularly in the case of the enzymatic catalytic process we have been able to show how closely our earlier stochastic model for the basic enzyme substrate reaction follows the queueing approach, which in turn forms a framework for the integration not only of the ideas immanent in the early stochastic model but also in certain aspects of chemical kinetics which are being studied deeply from the physico-chemical point of view. Similarly, the queue-theoretic approach underscores a number of difficult and neglected mathematical points in mathematical epidemiology, the solution of which should add to our understanding of the epidemic process. As we have pointed out here, suggestions for possible approaches to these unanswered questions come out of analogous situations arising, for example, in chemical and biochemical studies. In particular, the mechanism of activation of the epidemic process has been discussed along lines suggested by biochemical treatments of related problems.

Enzyme catalysis and epidemiological catalysis are certainly not the only two classes of realization of the GCQP. Time does not permit our following this further. Suffice it to say a variety of game theoretic and decision-theoretic processes can easily be conceived as further realizations of the GCQP.

REFERENCES

1. H. Muench. 1959. "Catalytic Methods in Epidemiology". Harvard Press, Cambridge, Massachusetts.

2. L. Takacs. 1962. "Introduction to the Theory of Queues." Oxford Press, New York.

3. A. F. Bartholomay. 1960. Bull. Math. Biophys. 22, 285.

4. A. F. Bartholomay. 1962. Ch. 1. in "Physicomathematical Aspects of Biology" (Ed. N. Rashevsky) (Course 16 Proceedings, Enrico Fermi International School of Physics) Academic Press, New York.

5. A. F. Bartholomay. 1958. Bull. Math. Biophys. 20, 175.

6. A. F. Bartholomay. 1959. Bull. Math. Biophys. 21, 363.

7. C. N. Hinshelwood. 1940. "The Kinetics of Chemical Change" Oxford Press, New York.

8. S. Friess, E. Lewis, A. Weissberger (Editors) 1961. "Investigations of Rates and Mechanisms of Reactions" (vol. VIII, Part I) Interscience Publishers, New York.

9. I. Langmuir. 1916. J. Am. Chem. Soc. 38, 2221.

10. I. Langmuir. 1918. J. Am. Chem. Soc. 40, 1361.

11. K. Laidler. 1958. "The Chemical Kinetics of Enzyme Action". Oxford Press, New York.

12. M. Kunitz. 1939. J. Gen. Physiol. 22, 293, 429.

13. R. Herriott. 1938. J. Gen. Physiol. 21, 501; 22, 65.

14. L. Michaelis and M. Menten. 1913. Biochem. Zeitsch. 49, 333.

15. J. B. S. Haldane. 1930. "The Enzymes". London.

16. D. Keilin and T. Mann. 1937. Proc. Roy. Soc., London B 122, 119.

17. B. Chance. 1943. J. Biol. Chem. 151, 553.

18. A. F. Bartholomay. 1962. Ann. N.Y. Acad. Sci. 96, 897.

19. A. F. Bartholomay. 1962. Biochemistry 1, 223.

20. A. T. Bharucha-Reid. 1960. "Elements of the Theory of Markov Processes and Their Applications." McGraw-Hill, New York.

21. K. Singer. 1953. J. Roy. Stat. Soc. B 15, 92.

22. B. L. Vallee, J. F. Riordan, J. E. Coleman. 1963. Proc. Nat. Acad. Sci. 49, 109.

23. R. T. Simpson, J. F. Riordan, B. L. Vallee. 1963. Biochemistry, 2, 616.

24. G. Schoellmann and E. Shaw. 1963. Biochemistry 2, 252.

25. S. Chandrasekhar. 1943. Rev. Mod. Phys. 15, 1.

26. F. A. Lindemann. 1922. Trans. Faraday Soc. 17, 598.

27. C. N. Hinshelwood. 1927. Proc. Roy. Soc. A 113, 230.

28. A. F. Bartholomay. Unpubl. data and lectures in Course "Introduction to Mathematical Biology." Harvard Med. Sch.

29. E. W. Montroll and K. E. Shuler. 1957. J. Chem. Phys. 26, 454.

30. E. W. Montroll and K. E. Shuler. 1958. in "Advances in Chemical Physics". v.i. p. 361 - Interscience, New York.

31. C. F. Curtiss. 1948. "The Equilibrium Assumption in the Theory of Absolute Reaction Rates." Univ. of Wisconsin Report CM-476

32. I. Prigogine and E. Xhrovet. 1949. Physica 15, 913.

33. S. K. Kim. 1958. J. Chem. Phys. 28, 1057.

34. M. A. Eliason and J. O. Hirschfelder. 1959. J. Chem. Phys. 1426.

35. B. Widom. 1959. J. Chem. Phys. 31, 1387.

36. H. Eyring and M. Polanyi. 1931. Zeits. Phys. Chem. B 12, 279.

37. H. Eyring. 1935. J. Chem. Phys. 3, 107.

38. W. Wynne-Jones and H. Eyring. 1935. J. Chem. Phys. 3, 492.

39. K. Takayanagi. 1951. Progr. Theoret. Phys. (Japan) 6, 486.

40. K. E. Shuler. 1959. J. Chem. Phys. 31, 1375.

41. B. J. Zwolinski and H. Eyring. 1947. J. Am. Chem. Soc. 69, 2702.

42. S. K. Kim. 1958. J. Chem. Phys. 28, 1057.

43. H. A. Kramers. 1940. Physica 7, 284.

44. L. Landau and E. Teller. 1936. Physik. Z. Sowjetunion 10, 34.

45. P. S. Cammarata and P. Cohen. 1950. J. Biol. Chem. 187, 439.

46. W. W. Umbreit and I. C. Gunsalas. 1946. J. Biol. Chem. 159, 333.

47. W. W. Umbreit, W. A. Wood, and I. C. Gunsalas. 1948. J. Biol. Chem. 165, 731.

48. A. F. Bartholomay. 1958. Bull. Math. Biophys. 20, 97.

49. N. T. J. Bailey. 1957. "The Mathematical Theory of Epidemics", Hafner Publ. Co., New York.

50. A. J. Lotka. "Elements of Physical Biology", Williams and Wilkins, Baltimore.

51. V. A. Kostitzin. 1939. "Mathematical Biology", London.

52. J. E. Gordon (ed.). 1955. "Control of Communicable Diseases in Man", An Official Report of the Amer. Pub. Health Assoc.

53. R. Ross. 1911. "The Prevention of Malaria" (2d Ed.) John Murray, London.

54. H. Waite. 1910. Biometrika 7, 421.

55. A. J. Lotka. 1923. "Contributions to the Analysis of Malaria Epidemiology", A. J. Hyg. (Jan. Supplement) 3, 1.

56. W. O. Kermack and A. G. McKendrick. 1927. Proc. Roy. Soc. A, 115, 700.

57. W. O. Kermack and A. G. McKendrick. 1932. Proc. Roy. Soc. A, 138, 55.

58. W. O. Kermack and A. G. McKendrick. 1933. Proc. Roy. Soc. A, 141, 94.

59. W. O. Kermack and A. G. McKendrick. 1937. J. Hyg. Camb. 37, 172.

60. W. O. Kermack and A. G. McKendrick. 1939. J. Hyg. Camb. 39, 271.

61. D. G. Kendall. 1956. Proc. Third Berkeley Symposium on Mathematical Statistics and Probability 4, 149, Berkeley.

62. P. Whittle. 1955. Biometrika 42, 116.

63. N. T. J. Bailey. 1953. Biometrika 40, 177.

64. N. T. J. Bailey. 1955. J. Roy Stat. Soc. B 17, 35.

65. E. B. Wilson and M. H. Burke. 1942. Proc. Nat. Acad. Sci. Wash. 29, 43.

66. H. Abbey. 1952. Human Biology 24, 201.

67. A. G. McKendrick. 1926. Proc. Edin. Math. Soc. 44, 98.

68. M. Greenwood. 1931. J. Hyg. Camb. 31, 336.

69. D. G. Kendall. 1948. Ann. Math. Stat. 19, 1.

70. D. G. Kendall. 1949. J. Roy. Stat. Soc. B, 11, 230.

71. N. T. J. Bailey. 1950. Biometrika 37, 193.

72. N. T. J. Bailey. 1956. Biometrika 43, 15; 322.

73. M. S. Bartlett. 1949. J. Roy. Stat. Soc. B, 11, 211.

74. R. A. Fisher. 1937. Am. Eugenics, London 7, 335.

75. M. G. Kendall. 1948. Proc. Camb. Phil. Soc. 44, 591.

76. J. G. Skellam. 1951. Biometrika 38, 196.

77. R. Barakat. 1959. Bull. Math. Biophys. 21, 141.

78. H. D. Landah. 1957. Bull. Math. Biophys. 19, 171.

79. H. D. Landah. 1959. Bull. Math. Biophys. 21, 153.

This work has been supported by Biomathematics Research Grant No. GM-10002 and Training Grant No. 5-Tl-GM-984 from the National Institutes of Health, Education and Welfare, and the Howard Hughes Medical Institute.

DISCUSSION PARTICIPANTS

Dr. H. P. Galliher
Operations Research Center, Massachusetts Institute of Technology, Cambridge, Massachusetts

Dr. George Weiss
Institute of Fluid Dynamics and Applied Dynamics, University of Maryland, College Park, Maryland

DISCUSSION

H. P. Galliher. Why call these processes queuing and stochastic processes, when they are descriptively more general and mathematically more deterministic?

Anthony F. Bartholomay. I do not know what you mean by the second part of your question unless you are referring to the same argument which was put up by Dr. Weiss, in which case I refer you to my reply to him for an answer to that part of your question. As fo the first part, I agree that the GCQP is more general than the corres ponding construct which is generally assumed within the Theory of Queues.

Perhaps it would be best to refer to the process as the General-ized Queue Process, as divorced from the particular catalytic realiz tions discussed. However, it should be emphasized that the main theme of this paper is that, looked at from both the deterministic an the stochastic mathematical point of view, widely divergent natural processes such as enzymatic catalysis and communicative disease point to the existence of an abstraction which is certainly analyzabl into queue-like features, with the extensions indicated in the GCQP In turn, this process has, I feel sure, a wide range of applicability, also characteristic of classical queueing theory. As Takács caution in the introduction to his book "Introduction to the Theory of Queues" "Many processes which seem to have very little to do with queues are in fact closely related to queueing processes."

George Weiss. Is there data on any enzymatic reaction which indicates that the deterministic kinetic theory is in any way deficient? I exclude random variations in data which might be due to experimental error. If there is no data which controverts the determi istic theory, is there any point of going to the stochastic equations, none of which have been solved even approximately?

Anthony F. Bartholomay. This is exactly the point. Exactly how much random variation do you exclude when you exclude that (part) which is due to experimental error? My own papers on stochastic models in chemical and biochemical kinetics (and the work of others referenced in my papers and discussed also by Bharucha-Reed in his book on Markov Process) in effect, deduce the existence of "inherent" random fluctuations in chemical processes. In my most recent studies, I have started with accepted principles, such as those which are contained in the Modern Theories of Reaction Rates and which in turn are derived from quantum and statistical mechanical considerations. Also, recent studies of the mechanism of biochemical reaction indicate that the final stage of decomposition is the resultant of a large number of passages from one intermediate and reversible enzyme-substrate complex to another, so that there is a compounding of probabilistic circumstances that are discussable in stochastic terms, which precede the final reaction step. K. Singer's work in England indicated a macroscopic random component in certain branching and nucleation processes. It is not possible to obtain biochemical data at this time that would allow us to differentiate between inherent and extrinsic or "experimental variation." On the other hand, I have seen kinetic data from time to time from a number of new enzymatic systems which contain so much random scattering as not to be interpretable - whereas the methods of determination would appear to be no different in terms of precision than those employed in other similar determinations. It is equally impossible to perform a complete error analysis of experimental methods. Biochemical kinetic data as well as chemical kinetic data in general are not rapidly enough obtained so as to rule out the strong possibility that any smoothness observed is only apparent and induced by the lack of resolution within the method itself. At the same time, the data we have seen is taken from in vitro experiments. In the in vivo situation where reactions are more dilute it is likely that inherent fluctuation would be more apparent.

Thus, if it is only descriptive mathematical modeling that you are interested in, then of course smooth curves are well described by smooth analytic (non random) formulations. If however, it is the underlying mechanism of reaction that is considered, then I do not see how one can avoid beginning with the stochastic model. It is after all more general and contains within it the allowance for smoothness in the context of statistical regularity and averaging procedures. It is true that final solutions to the equations have not been obtained - this I have myself emphasized. This does not mean that they should not be sought. The reformulation of such processes in this paper was in fact stimulated by my search for alternate stochastic approaches to the basic problem. I must say, I am somewhat surprised to have this question from you, in view of your own work; though perhaps I should not be, since I believe I have already had some previous correspondence with you on this subject.

J. O. IRWIN

The Contributions of G. U. Yule and A. G. McKendrick to Stochastic Process Methods in Biology and Medicine

1. In the last fifteen or twenty years the mathematical theory of stochastic processes has been put into a rigorous form and a constantly growing interest has been taken in its application in an ever growing domain. On the modern mathematical theory I have no competence to speak, but I have been struck by the extent to which the ideas and applications were anticipated by the work of Yule and McKendrick between 1914 and about 1930. In this field McKendrick's achievement was I think the more remarkable, but I shall speak first of Yule's contributions. His work on the subject is contained in three papers:

(1) (Jointly with Professor Major Greenwood) "An Inquiry into the nature of Frequency Distributions Representative of Multiple Happenings with Particular Reference to the Occurrence of Multiple Attacks of Disease or of Repeated Accidents" (J. R. Statist. Soc. (1920) 83, 255-279).

(2) "A Mathematical Theory of Evolution based on the Conclusions of Dr. J. C. Willis F.R.S." This was published in the Philosophical Transactions of the Royal Society in 1924 (Philos. Trans., B213, 21-87).

(3) "On a Method of Investigating Periodicities in Disturbed Series, with special reference to Wolfer's Sunspot Numbers", also published by the Royal Society (Philos. Trans. A(1927), 26, 267, 298.)

The first paper contains the solution for the general homogeneous-birth process. It is obtained by elementary methods, using reccurrence formulae without any explicit reference to the differential equation. Thus, the probability per unit of time that a person who has had i previous accidents will have another is taken as p_i, and $\lambda_i = p_i T$, and, for example, the frequency of 2 accidents in time T is found to be

(1.1)
$$\frac{\lambda_0\lambda_1 e^{-\lambda_2}}{(\lambda_0-\lambda_2)(\lambda_1-\lambda_2)} + \frac{\lambda_0\lambda_1 e^{-\lambda_1}}{(\lambda_0-\lambda_1)(\lambda_2-\lambda_1)} + \frac{\lambda_0\lambda_1 e^{-\lambda_0}}{(\lambda_1-\lambda_0)(\lambda_2-\lambda_0)}$$

Greenwood and Yule certainly did not know in 1920 that McKendric had already obtained the general solution as early as 1914, in essentially the modern way, by solving the differential equation, and had published the result in the Proceedings of the London Mathematical Society (McKendrick (1914)).

The third paper is perhaps the most well-known and contains the first introduction of the linear autoregressive model. It has been noticed and discussed by many writers notably by Wold (1938), M. G. Kendall (1946) and Bartlett (1955). I do not propose to deal with it here, but shall concentrate my remarks on the second paper which seems to me to be of particular interest.

2.1. Willis and Yule conceived species as arising by "specific mutation" within the genus. "Within any species, in any interval of time an 'accident' may happen that brings about a (viable) 'specific mutation', i.e. the throwing of a new form which is regarded as a new species, but a species within the same genus as the parent. The chance of this occurrence in any assigned interval of time (an hour, or a year or a century) is taken as the same for all species within the group considered and as constant for all time.

"Within any genus in any interval of time an 'accident' may happen that brings about the throwing of a (viable) 'generic mutation' i.e. a new form so different from the parent that it will be placed in a new genus. The chance of this occurrence in any assigned interval of time is similarly taken as the same for all genera within the group considered and as constant for all time."

Yule's first object was to obtain on these simple assumptions the frequency distribution of the number of species per genus - that is, of the size of genera - at any subsequent time, for example, the present day. Secondly, he wished to determine the frequency distribution of the ages of genera. In the former case he could compare the theoretical distribution obtained with actual data. In the latter case he could in general obtain no absolute measure of age, but the doubling time of genus-size could be taken as a unit.

In the earlier part of his work, he ignored the killing out of species "by agencies which act less continuously than spasmodically and may fairly be described as cataclysmic e.g. the sinking of land under the sea, the onset of a glacial epoch, or other great change of climate such as desiccation". In the later part he considered how his results would be modified by taking them into account. Here he considered the age of the flowering plants to be of the order of 100 million years. Assuming this, he was able to estimate the doubling period of this group which at present contains about 160,000 species and the rate of production of specific mutations making either the assumption (1) of no killing out, (2) continuous killing out or (3) discontinuous killing by a series of cataclysms.

2.2. Suppose the rate of increase of species per unit of time is s. Then the probability of n species at time t starting from one species at zero time, with no killing out, is given by the solution of the homogeneous-birth process, $f_n = e^{-st}(1-e^{-st})^{n-1}$. Yule obtained this result by simple algebra, using nothing more recondite than the binomial distribution, assuming p to be the probability of a mutation in a small finite time say h, and proceeding to the limit when $h \to 0$. He verified the result by solving the differential equation:

$$\frac{d}{dt} f_{n+1}(t) = s\{nf_n(t) - (n+1)f_{n+1}(t)\} \tag{2.1}$$

with $f_0(t) = e^{-st}$.

2.3. Similarly if g is the generic rate of mutation within a family starting with one primordial genus, the probability there are n at time t will be $e^{-gt}(1-e^{-gt})^{n-1}$ and the expected number at time t will be e^{gt}. Out of N primordial genera starting together, the expected number coming into existence at time t will be $Nge^{gt}dt$ and the number aged x at time T will be $Nge^{g(T-x)}dx$. The proportion aged x at time T is therefore $ge^{-gx}dx$. Yule notices that these are the <u>derived</u> genera only ignoring the primordial genera. However, <u>at first</u> he assumes the time to be infinite so that the number of primordial genera can be ignored in comparison with the derived. Since the probability that a genus aged x has n species is $e^{-sx}(1-e^{-sx})^{n-1}$ the probability in genera of all ages is

$$g\int_0^\infty e^{-(g+s)x}(1-e^{-sx})^{n-1}\,dx\,. \tag{2.2}$$

If we write $\rho = g/s$

(I am here for simplicity departing from Yule's notation; he puts $\rho = s/g$)

we find for the probability of n species

$$\rho s\int_0^\infty e^{-(1+\rho)sx}(1-e^{-sx})^{n-1}\,dx \tag{2.3}$$

or writing $e^{-sx} = u$

$$\rho \int_0^1 u^{\rho}(1-u)^{n-1}\, du$$

$$(2.4) \qquad = \frac{\rho\Gamma(\rho+1)\Gamma(n)}{\Gamma(n+\rho+1)} = \frac{(n-1)!\,\rho}{(\rho+1)(\rho+2)\ldots(\rho+n)} .$$

The generating function of the distribution is therefore

$$(2.5) \qquad A\left\{\frac{\rho}{\rho+1} + \frac{\rho A}{(\rho+1)(\rho+2)} + \frac{2!\,\rho A^2}{(\rho+1)(\rho+2)(\rho+3)} + \ldots\right\} .$$

This distribution has been called the Yule distribution by a number of writers including M. G. Kendall (1960). I have shown (Irwin 1962) it is only a particular case of the Waring distribution derived from the expansion

$$(2.6) \qquad \frac{1}{(x-a)} = \frac{1}{x} + \frac{a}{x(x+1)} + \frac{a(a+1)}{x(x+1)(x+2)} +$$

with $x = \rho + 1$ $a = 1$, and that this distribution is itself only a very particular case of a large family of frequency distributions, which can be derived from the expansion of various functions in convergent inverse factorial series of positive terms. They are particularly suitable, I think, for fitting distributions with exceptionally long tails.

Yule shows that when n is large and even for values as low as 10, with fair approximation, we can use

$$(2.7) \qquad f_n \simeq \rho\Gamma(1+\rho)n^{-(1+\rho)} .$$

Thus $\log f_n$ should be approximately linear when plotted against $\log n$. He was able to verify that this was indeed the case by plotting the logarithms of the number of genera against the logarithms of the number of species in a number of families of animals and plants. The paper contains three such diagrams for the beetles Chrysomelidae, Cerambycinae and for the Leguminosae. However although the law held very approximately up to genera of 30 species or so, beyond that the points began to fall away more or less rapidly from the line. Yule realized that the mistake was due to regarding the time as infinite. He therefore proceeded to correct equation (2.4) for finite time. At time T, out of unit total, there will be $ge^{-gx}dx$ derived genera of age x together with e^{-gT} of age T. Therefore to (2.4) must be added

(2.8) $$e^{-(g+s)T}(1-e^{-sT})^{n-1} = e^{-(1+\rho)sT}(1-e^{-sT})^{n-1}$$

and

(2.8 bis) $$\rho s\int_T^{\infty} e^{-(1+\rho)sx}(1-e^{-sx})^{n-1}\,dx$$

must be subtracted.

He got the corrections into workable form and proceeded to fit the corrected distribution to the data from four different genera. In this numerical work he took the doubling time for the genus as a unit. If this is λ, then we may put $T/\lambda = \tau$ the new measure of time and $e^{sT} = e^{\alpha T/\lambda} = e^{\alpha\tau}$ where $\alpha = \log_e 2$. The new g is then $\alpha\rho$, and two constants T and ρ have to be found from the data. He fitted these from the observed mean and first frequency given by the data. Table 2.1 summarizes the results for two genera of beetles, for snakes and for lizards.

2.4. Yule now proceeded to find the age distribution of genera containing n species. If time is taken as infinite, since the expected proportion of genera of age x is $ge^{-gx}dx$ the expected proportion of genera containing n species which are of age x will be

$gf_n^{-1} e^{-(g+s)x}(1-e^{-sx})^{n-1}dx$ where f_n is given by equation (2.4)

or

(2.9) $$\alpha\rho f_n^{-1} e^{-\alpha(1+\rho)\xi}(1-e^{-\alpha\xi})^{n-1}$$

where ξ is the age measured in terms of the doubling period for number of species within the genus. If time is finite, then at time T he finds the proportion of primordial genera of n species to all genera of n species is

$$q = {}_{\tau}f_n^{-1} e^{-\alpha(1+\rho)\tau}(1-e^{-\alpha\tau})^{n-1}$$

where ${}_{\tau}f_n$ is the corrected frequency of n species. The proportion of derived genera is $p = 1 - q$ and among these the age distribution is given by (2.8) truncated at age T. Yule worked out the age distribution of species of size 1 (1) 10, 20 (10) 100 for all the four genera of beetles, snakes and lizards and also showed their shape in diagrams. The probability that a genus is primordial (of

Table 2.1. Giving particulars respecting four frequency distributions for size of genus.

	Chrysomelidae	Cerambycinae	Snakes	Lizards
1. Number of genera	627	1,024	293	259
2. Number of species	9,997	5,718	1,475	1,580
3. Mean species per genus, M	15.94	5.584	5.034	6.100
4. Proportion of monotypes, f_1	0.3429	0.4580	0.4471	0.4054
5. τ	6.28	4.980	4.260	4.281
6. ρ	1.925	1.188	1.253	1.496
7. N_0	65.4	56.0	27.8	36.0
8. Mean from ρ, τ	15.77	5.593	5.038	6.130
9. Proportion of monotypes from ρ, τ	0.3428	0.4580	0.4466	0.4049
10. χ^2	11.21	13.76	13.77	3.50
11. n'	16	14	11	11
12. P	0.74	0.39	0.18	0.96

N_0 is the number of primordial genera.

age τ) increases with the number of species that it contains. For Chrysomelidae for example he finds 0.0004 for genera with one species and 0.655 for genera with 100 species, while $\tau = 6.28$.

2.5. In a final section, Yule attempted to estimate the doubling period for species for the flowering plants, and the present rate of occurrence of specific mutations. He assumed the age of the flowering plants to be 100 million years. The results he obtained varied somewhat according as he assumed (1) no killing out, (2) continuous killing out or (3) discontinuous killing by a series of cataclysms. The results were of the same order of magnitude whatever assumptions were made. "If the age of the flowering plants is 100 million years, or thereabouts the doubling period is of the order of some 2 or 3 million years; it is say almost certainly over 1 million and less than 6 millions. The present rate of production of viable specific mutations amongst all flowering plants on the whole surface of the globe is almost certainly less than 1 in 10 years or more than one in 60 years; it probably lies between 1 in 15 and 1 in 30 years. The assumption of a polyphyletic origin for the flowering plants would not very greatly affect these figures. Specific mutations must, therefore, be such exceedingly rare events that no valid argument, as it seems to me, can be based on the fact that we have no experience of such occurrences."

Needless to say, I would not be concerned, even if I had the knowledge, to discuss the biological plausibility of this particular theory in the light of modern evidence. We cannot but be struck, however, with the pioneering nature of the methods used, with the agreement between data and theory, and with the simplicity and elegance of the exposition.

3.1. A. G. McKendrick was in earlier life a lieutenant colonel in the Indian Medical Service and later became Curator of the College of Physicians at Edinburgh. Though an amateur, he was a brilliant mathematician, with a far greater insight than many professionals.

Nearly all his work on stochastic models in the medical field is contained in a paper written more than 35 years ago, which until comparatively recently had escaped notice altogether. It is entitled "Applications of Mathematics to Medical Problems" and was published in the Proceedings of the Edinburgh Mathematical Society, Vol. 44, in the session 1925-6. For thirty years this paper almost escaped notice altogether. On the other hand, the joint work of Kermack and McKendrick on epidemiological theory is well-known; it was done after the publication of the paper I am about to discuss and the approach was entirely deterministic.

I have given a very full account of this paper as an appendix to my Presidential address of the Royal Statistical Society (1962). Here

I must be rather more brief. In his introductory paragraphs McKendrick remarks: "I have been in the habit of employing vector diagrams for the representation of such problems. They have the advantage that the hypotheses which are adopted are clearly visualized as well by the non-mathematical reader as the mathematical, and they also aid in helping one to realize the various modifications which may occur, and so to treat the study of the general problem systematically. To fix ideas, let us consider a simple case; the relation of an assemblage of individuals to common colds. In the following series of compartments (Figs. 1, 2, 3) are classified at any instant the numbers who have experienced 0, 1, 2, 3 ... attacks of this complaint. The history of each individual consists of a series of unit steps, originating in the compartment which describes his initial condition. The arrows in the diagram indicate the chance of passage from one compartment to the next -- that is to say the chance of experiencing a further attack during the infinitesimal period of time dt .

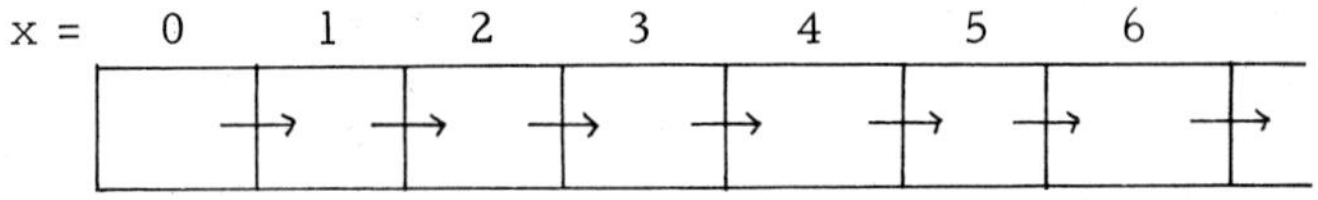

Figure 1

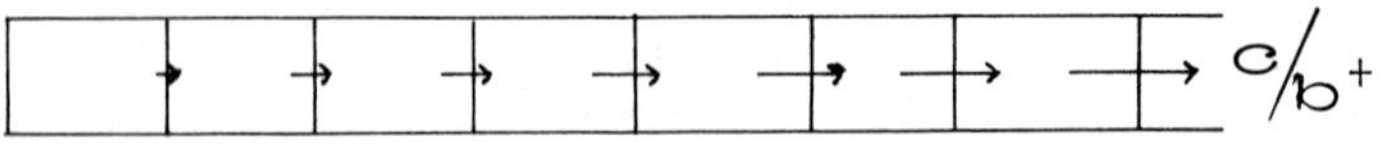

Figure 2

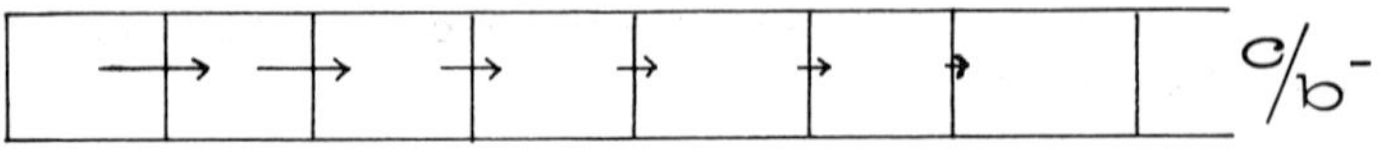

Figure 3

"In Figure 1 these arrows are of equal size, and by this we understand the successive chances were of constant value; in Figure 2 the arrows increase in size, denoting an increase of susceptibility with each attack; in Figure 3 they decrease, which denotes that the individual is becoming decreasingly liable, or in medical parlance he is developing an immunity.

"Guided by the diagram and using the nomenclature v_x = the number of individuals who have experienced x attacks (or shortly of grade x, $f_{t,n}$ = the probability that an individual of grade x will pass to grade $x + 1$ in the time dt, and noting that the variation of the number in any grade is the difference between the number of incomers into that grade, and the number who go out from that grade, we have

(3.1) $$dv_x = (f_{t,x-1} v_{x-1} - f_{t,x} v_x)\, dt \quad ."$$

You notice that v_x is defined rather loosely as "the number of individuals who have experienced x attacks". Nowadays we should have used the expected number, or most likely have used, instead of v_x, the corresponding probability p_x . In the subsequent work McKendrick considers only cases where $f_{t,x}$ is independent of the time. If $f_{t,x}$ is of the form $\phi(t)\,\psi(x)$, this may always be effected by a transformation of the time scale. When $f_x = b + cx$, he derives the negative binomial distribution- with the Poisson as a limiting case when $c/b \to 0$. He goes on to show (and the method is general for any discrete distribution) how when the zero class is missing the value of N, the total frequency including the zero class, may be estimated from the observed factorial moments. Clearly these do not involve a knowledge of the zero class frequency. Thus the missing frequency can be estimated by subtraction, and if necessary improved values can be obtained by iteration. This simple method had been overlooked until I mentioned it briefly in a paper in Biometrics (Irwin 1959). Some recent work of H. O. Hartley's shows that if a solution is obtained by this method, it will be the maximum likelihood solution. (Hartley 1958). McKendrick illustrates this by the following figures referring to an epidemic of cholera in a village in India (Table 3.1).

Table 3.1

	Observed	Expected
Houses with 0 cases	168	37
" " 1 "	32	34
" " 2 "	16	16
" " 3 "	6	5
" " 4 "	1	1
	223	93

and remarks: "This suggests that the disease was probably waterborne, that there were a number of wells, and that the inhabitants of 93 out of 223 houses drank from one well which was infected. On further investigation it was found that there was one particular infected well from which a certain section of the community drank."

3.2. McKendrick now considers reversible movement in one dimension (see Figure 4).

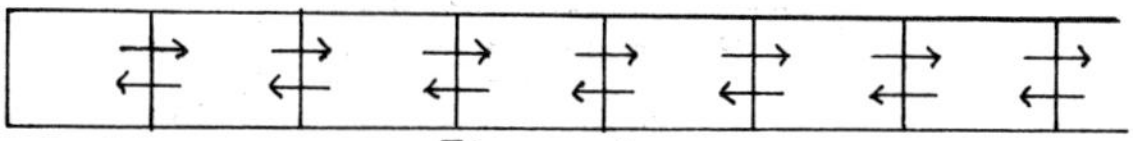

Figure 4

His equation is

$$(3.2) \qquad dv_x = (f_{x-1} v_{x-1} - f_x v_x)\,dt + (f'_{x+1} v_{x+1} - f'_x v_x)\,dt \ .$$

When $f = f' =$ constant, he find the solution

$$(3.3) \qquad v_x = Ne^{-2m} I_x(2m)$$

where I_x is the usual Bessel Function with imaginary argument and $2m$ is the variance of the distribution of x . When f and f' are constant but $f \neq f'$, he finds

$$(3.4) \qquad v_x = Ne^{-(m_1+m_2)} \left[\left(\frac{m_2}{m_1}\right)^{x/2} I_x\left(2\sqrt{(m_1 m_2)}\right) \right] \ .$$

I obtained (3.3) by elementary methods (not involving stochastic process arguments) in 1937 (Irwin 1937). I had then forgotten I had seen the result before in McKendrick's paper. The generalization (3.4) was published by Skellam in 1947. He also used an argument not involving stochastic processes.

In this section McKendrick also obtains the frequency when $f = f' = b + cx$. Here b/c is necessarily an integer, and as $t \to \infty$ we must have $x \to -(b/c)$ with probability unity, though McKendrick does not say this. The result is complicated (Irwin 1962) and I will not quote it here.

3.3. McKendrick now goes on to consider two dimensional cases (see Figures 5 and 6).

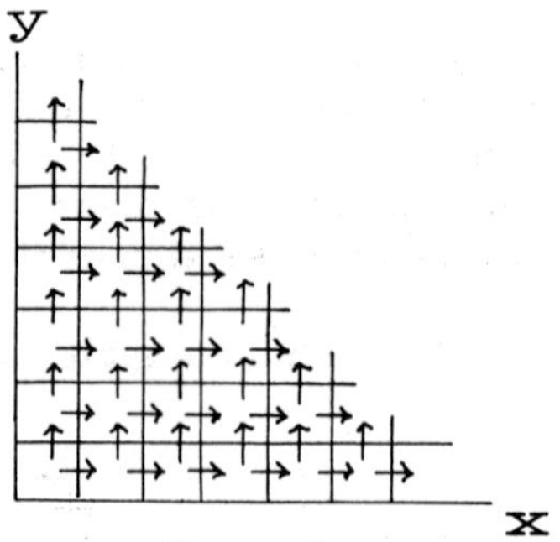

Figure 5

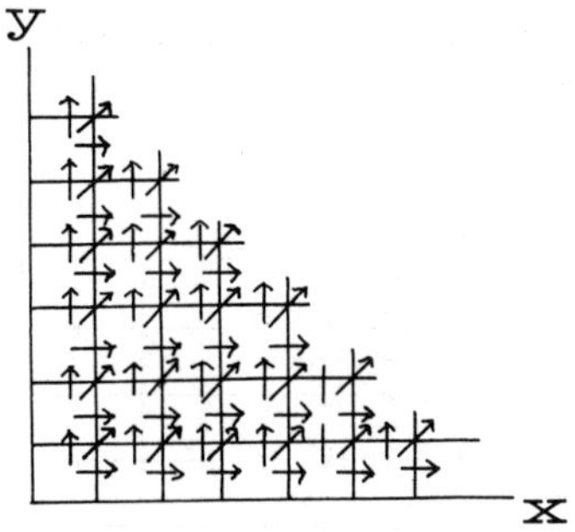

Figure 6

When there is no oblique movement his equation is

$$(3.5)\quad \frac{dv_{x,y}}{dt} = (f_{x-1,y}v_{x-1,y} - f_{x,y}) + (g_{x,y-1}v_{x,y-1} - g_{x,y}v_{x,y}) \,.$$

When $f_{x,y} = b + cx$, $g_{x,y} = d + ey$ he obtains the result as the product of two independent negative binomial distributions; which, when f and g are constants, reduces to the product of two Poisson distributions.

However the main interest here is when oblique movement occurs (see Figures 6 and 7). Figure 7 is meant to illustrate two ways in which correlation between x and y may be introduced. There is either a direct tendency for events x and y to occur together, or else the probability of an x event increases with y or vice versa. The former sort of correlation he calls oblique correlation the latter shear correlation. In either case a term $h_{x-1,y-1}v_{x-1,y-1} - h_{x,y}v_{x,y}$ is added to the right hand side of (3.5).

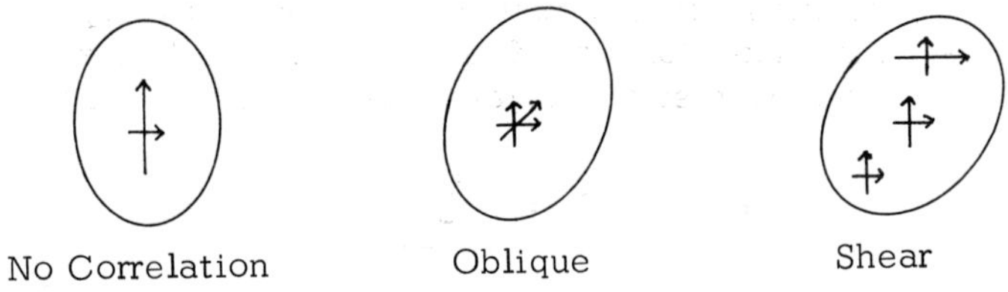

Figure 7

For f, g, h constant McKendrick obtains the solution as a bivariate analogue of the Poisson distribution. The margins are Poisson distributions; it is in fact the same bivariate analogue of the Poisson distribution which can be derived as a limiting form of the familiar fourfold table distribution when $ad - bc \neq 0$.

3.4. McKendrick now goes on to consider the effect of collecting values of $v_{x,y}$ in either diagonal direction (Figure 8) i.e. the distribution of $x + y$ and $x - y$.

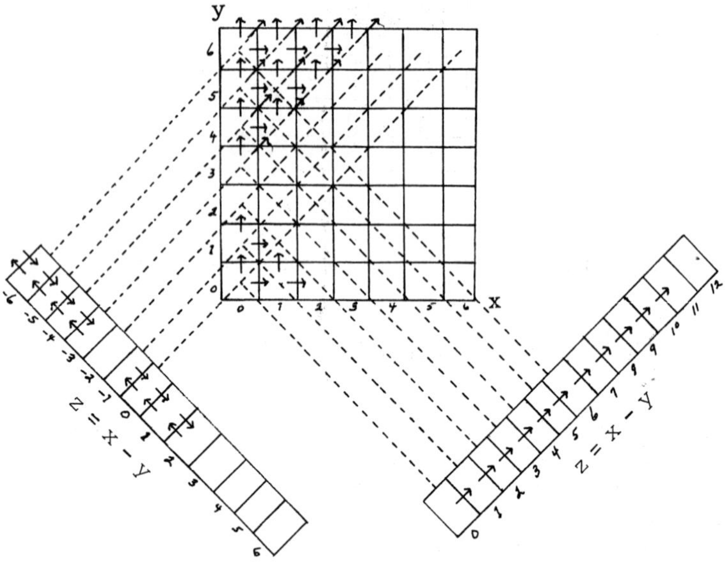

Figure 8

"These are important in medical statistical problems. For example if x denotes the number of fresh infections of a disease, and y denotes the number of relapses then $x + y = n$ denotes the number of attacks of the disease. The functions $f_{x,y}dt$ and $g_{x,y}dt$ for fresh infections and relapses, respectively, are certainly not identical, and as it is impossible to differentiate clinically between fresh infections and relapses statistics; are only available in the form S_n."

(3.6) Here $S_n = \sum_{x+y=n} v_{x,y}$.

"It is at once apparent from the figure, that where f, g, h are constant the results of the summation is to convert an irreversible two dimensional scheme into a reversible scheme in one dimension (the effect of oblique correlation does not appear) and the solution is the Bessel form which has already been dealt with."

Here we note the acuteness of his intuition. On reflexion I am sure that most of this audience will realize that this statement is correct and I will not enlarge upon the matter now, though I dealt with it in more detail in my 1962 paper.

McKendrick finds the distribution of $n = x + y$ and applies it to the following example.

"In a phagocytic experiment it seemed likely that the bacteria which were being ingested were not all discrete, some of them were united into pairs. If one considers for the moment that they were of two types, and that a pair consisted of one of each type, then the above analysis is applicable. The figures are given in Table 3.2."

Table 3.2

	Observed	Expected
Leucocytes containing 0 bacteria	269	268
" " 1 "	4	7
" " 2 "	26	23
" " 3 "	0	0.6
" " 4 "	1	1.1

and $r = 0.86$

The interesting point is that he derives the correlation coefficient between x and y from the distribution of $x + y$. On his model

$$V(n) = m_1 + m_2 + 2\rho\sqrt{(m_1 m_2)}$$

If

$$m_1 = m_2 \qquad V(n) = 2m(1+\rho) \quad .$$

Whence

$$\rho = \frac{V(n)}{E(n)} - 1 \quad . \tag{3.7}$$

3.5. McKendrick now goes on to consider restricted cases in which entry into certain compartments of the model are not possible. It is here that the applications of most interest to epidemiology occur. I only mention his next two examples (see Figure 9) without dealing with them in detail. The one is concerned with house to house infection; his x now denotes infections arising from outside the house. In this case since an internal infection is only possible after one from outside has taken place, the first column in his diagram is empty, except for the bottom square. He finds that from the total number of

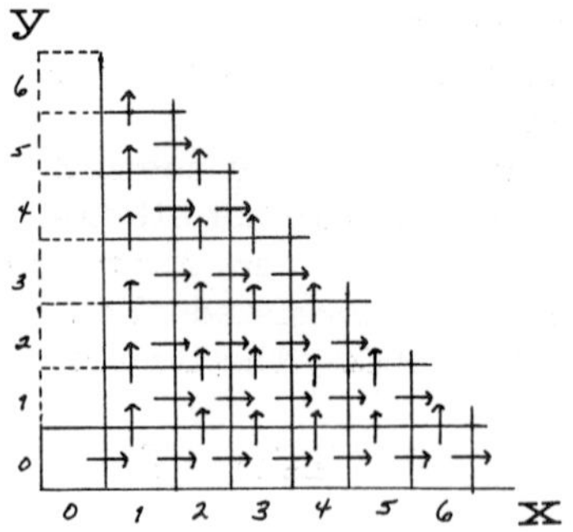

Figure 9

cases, the total number of houses and the number of infected houses, he can estimate the ratio of the probability of external infection to that of internal infection. From four epidemics of bubonic plague in a certain village, he found that the probability of internal infection was 200 times as large as that of external infection. He remarks that since the disease is transmitted by fleas, a species of animal which does not as a rule travel far from its own neighbourhood this may readily be understood. The next example is that of infection and relapse in malaria and is treated in the same way.

His next two examples I shall deal with in somewhat more detail.

(i) An unlimited population.

"Let us trace" says McKendrick "what is likely to be the number of epidemics in similar communities each starting from a single case, and let us adopt as variable the relation

$$\text{cases } (n) = \text{infections } (x) - \text{recoveries } (y) \ .$$

The course of affairs is illustrated in Figure 10.

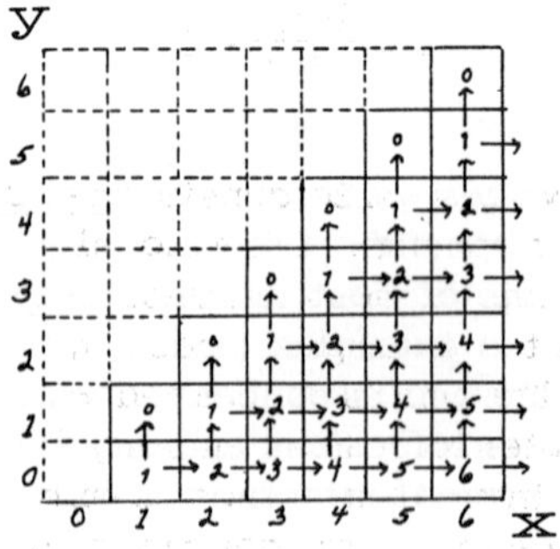

Figure 10

"We notice that each epidemic starts initially in the compartment (1, 0) i.e. one case which has not yet recovered, and that when a compartment $n = (x - y) = 0$ is arrived at, the epidemic has come to an end for there are no more cases. Thus when the probability of recovery exceeds the probability of infection, all epidemics must come to rest in one or other of the compartments $n = 0$. If we assume that $k\,dt$ is the chance that an individual may convey infection, then the probability that an epidemic of n cases will receive an additional case is $kndt$. We assume also, in the first instance, that the population concerned in each epidemic is unlimited."

He obtains the equation

$$\frac{dv_{x,y}}{dt} = k\{(x-1-y)v_{x-1,y} - (x-y)v_{x,y}\} + \ell\{(x-y+1)v_{x,y-1} - (x-y)v_{x,y}\} \quad (3.8)$$

This equation is in fact the usual equation for a continuous model with an unlimited population. It is in fact identical with a special case of equation 5.36 on p. 53 of Norman Bailey's book (1957). He finds the solution for the <u>total size</u> of an epidemic, i.e. of $v_{n,n}$ after infinite time

$$v_{n,n}(\infty) = a_n\left(\frac{k}{k+\ell}\right)^{n-1}\left(\frac{\ell}{k+\ell}\right)^{n} N \quad (3.9)$$

Here although McKendrick does not put it in this form

$$a_n = \frac{(2n-2)!}{n\{(n-1)!\}^2} \quad (3.9\ \text{bis})$$

(ii) McKendrick now considers the case where the population at risk is limited. This immediately leads to the equation

$$\frac{dv_{x,y}}{dt} = k\{(p-x+1)(x-1-y)v_{x-1,y} - (p-x)(x-y)v_{x,y}\} + \ell\{(x+1-y)v_{x,y-1} - (x-y)v_{x,y}\} \quad (3.10)$$

This is exactly the same as the equation given by Bailey for this case of the continuous infection model (see Bailey (1957) 5.31 where a different notation is used. See also M. S. Bartlett (1955)). Here again McKendrick succeeds in finding $v_{n,n}(\infty)$ equivalent to the determination of the distribution of epidemic size. He takes $N = 1$, $\ell/k = 2$ and finds

Table 3.3

	p = 5	p = 6
v_{11}	0.33	0.29
v_{22}	0.11	0.08
v_{33}	0.09	0.06
v_{44}	0.13	0.08
v_{55}	0.34	0.13
	--	0.37

Here we have an example of the U shaped distributions which have been discussed in recent years by D. G. Kendall, M. S. Bartlett and N. Bailey. There is a high probability of the epidemic dying down after a few cases and a high probability of a large epidemic, but intermediate size epidemics are comparatively unlikely.

3.6. McKendrick finally considers the limiting form of his stochastic equations, when variables such as he has been dealing with are not restricted to integral values but become continuous. "A consideration of continuous variables" he says "leads us from the foregoing general equation on the one hand into the domain of mathematical physics and on the other into wide statistical fields."

According to the way in which he proceeds to the limit, he derives:

(i) The three dimensional form of the diffusion equation where x, y, z may or may not be correlated, and realizes that a solution is given by the trivariate normal distribution.

(ii) The ordinary equation of continuity in hydrodynamics.

Here I think we have the clue to what has always been rather mysterious - the reason why McKendrick subsequently dropped the stochastic approach. As soon as one proceeds from discrete variables to continuous variables the distinction between the stochastic and continuous schemes may seem somewhat blurred. (I gave an example in my 1962 paper.)

McKendrick clearly got fascinated by those continuous variable models. That, I think, is the reason why he dropped the stochastic approach and in subsequent years, and in collaboration with Kermack developed deterministic epidemiological models.

REFERENCES

1. Bailey, N.T.J. (1957) The Mathematical Theory of Epidemics. London: Griffin.

2. Bartlett, M.S. (1955a) Stochastic Processes. Cambridge University Press.

3. ________ (1955b) "Deterministic and stochastic models for recurrent epidemics". Proc. Third Berkeley Symposium for Mathematical Statistics and Probability, 4, 81-109.

4. Greenwood, M. and Yule, G.U. (1920) "An inquiry into the nature of frequency distributions representative of multiple happenings with particular reference to the occurrence of multiple attacks of disease or of repeated accidents." J.R. Statist. Soc., 83, 255-279.

5. Hartley, H.O. (1958) "Maximum likelihood estimates from incomplete data." Biometrics, 14, 174-194.

6. Irwin, J.O. (1959) "On the estimation of the mean of a Poisson distribution with the zero class missing". Biometrics, 15, 324-326.

7. ________ (1962) "The place of mathematics in medical and biological statistics." J.R. Statist. Soc., 126, 1-44.

8. Skellam, J.G. (1946) "Frequency distribution of the difference between two Poisson variates belonging to different populations." J.R. Statist. Soc., 109, 296.

9. Wold, H. (1938) A Study in the Analysis of Stationary Time Series. Almquist and Wiksells. Uppsala.

10. Yule, G.U. (1924) "A mathematical theory of evolution based on the conclusions of Dr. J. C. Willis, F.R.S.". Philos. Trans. B 213, 21-87.

11. ________ (1927) "On a method of investigating periodicities in disturbed series, with a special reference to Wolfer's sunspot numbers." Philos. Trans. A 26, 267-298.

DISCUSSION PARTICIPANT

Professor Sewall Wright
Department of Genetics, University of Wisconsin
Madison, Wisconsin

DISCUSSION

Sewall Wright. I would like to comment on Yule's paper on evolution referred to by Professor Irwin. Yule demonstrated that under Willis' theory of abrupt origin of species and genera by rare mutations of appropriate magnitude, the frequency of genera with given numbers of species (within a large family) is inversely proportional to the number ($y = C/x$), except for large numbers. This is the "hollow" curve which Willis had demonstrated in many large families of plants and animals. Actually this agreement with the data does not contribute to confirmation of the evolutionary hypothesis, since it follows equally well from other hypotheses, such for example as Darwin's hypothesis of gradual origin by the accumulation of small changes under natural selection.

Joseph O. Irwin. I am grateful to Professor Sewall Wright for pointing out that the agreement of the data with Willis and Yule's theory does not contribute to the confirmation of this particular evolutionary hypothesis, because similar results follow from other hypotheses. Of this I was aware, as more than a possibility. In the last paragraph of my paper, I said "Needless to say, I would not be concerned, even if I had the knowledge, to discuss the plausibility of this particular theory in the light of modern evidence." That several different biological models may lead to the same form of distribution (cf. the well-known case of the negative binomial) is a fact that we should always keep in mind.

The interest of Yule's work for us now seems to me to lie in the fact that he was using essentially "stochastic process" methods long before the name was even invented, and using them (as I said) with simplicity and elegance of exposition.

NORBERT WIENER

On the Oscillations of Nonlinear Systems

When non-linear systems go into oscillation, a very general phenomenon is the concentration of the spectrum of oscillation into narrow bands, approximating to spectral lines. This phenomenon is probably responsible for the quantum phenomenon (Schrödinger equation) in physics [1]; the phenomenon of entrainment which is central in so many biological rhythms [2]; the sharpness of the frequencies exhibited in electrical nets of alternators in parallel, and the destructive oscillations which we find when oscillating systems of low dissipation are stimulated by a turbulence-field of small geometrical scale and high energy level [3]. As examples of the last type of phenomenon, we can cite:

1. The destruction of the Tacoma Narrows Bridge (Galloping Gertie) in a high wind. In this case the cinematographic films of the catastrophe show a remarkably close synchronism of oscillations of flexure and oscillations of torsion. This means that the energy of one form of oscillations was transferred at times almost totally to the other kind, thus greatly increasing the stresses upon individual members of the structure.

2. The much-publicized failure of the earlier models of the "Comet" airplanes, and later of the "Electra" airplanes. Here we probably do not have cinematographic records, and the complete nature of the failure is more conjectural. The final breakdown of the "Comets" seems to have been due to an elastic fatigue affecting primarily the sharply re-entrant corners of the windows -- a serious fault of design -- and spreading from these progressively along the skin. In the "Electras", the wings came off, apparently from flutter. In both cases, the final disintegration was merely the making good (or bad) of an excessive vibration, in which the phenomenon of non-linear resonance and the concentration of frequencies may easily have played a decisive role. In both cases, we have to begin with a non-linear oscillating system immersed in a turbulence field of high energy, due to a wind of high velocity. In both cases, this turbulence field produces fluctuation oscillation in the system of high frequency, as compared

with the final destructive oscillations of the structure itself. In both cases, the turbulence field at one time is substantially statistically independent of the turbulence field at a slightly later time. In both cases, we are dealing with a dynamical system in the bridge or plane which is dissipative, but only relatively slowly so in comparison with the time-scale of the fluctuations of turbulence.

In view of these matters, we can throw much light on the vibration of the structure by assuming a Hamiltonian dynamical system, stimulated at one time, and continuing to oscillate. We wish to examine the spectrum of such a system: that is, in accordance with the theory of Generalized Harmonic Analysis [4], the autocorrelation of the function expressing the state of the system at any time, and its harmonic analysis. We intend to discuss this later on a much more general basis, but for the present we shall discuss a system with a Hamiltonian dynamics, where the Hamiltonian is

$$H(p, q) = \sum_{n=1}^{N} \frac{p_n^2}{2} + F(q_1, \ldots, q_n) \quad . \tag{1}$$

The Hamiltonian equations for the dynamics of the system will be

$$\frac{dp_n}{dt} = -\frac{\partial F}{\partial q_n} \quad ; \qquad \frac{dq_n}{dt} = p_n \quad . \tag{2}$$

It at time 0, we have a (complex) distribution over phase space of the form

$$u(0, p, q) = e^{-\lambda \sum_{n=1}^{N} \frac{p_n^2}{2}} v(q) \quad , \tag{3}$$

which suggests a kinetic energy at each time due to the impact of a random turbulence, and if at time t, the distribution has become:

$$u(t, p, q) \quad , \tag{4}$$

then at time 0 we shall have:

$$\frac{du}{dt} = \frac{\partial u}{\partial t} + \sum \frac{\partial u}{\partial p_n}\left(-\frac{\partial F}{\partial q_n}\right) + \sum \frac{\partial u}{\partial q_n} p_n \quad . \tag{5}$$

If u remains constant along the time orbits of the Hamiltonian system,

$$\frac{\partial u}{\partial t} = \sum \frac{\partial u}{\partial p_n} \frac{\partial F}{\partial q_n} - \sum \frac{\partial u}{\partial q_n} p_n \quad , \tag{6}$$

and at time t = 0 ,

$$\frac{\partial u(0,p,q)}{\partial t} = e^{\frac{-\lambda \sum p_n^2}{2}} \sum \left(-\lambda p_n \frac{\partial F}{\partial q_n} v(q) - \sum p_n \frac{\partial v}{\partial q_n}\right) \quad . \tag{7}$$

Similarly,

$$\left[\frac{\partial^2 u}{\partial t^2}\right]_{t=0} = \left\{ \sum_\nu \left(\frac{\partial F}{\partial q_\nu} \frac{\partial}{\partial p_\nu} - p_\nu \frac{\partial}{\partial q_\nu} \right) \right\} \left\{ \sum_n \frac{\partial F}{\partial q_n} \frac{\partial u}{\partial p_n} - p_n \frac{\partial u}{\partial q_n} \right\} \Bigg|_{t=0} \tag{8}$$

$$= \sum_\nu \sum_n \left\{ \frac{\partial F}{\partial q_\nu} \frac{\partial F}{\partial q_n} \frac{\partial^2 u}{\partial p_\nu \partial p_n} - p_\nu \frac{\partial^2 F}{\partial q_\nu \partial q_n} \frac{\partial u}{\partial p_n} - p_\nu \frac{\partial F}{\partial q_\nu} \frac{\partial^2 u}{\partial q_\nu \partial p_n} \right.$$

$$\left. - \delta_{n\nu} \frac{\partial F}{\partial q_\nu} \frac{\partial u}{\partial q_\nu} - p_\nu \frac{\partial F}{\partial q_n} \frac{\partial^2 u}{\partial q_n \partial p_\nu} + p_n p_\nu \frac{\partial^2 u}{\partial q_\nu \partial q_n} \right\} \Bigg|_{t=0}$$

$$= e^{\frac{-\lambda \sum p_n^2}{2}} \left\{ \sum_n \left[\left(\frac{\partial F}{\partial q_\nu} \right)^2 (\lambda^2 p_n^2 - \lambda) \nu + \lambda \sum p_n^2 \frac{\partial^2 F}{\partial q_n^2} v \right. \right.$$

$$\left. \left. + (2\lambda p_n^2 - 1) \frac{\partial F}{\partial q_n} \frac{\partial \nu}{\partial q_n} + p_n^2 \frac{\partial^2 \nu}{\partial q_n^2} \right] + \text{terms in } p_n p_\nu (n \neq \nu) \right\} .$$

Then since

$$\int_{-\infty}^{\infty} \cdots \int_{-\infty}^{\infty} p_n p_\nu e^{-\lambda \sum p_n^\nu} dp_1 \ldots dp_N = \frac{1}{2\lambda} \delta_{n\nu} \int_{-\infty}^{\infty} \cdots \int_{-\infty}^{\infty} e^{-\lambda \sum p_n^2} dp_1 \ldots dp_n \tag{9}$$

if

$$(10)\quad U(t,q) = \int_{-\infty}^{\infty} \cdots \int_{-\infty}^{\infty} u(t,p,q)\, e^{\frac{-\lambda \sum p_n^2}{2}}\, dp_1 \ldots dp_N ,$$

we shall have at time $t=0$,

$$(11)\quad \frac{\partial^2 U}{\partial t^2} = -\frac{\lambda}{2}\, U \sum \left(\frac{\partial F}{\partial q_n}\right)^2 + 1/2\, U \sum \frac{\partial^2 F}{\partial q_n^2} + 1/2\lambda \sum \frac{\partial^2 U}{\partial q_n^2} .$$

Now

$$(12)\quad \int_{-\infty}^{\infty} \cdots \int_{-\infty}^{\infty} \frac{\partial^2 u(t,p,q)}{\partial t^2}\, \overline{u(0,p,q)}\, dp_1 \ldots dp_N dq_1 \ldots dq_N$$

$$= \int_{-\infty}^{\infty} \cdots \int_{-\infty}^{\infty} u(t,p,q) \left[\frac{\partial^2}{\partial t^2} u(0,p,q)\right]_{t=0} dp_1 \ldots dq_N$$

$$= \int_{-\infty}^{\infty} \cdots \int_{-\infty}^{\infty} dq_1 \ldots dq_N \int_{-\infty}^{\infty} \cdots \int_{-\infty}^{\infty} u(t,P,q)\, e^{\frac{-\lambda \sum P_n^2}{2}}\, dP_1 \ldots dP_N$$

$$\times \frac{\left[\frac{\partial^2 U}{\partial t^2}(0,q_n)\right]_{t=0}}{\int_{-\infty}^{\infty} \cdots \int_{-\infty}^{\infty} e^{-\lambda \sum x_n^2}\, dx_1 \ldots dx_N}$$

$$= \frac{\int_{-\infty}^{\infty} \cdots \int_{-\infty}^{\infty} dq_1 \ldots dq_n\, U(t,q)\, \overline{\frac{\partial^2 U(0,q)}{\partial t^2}}}{\int_{-\infty}^{\infty} \cdots \int_{-\infty}^{\infty} e^{-\lambda \sum x_n}\, dx_1 \ldots dx_N}$$

$$= \frac{\int_{-\infty}^{\infty} \cdots \int_{-\infty}^{\infty} dq_1 \ldots dq_N\, U(t,q) \left\{ -\lambda/2\, U(0,q) \sum \left(\frac{\partial F}{\partial q_n}\right)^2 + 1/2\, U(0,q) \sum \frac{\partial^2 F}{\partial q_n^2} + \frac{1}{2\lambda} \sum \frac{\partial^2 U}{\partial q_n^2} \right\}}{\int_{-\infty}^{\infty} \cdots \int_{-\infty}^{\infty} e^{-\lambda \sum x_n^2}\, dx_1 \ldots dx_N}$$

Let

$$(13)\qquad \int_{-\infty}^{\infty}\cdots\int_{-\infty}^{\infty} e^{-\lambda\sum x_n^2}\, dx_1\ldots dx_N = A\ .$$

If

$$(14)\qquad V(t,p,q) = U(t,q)\, e^{-\frac{\lambda\sum p_n^2}{2}}$$

then

$$(15)\qquad \int_{-\infty}^{\infty}\cdots\int_{-\infty}^{\infty} \frac{\partial^2}{\partial t^2} V(t,p,q)\, V(0,p,q)\, dp_1\ldots dq_N$$

$$= \int_{-\infty}^{\infty}\cdots\int_{-\infty}^{\infty} \frac{\partial^2}{\partial t^2} u(t,p,q)\, \overline{u(0,p,q)}\, dp_1\ldots dq_N$$

$$= A\int_{-\infty}^{\infty}\cdots\int_{-\infty}^{\infty} U(0,q)\, \frac{\partial^2}{\partial t^2} U(t,q)\, dq_1\ldots dq_N$$

$$= A\int_{-\infty}^{\infty}\cdots\int_{-\infty}^{\infty} \overline{U(0,q)} \left\{-\lambda/2\, U(t,q)\sum\left(\frac{\partial F}{\partial q_n}\right)^2 + 1/2\, U(t,q)\sum\frac{\partial^2 F}{\partial q_n^2} + \frac{1}{2\lambda}\sum\frac{\partial^2 U}{\partial q_n^2}\quad dq_1\ldots dq_N\right\}.$$

This will be true whenever

$$(16)\qquad \frac{\partial^2}{\partial t^2} U(t,q) = \left\{-\frac{\lambda}{2} U(t,q)\sum\left(\frac{\partial F}{\partial q_n}\right)^2 + \frac{1}{2} U(t,q)\sum\frac{\partial^2 F}{\partial q_n^2} + \frac{1}{2\lambda}\sum\frac{\partial^2 U}{\partial q_n^2}\right\}$$

A set of particular cases where this will be true is if

$$(17)\qquad U(t,q) = e^{i\omega t}\,\phi_\omega(q)\ ,$$

while

$$(18)\quad -\omega^2 \phi_\omega(q) = -\lambda/2\, \phi_\omega(q) \sum\left(\frac{\partial F}{\partial q}\right)^2 + 1/2\, \phi_\omega(q) \sum \frac{\partial^2 F}{\partial q_n^2} + \frac{1}{2\lambda} \sum \frac{\partial^2 \phi_\omega}{2 q_n^2}$$

In this case,

$$(19)\quad \int_{-\infty}^{\infty} \cdots \int_{-\infty}^{\infty} u(t,p,q)\, \overline{u(0,p,q)}\; dp_1 \ldots dq_N$$

$$= A\, e^{i\omega t} \int_{-\infty}^{\infty} \cdots \int_{-\infty}^{\infty} |\phi_\omega(q)|^2\, dq_1 \ldots dq_N \quad .$$

It is easy to show that if there are two values of ω, (ω_1 and ω_2) for which

$$(20)\quad \int_{-\infty}^{\infty} \cdots \int_{-\infty}^{\infty} |\phi_\omega(q)|^2\, dq_1 \ldots dq_n \neq 0 \;,$$

then

$$(21)\quad \int_{-\infty}^{\infty} \cdots \int_{-\infty}^{\infty} \overline{\phi_{\omega_2}(q)}\, dq_1 \ldots dq_n = 0 \;.$$

Since it is well known that

$$dp_1 \ldots dq_N$$

is independent of the time, it is easy to deduce that

$$(22)\quad \int_{-\infty}^{\infty} \cdots \int_{-\infty}^{\infty} u(t+\tau,\, p,\, q)\, \overline{u(\tau,p,q)}\, dp_1 \ldots dq_N$$

$$= \int_{-\infty}^{\infty} \cdots \int_{-\infty}^{\infty} u(t,p,q)\, \overline{u(0,p,q)}\; dp_1 \ldots dq_N \quad .$$

This therefore will be the same as

$$(23) \qquad \lim_{T\to\infty} \frac{1}{T} \int_0^T d\tau \int_{-\infty}^{\infty} \cdots \int_{-\infty}^{\infty} u(t+\tau, p, q)\, \overline{u(\tau, p, q)}\, dp_1 \ldots dq_N \quad .$$

This is the average over phase space of the autocorrelation of $u(t, p, q)$ in the time. The trigonometric development of this in the time, in the case that

$$(24) \qquad V(t, p, q) = \sum_\nu a_\nu \, \phi_{\omega_\nu}(q) \, e^{i\omega_\nu t - \lambda \frac{\sum p_n^2}{2}} \quad ,$$

where the a_ν are characteristic values and the ϕ_{ω_ν} characteristic functions of (18) will be

$$(25) \qquad \sum_\nu |a_\nu|^2 \, e^{i\omega_\nu t} \quad .$$

This will be a line spectrum.

Thus in this special case, whenever the equation (18) has discrete characteristic values, and the non-linear Hamiltonian system is stimulated at any time by momenta with a Gaussian distribution, the mean spectrum of the non-linear oscillations stimulated will contain sharp lines. If the system is stimulated at successive times by similar momenta with Gaussian distributions, this will still be the case. Even if the system is not strictly conservative, but slightly dissipative, with slow decay, this will approximately be the case. Thus we see how Hamiltonian (or nearly Hamiltonian) systems, excited by a random turbulence from outside, in case the Hamiltonian oscillations are slow compared with the time needed for the Hamiltonian system to go approximately through its total orbit for a sufficiently high energy level, can generate non-linear oscillations confined to narrow frequency bands -- the phenomenon to which we have attributed the breakdown of the Tacoma Narrows Bridge and various models of airplanes.

Let it be said once for all that the treatment given here is only tentative. We have taken only a particular uniform type of turbulence excitation, and only a Hamiltonian system where the kinetic energy is one half the sum of the squares of the squares of the momenta (times a constant, if we wish).

To put the work we are undertaking into definite form, we need to work with Hamiltonian systems of more general form, with more general distributions of the momentum, with a more complete statistical account of the changes of the imposed momentum distribution with time, and with a fuller treatment of the statistics of change of the impressed momenta with the relatively long-time momenta of the vibrations excited in the non-linear dynamical system. We also need to discuss the characteristic functions of equation (18), whether they be discrete or form a continuous spectrum. This I leave for further work by others and myself.

REFERENCES

1. Wiener, N., Della Riccia, G., "Random Theory in Classical Phase Space and Quantum Mechanics", (Talk presented at the conference on "The Theory and Application of Analysis in Functic Space", at the Massachusetts Institute of Technology, Cambridg Mass., June 1963.

2. Wiener, N., Cybernetics, second edition, Chapter X, John Wile and Sons, New York, 1961.

3. Crandall, Steven H., "Random Vibration", Applied Mechanics Reviews, Vol. 12, 739-742 (1959).

4. Wiener, N., "Generalized Harmonic Analysis," Acta Mathematic 55, 117-258 (1930).

DISCUSSION PARTICIPANTS

Dr. Anthony F. Bartholomay
Mathematical Biology, Harvard University Medical School and Peter Bent Brigham Hospital
Boston, Massachusetts

Professor R. M. Bock
Department of Biochemistry, University of Wisconsin
Madison, Wisconsin

Professor A. Charnes
Departments of Mathematics, Economics and Engineering Sciences, Northwestern University
Evanston, Illinois

Dr. S. M. Shea
Department of Pathology, Harvard University Medical School and Peter Bent Brigham Hospital
Boston, Massachusetts

DISCUSSION

Anthony F. Bartholomay. Is this set of ideas an outgrowth of the work which you did earlier on using the Wiener Differential Space as a basis for quantum mechanics?

Norbert Wiener. Yes.

Anthony F. Bartholomay. Are you saying that in effect you have here a probability sample space for quantum theory which makes closer contact with classical probability theory, in contrast with the usual quantum postulates that have a "pseudoprobabilistic flavor"?

Norbert Wiener. Yes.

Anthony F. Bartholomay. Am I correct in inferring then that you wish to imply that given this new system of postulates, in principle we may deduce formally certain mechanical behaviors which may be different from classical expectations, including actually "observable" phenomena?

Norbert Wiener. While we have not arrived at the point of doing so, yes.

R. M. Bock. Is there hope of using your approach to predict periodic Brownian motion phenomena such as Liesegang rings or striated colloid sediment by considering the way these motions couple with perturbations of their physical environment?

Norbert Wiener. Yes.

A. Charnes. In the theory of plastic collapse, e.g. of a pin-jointed truss with elastic perfectly plastic members in which the intensity of the applied forces vector is raised until collapse occurs, the dynamic mechanism is a highly non-linear one, yet the collapse states can be predicted by a linear, "tangential" system (more explicitly by a linear extremal principle due to Prager, Drucker, Greenberg, Neal, etc.). This extremal system is obtained however only by analysis of conditions at the instant of collapse. Would your theory (and Della Roccio's) yield such systems by generation of some asymptotic "final" or "steady-state" expression directly from your non-linear Hamiltonian type representation of the dynamics?

Norbert Wiener. In my Wisconsin paper I discuss the point.

S. M. Shea. Professor Wiener, do you anticipate that your theory can be used to account for the operation of biological clocks?

Norbert Wiener. I definitely anticipate that the theory which I am giving of vibrations in non-linear systems can be applied to biological clocks. I am working on this with Dr. John Barlow of the Massachusetts General Hospital.

W. J. SCHULL and B. R. LEVIN

Monte Carlo Simulation: Some Uses in the Genetic Study of Primitive Man

Through most of his existence man has been a hunter and gatherer of food -- shaped by rather than shaping his environment. This way of existence imposed a substantial number of restrictions, social and biologic, upon his evolution. Clearly these restrictions have varied with time, but it seems reasonable to suppose that the first major change occurred with man's recognition that he could exercise some control over his source of food either through farming or herding, or both. The earliest evidence of this important step is to be found in the Shanidar valley culture of Northern Iraq of some 80 centuries before Christ (Solecki, 1963).

As a hunter and gatherer man's numbers must have been sharply limited -- a response to the limitations of food and the obvious need for mobility. The smallness of the groups in which he lived was both an asset and a handicap. It restricted rather markedly the number and kind of his diseases and by so doing lessened the role played by disease in his evolution. (For a discussion of the role of disease in evolution, see Haldane, 1948). But this same smallness exposed the individual group to the constant threat of extinction either from beasts or marauding fellow men. With the advent of agriculture and a more sedentary way of life, man's culture changed dramatically, as did the selective forces which operated upon him. Of particular importance was the changed role of disease. Some have held that contemporary man is largely, if not wholly, a product of events since the advent of agriculture. If this is so, then the exploration of the manner in which primitive man's way of life influenced his genetic structure has only heuristic interest, but we believe that it holds more.

Stochastic models in genetics

The processes which shape the genetic composition of a population are generally regarded as either systematic or dispersive. The former consist of those directional processes such as mutation, migration, and selection; whereas the latter, the dispersive forces, are the fluctuations in gene frequencies due to random sampling of gametes generally referred to as "genetic drift," random variation in selection intensities, and random variation in migration rates. The effects of most of these processes are dependent upon the mating behavior of the population under scrutiny. The study of the relationship of these processes to the persistence and spread of a gene or group of genes forms the core of population genetics. Much of the present theory we owe to Sewall Wright, the late R. A. Fisher, J. B. S. Haldane, and more recently, Motoo Kimura. Attention has, in general, centered upon those situations where mathematically explicit statements were possible, but even here it has been frequently necessary to make simplifying assumptions which limit the generality of the result. Clearly, difficult or not, an explicit, comprehensive, and preferably stochastic statement of evolutionary theory is desirable. Such a statement does not now exist and because of the complexity of the problem progress toward it is slow. It is tedious to separate the relevant from the irrelevant, the important from the unimportant. However, digital computers and Monte Carlo solutions now afford us the opportunity to seek numeric answers to some of the problems which have thus far proven to be mathematically intractable. Simulation methods admittedly lack the appeal of explicit mathematical statements, but if one is pragmatic, these methods hold great promise for an early insight into a variety of interesting and important problems. In fact, at this juncture, it may well be that numeric analysis is more rewarding than an analytic, mathematical approach. What, now, are some of these problems which have proven intractable to formal methods?

Most population genetic theory has been until quite recently largely of a deterministic nature -- a matter of limited concern, perhaps, if emphasis is upon expected or average behavior in large populations. Clearly, in small populations, such as those which must have characterized primitive man, the stochastic element can not be ignored. Until 1954 and Kimura's work on the role of random fluctuations in selection intensities in the quasi-fixation of genes, the only random element prominently incorporated into the theory was that associated with the sampling of gametes. Earlier work, notably that of Fisher and Wright, had concentrated on the steady state distributions. Kimura has subsequently incorporated several other factors into the stochastic model, but to do so he has generally been obliged to assume a constancy of population size, randomness of mating, frequency independent selection intensities, etc. Thus, the case which he analyzes, though undoubtedly biologically meaningful for a variety of animals, may be an exceptional situation in man. Many of the cases which he as well as others have studied fail to take into account the simultaneous action of all of the processes, systematic and dispersive, which shape gene frequencies, although there are notable and important exceptions to this statement. The program which we propose to discuss shortly admits of some 50 different parameters which may be varied singly or in groups.

Among the important unsolved problems which can be readily studied numerically are the following: (1) The effect on the extinction of a gene of frequency-dependent selection intensities. (2) The effects on the genetic processes of age-specific birth and death rates. (3) The effects of a variety of kinds of phenotypic selection on gene frequencies in a natural population. (4) The rate of approach to homozygosity in the case where a population is subdivisible into two or more interbreeding subunits or demes in which the selection coefficients differ among the units. (5) Some years ago, the chairman (Crow, 1955) suggested on intuitive grounds, as nearly as we can tell, that in nature non-constant selective values must more often lead toward fixation than toward maintenance of variability in a panmictic, that is, in a randomly breeding, population. If our surmise that this was intuition is correct and there is no formal proof of the statement, then the problem could be answered by numeric means. (6) Finally, virtually every problem which has thus far been solved could be reinvestigated treating population size as a random variable. Situations in man can be cited which approximate virtually all of the problems we have enumerated. For example, in the case of the interbreeding subunits with different selection intensities, we know that the Birhor of India (Williams, 1963) live in bands, or demes of 25 to 35 persons. They are a hunting and gathering people and each band has a strong sense of territoriality. At any given time, some groups are relatively more affluent than others. It seems reasonable to assume that selection may, as a consequence, be unevenly distributed over neighboring bands. However, each band exchanges wives in a seemingly fixed pattern with the bands which surround it; hence the frequency of a given gene in a given band may be some complex function of a variety of selective forces.

To indicate how some of these problems might be approached let us examine the simulation program we have begun to use. We begin with a few general remarks on the nature of this program and the uses to which it, as well as other programs, have been put.

Some general remarks on the program

The applicability of simulation methods to genetic problems has been recognized by many, and, as a consequence, there already exists a modest but promising literature which attests to the broad potential of these techniques. Fraser (1957, 1962), for example, has applied them to a study of the effects of linkage and epistasis on selection. Lewontin and Dunn (1960) have investigated with a stochastic model the effect of a positive gametic selection on the t-allele polymorphism in the house mouse. Levin, Petras, and Rasmussen (1963) have extended the Lewontin and Dunn model to include intra-demic migration. Crosby (1963) has simulated certain evolutionary problems in Oenothera, the primrose. Martin and Cockerham (1960) have modeled several problems involving mass selection and linkage such as may arise in plant and animal breeding. Finally, Brues (1963) has used simulation methods in a study of the interaction of genetic drift with maternal-fetal incompatibility reactions and selection in the maintenance of the ABO blood group polymorphism in man. Ultimately the value of the models used by these investigators as well as the one to be proposed by ourselves is dependent upon the validity of the assumptions made in their construction. In the case of Monte Carlo simulations, the basic assumptions are set out in the form of a series of simple decisions, for example, the choice of a male parent, the segregation of two alleles, or the determination of the sex of an individual. Under these circumstances, it seems unlikely that the user of Monte Carlo methods is apt to incorporate unwittingly many cryptic assumptions. Be this as it may, decisions are made by comparing the various probabilities of the different outcomes of an event to a random number, r, where $0 \leq r \leq 1$. As an illustration, in the choice of a parent from a popultion in which the various genotypic frequencies are f(AA), f(Aa), and f(aa), if the random number is less than or equal to f(AA), the parent is taken to be homozygous AA. If the random number is greater than f(AA) but less than or equal to the sum f(AA) + f(Aa), the parent is heterozygous. Finally, if the random number is greater than the latter sum, the parent is homozygous aa. Quite clearly the integrity of this simulation is dependent upon the randomness of the so-called random numbers. In our case, these are generated by a subroutine which uses the power residue method (IBM Reference Manual, 1959). The random number generation sequence which is generated has a periodicity of 2^{b-2} terms when the word size is of b-bits and the arithmetic assumes the binary point to be at the extreme right of the word. With the IBM 7090 this means a periodicity of 2^{33}. A difference in runs is obtainable by merely starting at a different place in the sequence.

The various steps and decisions in the program are presented diagrammatically in Figure 1. In the main, the figure is self-explanatory but a few remarks seem in order. Although all events occur in a serial fashion in the program, individuals in the same generation or age-set are mated at the same instant in biological time. The sampling of mates from the parental pool alters the genotypic frequencies in these pools, that is, sampling is without replacement. Selection in the form of differential mortality is represented by storage decisions. Individuals selected against simply are not stored. Selection in the form of differential fertility is represented, obviously, by the differential production of offspring. At the moment, immigration is viewed as being a draw from an infinite source which is supposedly representative of the surrounding populations. Emigration is a random reduction of the population under scrutiny.

As most of you are well aware, Monte Carlo methods are, by their very nature, inefficient in terms of computer time. In this simulation, which was programmed in MAD (Michigan Algorithm Decoder), and run on an IBM 7090, with a binary deck, about one-third of a second is required per generation to produce a population of 100 individuals. A single 200 generation run requires slightly more than one minute. Needless to say, the number of runs required depends primarily upon the relative stability of the system being simulated. At this preliminary stage, we have usually been content with 15 runs. These are averaged and the variation in the system at a given generation judged by the mean of the ranges derived from successive sets of five runs. There is as yet no consensus with respect to the optimal number of runs. Clearly, to document with precision some specific model more than 15 runs may be needed, but as a screening procedure this number may be adequate.

The input parameters

One of the major justifications for simulation programs is, as we have indicated, the opportunity they afford to study the effect on any given genetic model of concurrent variation in a number of parameters. In a very real sense, the limiting factor to this variation is the inefficiency of the conventional digital computer where one is obliged to achieve stochastic operations through machine elements which are essentially deterministic in behavior and are programmed serially. Recently, Connelly and Justice have advocated a special computer with statistical switches, the latter being biasable binary random function generators. This computer would not be obliged, presumably, to spend most of its time generating or examining random numbers.

As we have previously stated, we can vary some 50 parameters in the present program, and can readily extend this with the addition of a few more statements (we presently employ about 370). We would be remiss, however, if we led you to believe that our present program is capable of solving all of the problems previously outlined. It is not; in fact, it is still quite crude but we believe that it has promise.

We turn, now, to a brief consideration of the parameters of interest to us, and the values which seem appropriate for our purposes.

Population size. -- Our notions on the probable size of the bands of primitive man stem from contemporary hunting and gathering cultures. The representativeness of these groups is open to challenge. This notwithstanding we have selected the population sizes we have used largely on the basis of information on three such groups of people. We know that the Xavante, a primitive group living along the Rio das Mortes in Brazil, usually live in bands of approximately 200 (Neel et al., 1963). The Birhor of India, who like the pygmies of the Ituri forest may represent a highly specialized case of hunting and gathering culture, travel in groups of approximately 25 during the wet season and in groups averaging 30-35 in the dry period of the year (Williams, 1963). Finally, the average tribal size for the Australian aboriginal, as judged by linguistic standards, is given as 523 (Birdsell, 1950) although the hunting band size is undoubtedly much smaller. We are, of course, interested in the size of the effective breeding population, and the figures just quoted are not necessarily breeding sizes. Accordingly, we have generally assumed the effective population size to be between 50 and 200.

We can with our present program view population size as a fixed constant or as a random variable subject to some distribution. While most of our runs to date have been on populations of constant size, we have attempted a few where the size was permitted to vary randomly between two limits. When the upper bound was reached, the group automatically divided into two, fissioned so to speak. When the lower bound was attained, a fusion occurred to return the population to the mean value. Our interest in population bounds stems from the belief that empirically at least, the more sagacious of primitive men must have recognized that there was an optimum population size and that drastic departures from this optimum threatened the existence of the group. In support of this contention, it is known that certain contemporary but primitive groups practice a form of population control through infanticide, and that others do on occasion bud-off groups comprising several families. The Xavante studied by Neel and his colleagues have recently gone through such a process.

Age stratification. -- Most primitive peoples have a less quantitative sense of time than characterizes our own culture. Exact ages are, as a rule, unknown, and moreover they are generally viewed as unimportant. Age differentials tend to be recognized not in terms of seasons or years but rather in terms of the age-sets to which individuals belong. The persons comprising a given age-set move together through life much as a cohort; they attain manhood or womanhood simultaneously; they marry in a prescribed manner; etc. As a generality, the regulations governing the males are the more rigid. While the difference between oldest and youngest in an age-set undoubtedly varies somewhat between age-sets, the average difference can be estimated on the basis of dentition, bone age, etc. in those instances where it is not a matter of tradition. The interval associated with an age-set in the Xavante, for example, appears to amount to five years, on the average. We have, for convenience, elected to recognize, with a given sex and generation, three age-sets rather than the five or six the Xavante data would suggest. Thus, in our simulation, each age-set corresponds to a span of approximately ten years.

Mating formula. -- Man appears to have exercised more ingenuity in the restrictions he has formulated to control his mating behavior than in ways of distributing the economic burden of his culture. He may be monogamous or polygamous, and if polygamous, either polyandrous or polygynous. His polygamy may be concurrent or serial since marriages may be arranged for some lesser period than life. Temporary arrangements such as wife lending further complicate his behavior. Moreover, he frequently favors a choice of spouse which gives rise to a correlation between uniting gametes either as a consequence of inbreeding or a phenotypic assortative mating. Finally, he generally has fixed but not inviolate notions about an acceptable age differential twixt husband and wife. With respect to man, in no other area, perhaps, are our present models more unrealistic than in their treatment of the manner in which he mates.

The occurrence of overlapping, or possibly we should say, interbreeding generations has long been a matter of concern in population genetics. When it has been possible to incorporate a sense of this overlapping into the model it is generally assumed that overlapping is a continuous phenomenon, a reasonable assumption in our culture (see Moran, 1962). However, in primitive man with his age-set notion of time, this would hardly seem to be the case. The overlapping must have been discontinuous. We can and have incorporated interbreeding generations into our runs through the specification of the manner in which mating occurs between age-sets. One simply requires the female to be drawn from an age-set younger than the male.

Again, to give some dimension to the variation in marital practices we cite the Xavante. In this group, chiefs, heads of clans, and other important members of the tribe are generally polygynous, with the number of wives varying from two to five. Lesser males are either monogamous or go unmarried. Among the Xavante studied by Neel and his colleagues, of 37 living adult males 23 were monogamous and 14 polygynous. Of the latter 14, 11 had two wives, two had three, and one, the chief, had five wives.

Selection. -- Selection intensity may be considered at several levels in the program, but in all cases selection implies that some individuals are differentially represented by progeny in succeeding generations. This may arise either as a consequence of differential survival, or differential fertility, or both. Selection to be genetically meaningful, and, therefore, of evolutionary significance, must correlate either with one's phenotype or one's genotype. In general, it is much easier to treat differential mortality than differential fertility, for, as we have stated, the former is merely a decision with respect to storage and this decision can be made in such fashion that the selection intensity is a fixed constant with or without random fluctuations. Differential fertility is, however, the more interesting. For example, among the Xavante to which reference has been made, the present chief has fathered a minimum of 25 per cent of the next generation -- the precise figure being a function of how one elects to define a generation. If this is a continuing custom, its consequences would seem large.

At present, we treat fertility as if it were an attribute of a mating. This attribute, however, is viewed as being a multiple of a linear function of a constant associated with the male and a constant associated with the female, and these latter constants are genotype dependent. This permits us to assign specific genotypic values, but still have differences in fertility between reciprocal crosses. In man an important case in point would be the probable difference in fertility between the mating of an Rh+ male with an Rh- female and the reciprocal, namely, the marriage of an Rh- male with an Rh+ female. Rucknagel and Neel (1961) have presented data which can be interpreted as suggesting that a similar situation may obtain in Africa in matings of normal individuals with those heterozygous for the gene which when homozygous gives rise to sickle cell anemia.

We can not accommodate at present a phenotypic selection in the usual sense. There are numerous interesting problems in this area, however. A case in point occurs in those groups of people where the chiefs are polygamous, contribute, therefore, disproportionately to subsequent generations, and where the selection of the chief is essentially phenotypic.

Migration and mutation. -- These two processes differ essentially only in the frequency of their occurrence. We do not at present allow for mutation, but this can be readily done. We can accommodate migration either in or out, but have, as previously stated, been more concerned with notions of a critical population size and sporadic but relatively large-scale migration rather than the case of a constant, small and perhaps fluctuating migration pressure.

Number of loci. -- At present we can only simulate models which involve one genetic locus, but we are currently extending this to two loci.

Number of alleles at a locus. -- Two alleles are routinely considered, but extension to three, four, or some other small number is a simple matter.

Some preliminary results

As frequently happens in any complex program a surprising amount of time can be invested in debugging. Our experience is no exception

Accordingly, the results which we have to show are less exciting than we should like. They are essentially of two kinds. On the one hand, they represent tests of the program through contrasting stochastic with deterministic results for certain simple situations. On the other hand, they afford an insight, admittedly limited, into the effect of a discontinuous overlapping of generations and some kinds of fertility differentials. We propose to expose these cases by enumerating the restrictions under which the runs occurred and then commenting briefly on what we view as the salient features of each case.

Case 1. Effect of discrete overlapping of generations on genetic drift.--Kimura's model of genetic drift assumes non-overlapping generations but views the changes in gene frequency as continuous. As we have indicated, in primitive man and in time spans of tens of generations this may not be true. Our model permits us to examine this proposition. The population which we simulated was one of fixed size mating monogamously and at random. The sizes chosen were 48, 102, and 198 so that we might have six age-sets of equal size, three male and three female. The age-sets were ranked, and the mating system assumed that a male drew his spouse from the next age-set in rank to the rank of his own set. For example, males of age rank 1 would mate with females of age rank 2 and their offspring would constitute the age rank 1 (male and female) of the next generation. Thus, in each generation one-third of the males obtained their spouses from the next generation. All matings were assumed to produce two offspring, one male and one female. No selection, mutation, or migration operated on the system, and the initial population was assumed to be completely heterozygous. The results are to be found in Figure 2.

Case 2. A locus with incomplete selection against one homozygote, and reproductive compensation -- Among the San Blas Indians of the Caribbean, albinism reaches extraordinary frequencies for human populations or any population for that matter. The maintenance of these high gene frequencies in the face of obvious selection has been an intriguing problem. We know that, in the past, albino infants were often destroyed, and that among those who reached adulthood the males were not permitted to marry and the females, though marriageable, were not viewed as particularly desirable spouses. Albinism is also relatively common among the Hopi Indians of the United States. Woolf and Grant (1962) have suggested that genetic drift, cultural selection favoring the albino, or a small heterozygous advantage could account for the Hopi frequency.

We have simulated the San Blas case in the following manner: We have assumed a population of fixed size, 102, breeding randomly with overlapping generations as outlined in Case 1. Monogamy was the rule. There was no mutation nor migration. However, the albino, the recessive homozygote, was assumed to have a survival frequency of only 0.25. But we assumed that all matings ultimately produced exactly two children, one male and one female. Thus, in a mating of two heterozygotes, if an albino is produced and eliminated by selection, this mating produces another child! This has been called reproductive compensation. Again, the initial population was assumed to be completely heterozygous. This choice of input parameters is, of course, a value judgment, but we have no reason to believe that the shape of these curves will be a function of the input parameters. There exists a deterministic solution for a closely related case, and this along with our results will be found in Figure 3. We note that the two models agree moderately well. Exact agreement is not to be expected for the stochastic model includes reproductive compensation which is not present in the deterministic model. Reproductive compensation can only slow down the rate of elimination of the gene, and the figure is in agreement with this.

Case 3. A balanced polymorphism with complete selection against one homozygote and 20 per cent selection against the other. -- This may be viewed as a somewhat extreme version of the situation which appears to obtain with respect to sickle cell anemia in man in malarious areas of the world. Our simulation invoked the following restrictions: The population was assumed to have a constant size, namely 102 individuals. Mating was at random between age-sets but such that overlapping generations occurred. The population was monogamous. No individuals of one homozygous class survive, and only 80 per cent of the other homozygous group. All matings, however, ultimately produced two offspring, one male and one female. Again, the initial population was taken to be completely heterozygous. The steady state frequency on a deterministic basis for a population where the fitness of the homozygotes are 0.8 and 0 can be readily computed. Our stochastic model differs from this, however, in that reproductive compensation occurs. The steady state value for the case just cited is approximately 0.166; the results of our simulation are to be found in Figure 4. It is patent on inspection that a stable equilibrium exists at a gene frequency somewhat greater than 0.1, but not as high as the deterministic value. This is undoubtedly attributable to the reproductive compensation.

Case 4. A locus in which differential fertility is a function of the mating type rather than the genotype. -- We know that in man maternal-fetal incompatibilities occur, and that some of these may take the form of hemolytic disease of the newborn, a serious and often fatal anemia. Thus, in the Rh system an Rh+ child conceived by an Rh- mother runs a risk of dying not run by an Rh- child of the same mother. Selection is not complete against the Rh+ children of Rh- mothers, however, for immunization of the mother is a necessary condition before hemolytic disease can occur. Immunization requires either a transfusion or the conception of at least one previous Rh+ child. The system is more complicated than this in that hemolytic disease as a consequence of Rh incompatibility depends, in part, upon the compatibility of mother and child with respect to another genetic locus, namely, that associated with the ABO system. This situation leads us to consider the simulation of a population in which selection occurred through ascribing differentials in fertility to matings rather than to specific genotypes. Our model does not describe the Rh system exactly, but it is a step in this direction. Specifically, we assume a population of fixed size, 100, discrete and non-overlapping generations. Mating is monogamous but at random. There is no mutation, nor migration. Of the nine possible mating types when the sex of the parents are considered, all are assumed to have equal fertility save for the case of an RR x rr, and Rr x rr . These are assumed to have only half, and three-fourths the fertility of the others. The sex ratio is not a random variable. The initial population is completely heterozygous. The results are to be seen in Figure 5. Of particular interest to us was the relatively slow rate of decay and the variability of the 15 runs; compare the range with those seen in Figure 2 and 3.

As we stated at the outset of the consideration of these cases, the data are primarily of a program proofing kind. We have specifically limited ourselves to date to cases where a deterministic solution exists or where intuition can be assumed to be a reliable guide. We have satisfied ourselves that the program contains no flaws in logic, and that we may now turn to more exciting pursuits. Specifically, and at an early date, we expect to simulate a human population of the kind the Xavante presently appear to be. That is to say, we propose to assign to the parameters values consistent with those estimated from the Xavante, and to examine questions of the persistence and spread of major genes under circumstances so defined.

Summary

In summary, despite some quite sophisticated and ingenious mathematical arguments, progress toward a stochastic theory of evolution which incorporates all of the processes which perturb gene frequencies has been slow. Most of the cases which have been investigated seem to have more relevance for subhuman forms than for man. Numerous interesting problems in the evolution of man exist, and are presently unsolved. Monte Carlo simulation offers a means of investigating many of these. We are currently engaged in developing and testing a program which would permit us to describe the genetic consequences associated with certain existing hunting and gathering cultures.

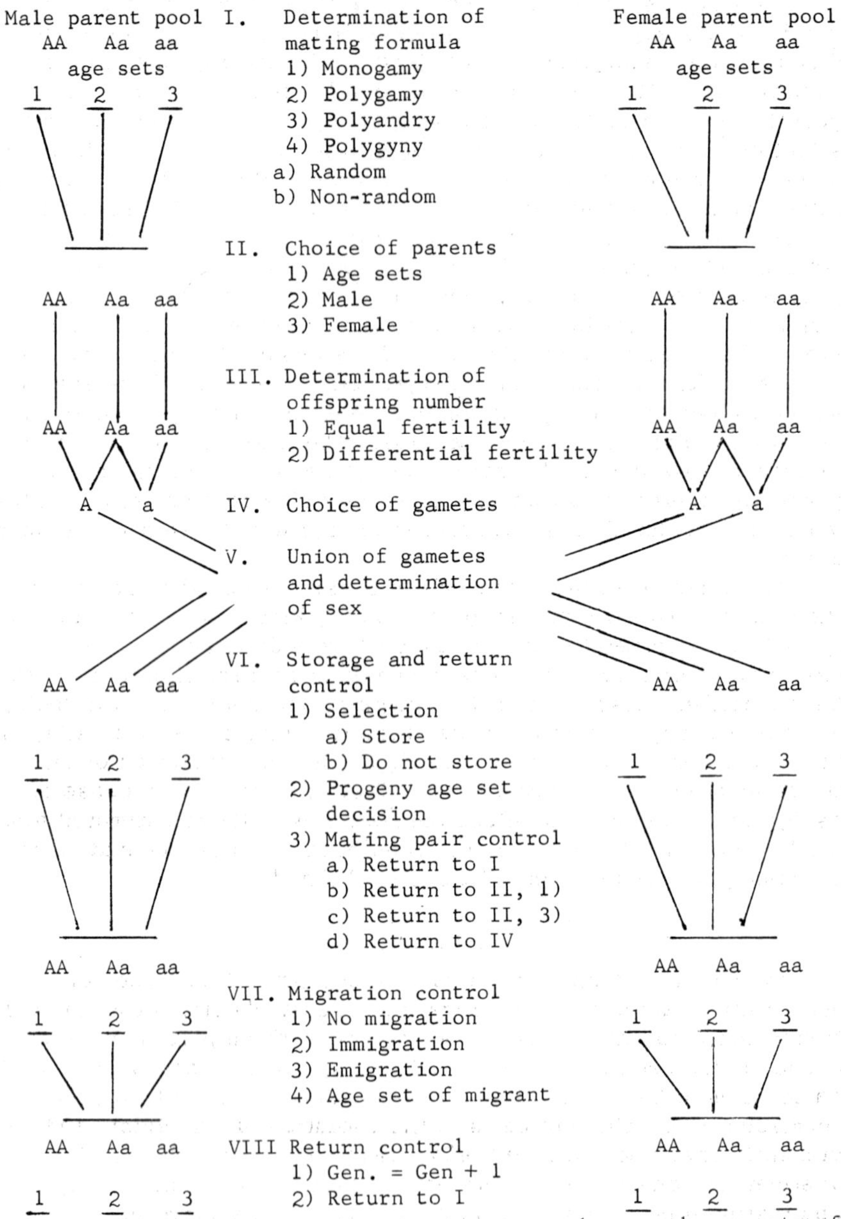

1) Individuals in the male and female storage become the parents of the next generation.
2) Continues iterations until Gen. = desired number or fixation occurs.

FIGURE 1. A diagrammatic representation of the various steps and decisions represented in the simulation program under discussion.

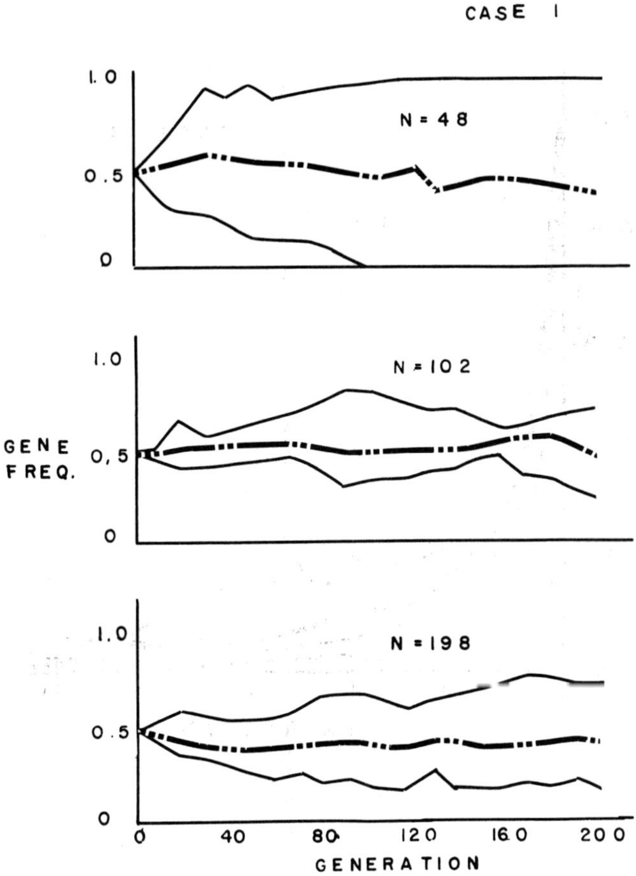

FIGURE 2. Effects of discrete overlapping of generations on genetic drift. The average of six runs is indicated by the heavy interrupted line; the solid lines define the range described by the six runs.

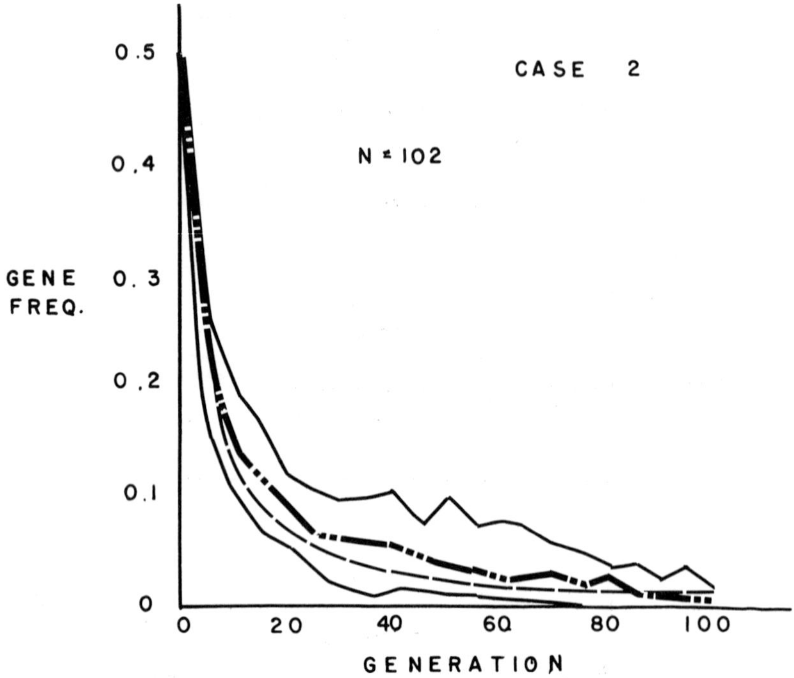

FIGURE 3. Change in gene frequency associated with a locus where selection proceeds against one homozygote but reproductive compensation occurs. The average of the 15 runs is indicated by the heavy interrupted line while the solid lines define the mean range for each point. The deterministic solution is represented by the light interrupted line.

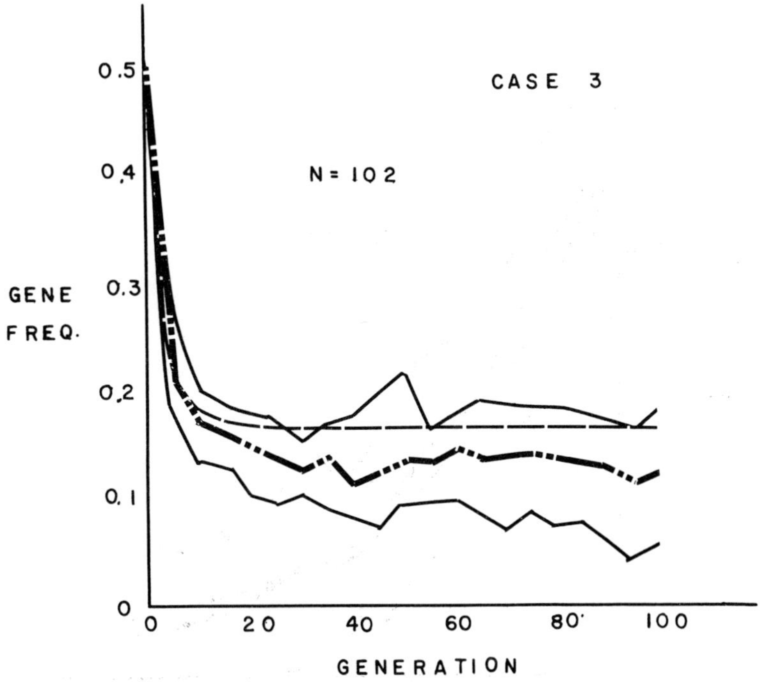

FIGURE 4. Change in gene frequency associated with a locus with complete selection against one homozygote and 20 per cent selection against the other. The average of 15 runs is indicated by the heavy interrupted line represents the deterministic solution associated with a similar but not identical situation. The solid lines define the mean range for each point.

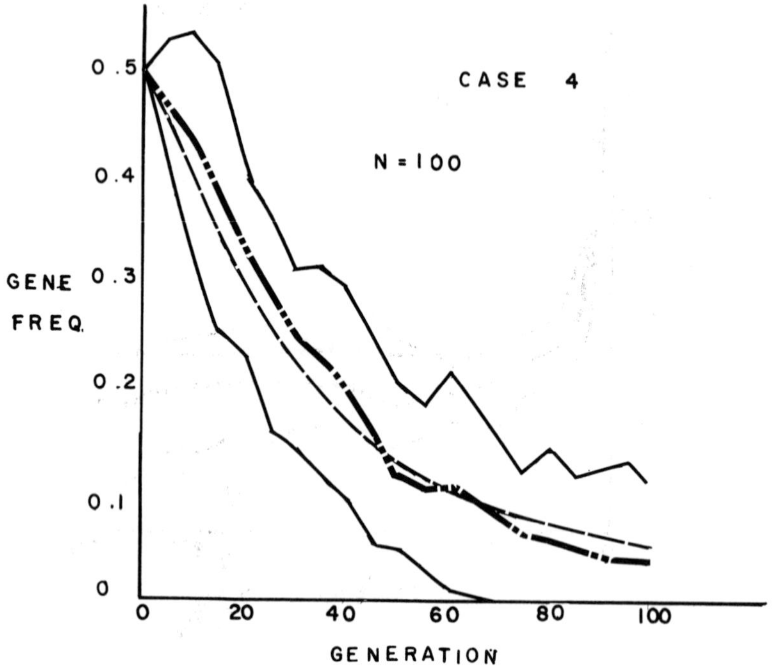

FIGURE 5. Change in gene frequency associated with a locus in which differential fertility is viewed as a function of the mating type rather than the genotype. The heavy interrupted line is the average of 15 runs; the light interrupted line is the deterministic solution. The range at each generation is described by the uninterrupted lines.

REFERENCES

1. Birdsell, J. B. 1950. Some implications of the genetical concept of race in terms of spatial analysis. Cold Spring Harbor Symposium 15: 259-314.

2. Brues, A. M. 1963. Further contributions to the problem of ABO blood group polymorphism. Paper read at the Annual Meeting of the American Association of Physical Anthropologists.

3. Crosby, J. L. 1963. Evolution by computer. New Scientist No. 327: 415-417.

4. Crow, J. F. 1955. General theory of population genetics: Synthesis. Cold Spring Harbor Symposium 20: 54-59.

5. Fraser, A. S. 1957. Simulation of genetic systems by automatic digital computers. I. Introduction. II. Effects of linkage on rates of advance under selection. Aust. J. Biol. Sci. 10: 484-491, 492-499.

6. Fraser, A. S. 1962. Simulation of genetic systems. J. Theoret. Biol. 2: 329-346.

7. Haldane, J. B. S. 1949. Disease and evolution. La Ricerca Scientifica (Suppl.) 19: 3-11.

8. IBM Reference Manual 1959. Random number generation and testing.

9. Kimura, M. 1954. Process leading to quasi-fixation of genes in natural populations due to random fluctuations of selection intensities. Genetics 39: 280-295.

10. Levin, B., Petras, M., and Rasmussen, D. 1963. The effect of migration on maintaining a polymorphism in the house mouse. (In manuscript.)

11. Lewontin, R., and Dunn, L. C. 1960. The evolutionary dynamics of a polymorphism in the house mouse. Genetics 45: 705-722.

12. Martin, F., and Cockerham, C. 1960. High speed selection studies. In: Biometrical Genetics (). Kempthorne, ed.) New York: Pergamon Press. pp. 35-45.

13. Moran, P. A. P. 1962. The statistical processes of evolutionary theory. Oxford: Clarendon Press. pp. viii and 200.

14. Neel, J. V., Junqueira, P. C., Salzano, F. M., Keiter, F., and Maybury-Lewis, D. 1963. Studies in the Xavante Indians of the Brazilian Mato Grosso. (In manuscript.)

15. Rucknagel, D., and Neel, J. V. 1961. The Hemoglobinopathies. In: Progress in Medical Genetics (Ed.: A. Steinberg). New York: Grune and Stratton, Inc. pp. 158-260.

16. Solecki, R. S. 1963. Prehistory in Shanidar Valley, Northern Iraq. Science 139: 179-193.

17. Stout, D. B. 1946. Further notes on albinism among the San Blas Cuna, Panama. Amer. J. Phys. Anthrop. 4: 483-490.

18. Williams, B. J. Unpublished observations.

19. Woolf, C. M., and Grant, R. B. 1962. Albinism among the Hopi Indians in Arizona. Amer. J. Human Genet. 14: 391-400.

20. Wright, S. 1951. The genetical structure of populations. Ann. Eugen. 15: 323-354.

DISCUSSION PARTICIPANT

Dr. James F. Crow
Professor of Medical Genetics and Acting Dean, School of Medicine, University of Wisconsin Hospitals
Madison, Wisconsin

DISCUSSION

James F. Crow. Some of the problems worked on by Dr. Schull can be worked out, at least to a good approximation, by a continuous diffusion model. Might this not provide a useful cross check?

William J. Schull. The cross check which Dr. Crow has suggested would be most useful. In point of fact we have attempted just this although on a very limited scale. With respect to "genetic drift", for example, we have compared our results with those obtained by Kimura through the use of diffusion equations.

SEWALL WRIGHT
Stochastic Processes in Evolution

The idea that evolution comes about from the interaction of a stochastic and a directed process was the essence of Darwin's theory. The stochastic process that he invoked was the occurrence of small random variations which, he supposed, provide raw material for natural selection, a process directed by the requirements of the environment, and one that builds up, step by step, changes that would be inconceivably improbable at a single step.

Mutation (in the broad sense), and natural selection are still considered by all geneticists to form the ultimate basis of evolution though there has been a wide spectrum of opinions on their roles.

Evolution as a succession of major mutations

The basic principles of heredity were discovered by Mendel in 1865 but did not effectively come to the attention of biologists until rediscovered in 1900, simultaneously by de Vries, Correns and Tschermak. de Vries' primary interest had been in evolution. It is not surprising that his theory, the abrupt origin of species by single major mutations, for which he seemed to have direct evidence, had much influence among geneticists. It turned out that what he had observed were gross chromosome aberrations. These undoubtedly play a real part but, it is generally agreed now, a subordinate part in evolution, which I will not go into.

de Vries attributed a cumulative effect to natural selection only in shaping genera and higher categories. Some of his followers including Willis in his "age and area" theory and most recently Goldschmidt (1940) went farther and assumed that genera could only arise from generic mutations, families from family mutations and so on. There is only the faintest possible recognition of selection in Goldschmidt's phrase "hopeful monsters" for mutations that succeed. Most biologists, contemplating the complex and marvelously precise adaptations to the various ways of life of species, have felt that all theories of abrupt origin are essentially begging the question by invoking miracles.

Evolution as a succession of minor mutations

Almost from the first, most geneticists adopted the view that a species difference must be built up by an accumulation of minor mutations that differ from those ordinarily observed in the laboratory mainly in being favorable. This theory, which is still perhaps that most widely held, is well expressed by Morgan (1932) in the following quotation in which selection is recognized only in the phrase "better adapted".

"If we had the complete ancestry of any animal or plant living today, we should expect to find a series of forms differing at each step by a single mutant change in one or another of the genes and each a better adapted or differently adapted form from the preceding".

Evolution as steady progress under selection

Before the rediscovery of Mendelian heredity, there had been a group, led by Karl Pearson, who had been studying the heredity of quantitatively varying characters by statistical methods, and who, following Darwin, interpreted evolution as the accumulation of changes in such characters. A vigorous polemic arose between this group and the Mendelians but this was followed by a reconciliation to which Pearson himself, Yule, Hardy and Weinberg contributed on the theoretical side in papers between 1904 and 1910 and the experimental geneticists Nilsson-Ehle, East, Shull, Emerson and others contributed from 1908 on, by demonstrating the validity of the multiple factor theory of quantitative variability. L. H. Smith, Castle, Payne and others contributed in this period by demonstrating the effectiveness of selection in carrying the mean of such characters far beyond the original limits of variation. My first active contact with the subject came as Dr. Castle's assistant from 1912-15 in his selection experiment with the hooding patterns of rats.

J. B. S. Haldane in a series of papers in the 1920's summarized in 1932, worked out the mathematics of the orderly progress toward fixation of favorable mutations under a great variety of complicating conditions. These included interaction among the effects of genes, but largely as an impediment to rapid progress, rather than as something that would enormously amplify the field of significant variability if there were any way in which favorable combinations could be seized upon by selection. Unfortunately the same process of recombination that may produce an exceptionally favorable genotype, at once breaks it down in a sexually reproducing species. Thus Haldane treated the evolutionary process as a quasi-deterministic one in which the future state of a population could be estimated by integration of formulae describing the momentary changes in gene frequency ratios due to selection coefficients attributed to the individual genes.

R. A. Fisher (1930) developed what he called the "fundamental theorem of natural selection". He defined two properties of each pair of alleles that affect any character, the average excess (a) of the portion of the population with one allele, over the portion with the other (apportioning heterozygotes equally); and the average effect (α) produced in the population as genetically constituted by the substitution of one for the other. He showed that the additive contributions of such a pair to the variance is given by $q(1-q)\,a\alpha$ where q is the frequency of one. On applying these concepts to "fitness", defined for individuals as their net productivity, he showed that its rate of increase in the population under given conditions is $\sum \alpha \frac{dq}{dt}$ and that this is equal to the genetic variance of individual fitness, $\sum a\alpha\, q(1-q)$, where by genetic variance he meant the additive component. Summation is over all loci. This was generalized to allow for multiple alleles.

"The rate of increase in fitness of any organism at any time is equal to its genetic variance in fitness at that time".

It may be noted that fitness is used here in two senses; as a property of the population that can never decrease (under given conditions) and as a property of individuals that has a variance. It is not easy to grasp just what the former means, a point to which we will return.

This theorem gives a formal demonstration of the principle that mass selection can operate only on the momentary net effects of the separate genes. Interaction effects merely reduce the additive portion of the variance and thus cut down by just that much the rate of change of fitness.

It is, indeed, possible that in the process of fixation of a favorable mutation, the selection coefficient of other interacting genes may be reversed in sign. The process thus may lead to a chain of readjustments. This, however, does not imply any selection among genotypes as wholes at any given moment. The evolutionary process under given conditions is largely limited by the rate of occurrence of novel favorable mutations, which is exceedingly low.

Treadmill evolution

Conditions, however, do not remain constant. A change of conditions may bring about reversal of the direction of selection at many loci and thus initiate a rapid evolutionary readjustment. Continual change of condition thus brings about continuous evolution of a sort.

The nature of the progress is, however, somewhat like that on a treadmill. The species merely holds its own as each new rough adaptation accompanies the undoing of an old one (Wright 1932). Observec evolutionary changes in nature and successful selection experiments come, however, almost wholly in this category.

The shifting balance theory of evolution

This theory (Wright 1931) grew out of my attempt to formulate the roles of inbreeding, crossbreeding and selection in the improvement of livestock (Wright 1920, 22, 23). It resembled the theories of Haldane and Fisher in being based on the mathematical consequences of Mendelian heredity but differed considerably in the biological premises that were stressed. It will be desirable to list some of the more important premises, especially as there have been recent assertions that these were the opposite in most respects of what they actually were.

Premises

A. Multiple factor theory of quantitative variability.

Evolution depends largely on the cumulative effects of changes in the frequencies of multiple minor factors, responsible at any given time for merely quantitative variability. There are numerous isoalleles at each locus. Major mutations may be utilized but require extensive readjustments of frequencies among multiple modifiers.

B. Multiple selective peaks.

The ramifications from the primary effect of any gene replacement (assumed from the first to be on the specificity of an enzyme), through the networks of metabolic reactions and of intercellular developmental processes to the characters with which the organism confronts its environment is such that each replacement has effects (not necessarily obvious) on numerous characters. The pleiotropic effects of multiple alleles are in general not parallel. Universal pleiotropy is assumed.

The occurrence of joint reactions in the above networks implies extensive interactions among the effects of genes. Moreover, all characters contribute to a single character "selective value". Because of factor interaction and pleiotropy there is the potentiality for a vast number of different harmonious combinations corresponding to different "selective peaks" is the "surface" of selective values relative to the multi-dimensional field of gene frequencies, instead of the single best type, implied by mere summation of absolute effects attributed to the separate genes. Even for gene effects that are cumulative with respect to a quantitatively varying character, the prevailing intermediacy of the optimum grade insures the potentiality for a vast number of discrete selective peaks, and pleiotropy insures that these be at diverse values.

C. Multiple partially isolated demes.

Most species contain numerous small, random breeding local populations (demes) that are sufficiently isolated (if only by distance) to permit differentiation of their sets of gene frequencies (not necessarily associated with detectible phenotypic differentiation) but not so isolated as to prevent gradual spreading of a favorable genetic complex throughout the species from its center of origin.

These premises were indicated briefly in 1931 and those on the relation of genes and characters at considerable length in 1934.

The first premise differentiates this theory sharply from those which see evolution as a succession of mutations, major or minor. Much more emphasis is put on pleiotropy (second premise) than by Haldane or Fisher. The latter virtually denied its importance in his theory of the evolution of dominance (1928, 29), (Wright 1929a, 34). The possibility of multiple peaks has been accepted by Haldane but virtually denied by Fisher (1941). The last premise is perhaps the most distinctive and probably also the most controversial.

A three-phase evolutionary process was deduced from these premises. Change of gene frequency is treated as the elementary evolutionary process since it permits reduction of all factors to a common basis.

Phases of the evolutionary process

1. Phase of random drift.

In each deme, each set of gene frequencies drifts at random in a multi-dimensional stochastic distribution about the equilibrium point, characteristic of one of the multiple selective peaks. The set of equilibrium values is the resultant of three sorts of "pressures" on gene frequencies (a) those of recurrent mutation, (b) those of selection and (c) those of immigration from other demes. The fluctuations, responsible for random drift, may be due either to accidents of sampling or to fluctuations in the values of the coefficients for the various pressures.

2. Phase of intrademic selection.

From time to time a set of gene frequencies drifts across one of the many two-factor saddles in the probability distribution. There ensues a period of rapid systematic change, dominated by selection among individuals until the set of gene frequencies approaches the equilibrium associated with the new, higher selective peak, about which it now drifts at random for a long time as in the first phase.

3. Phase of interdemic selection.

A deme that comes under control of a selective peak superior to that controlling the neighboring demes, produces a greater surplus population and by excess dispersion systematically shifts the positions of equilibrium in the neighboring demes toward its own position, until they are pulled across the same saddle, and come under the second phase. This process spreads in concentric circles among the inferior demes. The process may go on indefinitely because of the indefinitely large number of selective peaks, with only the small amount of novel mutation necessary to replace alleles occasionally lost in the third phase.

There is a higher level of adaptation at which a high mean rate of reproduction becomes an inadequate criterion of success. Such a rate may lead to over-population in a large area that threatens persistence of the group by exhaustion of resources or poisoning of the environment. Long time adaptation requires selection at a level that puts a premium on the achievement of a proper balance with natural resources rather than a maximum rate of reproduction.

Ecologic opportunity

It is here assumed that selection at various levels is always the guiding principle but this leaves it unexplained why some forms have changed only slightly in hundreds of millions of years, others have progressed steadily along rather narrowly restricted lines, while still others have developed with relatively explosive rapidity and diverged along many lines (bradytely, horotely and tachytely of Simpson 1945).

The interpretation that fits best the rest of the theory is summed up in the words "ecologic opportunity". Most species are restricted to progress, if any, along the line of increasing perfection in the niche that they occupy, by the occupation of all slightly different niches, by other species. Occasionally, however, an unusually favorable ecologic opportunity may be presented (1) by arrival of a colony in territory in which many niches, possible for it, are unoccupied or (2) by some degree of preadaptation to a drastically altered environment in which most rival forms become extinct or (3) attainment in the course of specialization of a complex of adaptations that opens up an extensive new way of life. A new higher category may evolve rapidly by branching out of the species in different directions in different localities in exploitation of one of these opportunities, (Wright 1942, 1949).

As the shifting balance theory pertains to transformation of species, the problems of the splitting of species are not here considered (cf. Wright 1949).

Mathematical framework

As noted earlier, the systematic "pressures" on gene frequency have been grouped into three categories, those from recurrent change of the genetic material itself (mutation pressure), those from introduction from without (immigration pressure) and those from change in gene frequency without either of the above (selection pressure). Selection pressure includes changes from differential viability at any stage, differential emigration, differential mating, differential productivity and inequalities in the segregation process itself (meiotic drive).

These are measured by the changes (Δq) in gene frequency (q) which they tend to bring about per generation. The total pressure is the sum of the three partial pressures (at least if small). In the simplest case, with mutation rates v and u, to and from the given gene, with replacement of the proportion, m, of the deme by immigrants with mean gene frequency Q and with a momentary selective advantage, s, of the gene over its alleles collectively, this total pressure is measured by the following (Wright 1931):

$$(1) \qquad \Delta q = [v(1-q) - uq] - m(q-Q) + sq(1-q) \quad .$$

The various terms may be elaborated to deal with situations more realistically. For example any degree of dominance may be taken care of by expressing selection pressure in the form $(s + tq)\, q(1-q)$ (Wright 1937). A special case of interest is that in which the heterozygote has an advantage s' over one homozygote and t' over the other, $\Delta q = [t' - (s' + t')q]\, q(1-q)$.

In most cases, some of the pressures are positive, others negative. In the last case above, selection pressure by itself involves opposed components. The net effect is to push gene frequency to an equilibrium value, $\hat{q}$, calculated by putting $\Delta \hat{q} = 0$.

Similarly, the effects of undirected random processes on gene frequency can be given condensed expression in terms of their contributions to the variance of fluctuations about the equilibrium value per generation (Wright 1931, 1948, 1956b).

$$(2) \qquad \sigma^2_{\Delta q} = (1/2N)\, q(1-q) + \sigma^2_s q^2 (1-q)^2 + \sigma^2_m (q-Q)^2 + m^2 \sigma^2_Q \quad .$$

The first term is the contribution from accidents of sampling in a population of effective size N; the second is that from fluctuations, σ_s^2, in the selection coefficient, the third from fluctuations, σ_m^2, is the amount of immigration and the last from fluctuations, σ_Q^2, in the gene frequencies introduced by immigration. The last two are usually unimportant.

The directed and random processes operate jointly to determine a probability (or stochastic) distribution which describes the extent of random drift about the equilibrium value.

The distribution of frequencies for a single gene

The first attempt to determine this distribution was made by Fisher (1922) who used the heat diffusion equation. His results were expressed in terms of the quantity $\vartheta = \cos^{-1}(1-2q)$, instead of gene frequency (q), in order to make the sampling variance uniform throughout the range between $q = 0$ and $q = 1$.

A discrepancy between the rate of decay under inbreeding alone ($\Delta q = 0$), given by him as $1/(4N)$ where N is population number, and the value $1/(2N)$ which I had obtained independently of the distribution, (and lack of familiarity with differential equations), led me to try to derive the formula for the distribution in another way. The results were reported briefly and in one respect incorrectly in a note (Wright 1929b). In the course of correspondence, initiated by Fisher, I sent him my full manuscript. He found that he had omitted a term (last below) in his diffusion equation, made necessary by the transformation of scale. His revised equation for the above case and the solution were as follows:

(3) $$\frac{\partial y}{\partial t} = \frac{1}{4N}\frac{\partial^2 u}{\partial \vartheta^2} + \frac{1}{4N}\frac{\partial}{\partial \varphi}(y \cot \theta)$$

(4) $$y = A_0^{e^{-t/2N}} \sin \theta \qquad t = \text{number of generations.}$$

With this correction, he agreed with the rate of decay that I had obtained. The form of the distribution is also in agreement. He also corrected his formulae for cases in which $\Delta q = 0$ except for minute amounts of mutation in one or both direction, and for ones assuming selection without dominance, $\Delta q = sq(1-q)$, again associated with minute amounts of mutation. These corrections were made in his book (1930). On transforming his formulae from θ to q, I noted a discrepancy in the selection term in my 1929 formula. This time it was my turn to make a correction which I was able to do in correcting proof for my 1931 paper as noted therein. The method that

I used was a cumbersome one but it may be of interest to compare it with other methods that I have used.

Stochastic distributions from an integral equation

This equation was based on the concept that a class of populations, characterized by the frequency q of gene A and subject to change of frequency at the rate Δq per generation makes a contribution to the class of populations characterized by gene frequency q_1, by the appropriate term in the expansion of $[(1-q-\Delta q)\,a + (q+\Delta q)\,A]^{2N}$ i.e. $\binom{2N}{2Nq_1}(q+\Delta q)^{2Nq_1}(1-q-\Delta q)^{2N(1-q_1)}f(q)$ where $f(q)$ is the frequency of the parent class. If there is constancy of the form of the distribution but decay at rate K, the sum of the contributions from all classes to any given offspring class must be the same as the frequency of the parent class with the same gene frequency except for reduction by the factor $(1-K)$. It is convenient to use p, for $1-q$

$$(5)\qquad \binom{2N}{2Nq_1}\sum_{0}^{1}\left[(q+\Delta q)^{2Nq_1}(p-\Delta q)^{2Np_1}\right]f(q) = (1-K)\; f(q_1) \;.$$

Since q varies by very small steps, $1/(2N)$, if N is large, it seems to be a legitimate approximation to deal with q as if it were continuous between 0 and 1, replacing summation by integration, $f(q)$ by $\varphi(q)\,dq$, $f(q_1)$ by $\varphi(q)/2N$ (noting that care must be taken near the boundaries 0 and 1).

$$(6)\qquad \frac{\Gamma(2N)}{p_1q_1\,\Gamma(2Np_1)\,\Gamma(2Np_1)}\int_0^1 (q+\Delta q)^{2Nq_1}(p-\Delta q)^{2Np_1}\,\varphi(q)\,dq = (1-K)\;\varphi(q_1)\;.$$

It may readily be seen that if $\Delta q = 0$ and it is assumed that $\varphi(q) = 1$, the left hand member becomes $\frac{2N}{2N+1}$ which agrees with the right hand member if $\varphi(q_1) = 1$, $K = \frac{1}{2N+1}$. This is very close to the value $1/(2N)$ known for independent reasons, to be correct (for completely random union of gametes from N monoecious individuals). The correct value for random union of gametes if there are $N/2$ males, $N/2$ females, or if there are N monoecious individuals with self fertilization excluded, is closer to $1/(2N+1)$. The form $\varphi(q) = 1$ is thus indicated to be very nearly correct though there is still a slight discrepancy with the result from Fisher's formula, which gives $1/(2N)$ exactly. This case is illustrated in figure 1.

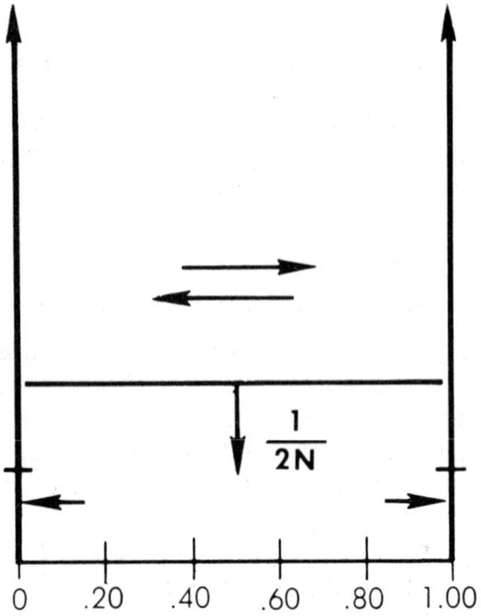

Figure 1

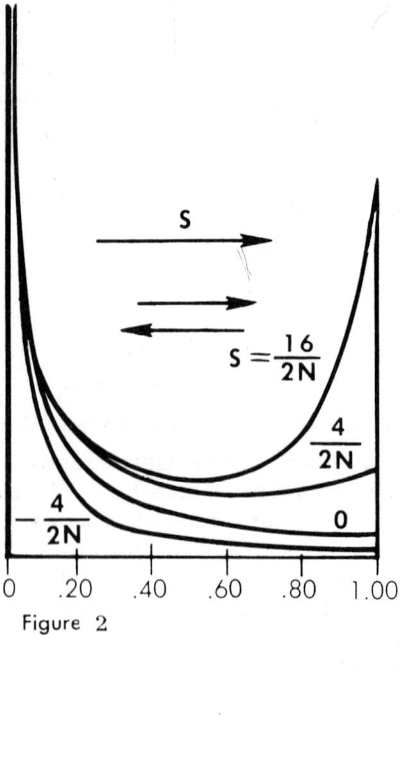

Figure 2

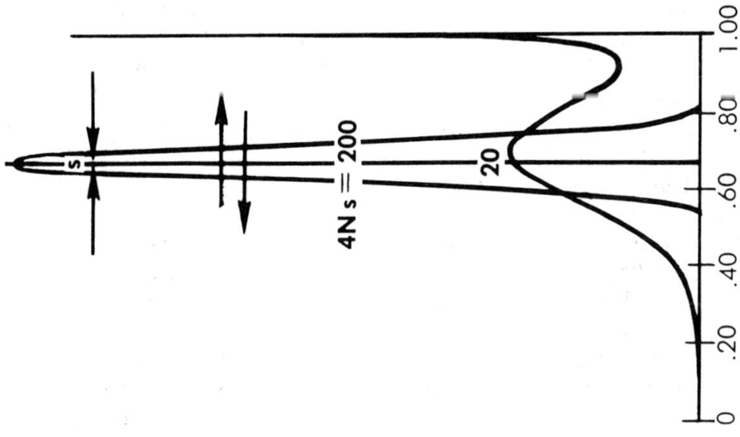

Figure 3

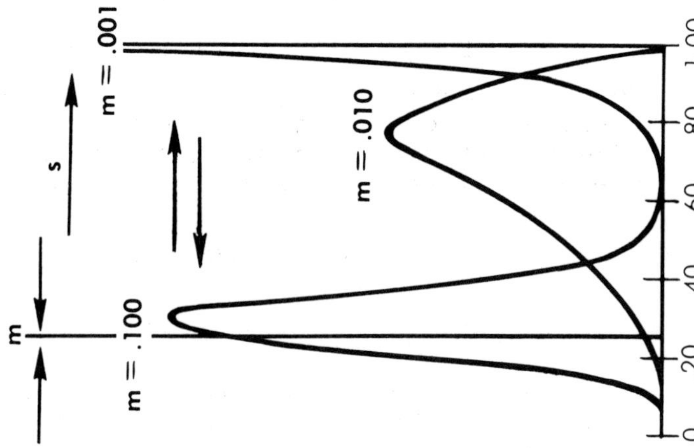

Figure 4

The necessity of considering the situation at the boundaries may be illustrated by certain simple cases. Let Δq be negligibly small except that irreversible fixation $(q = 1)$ or loss $(q = 0)$, is prevented by very small rates of mutation $(\Delta q = v(1-q) - uq)$ in both directions. It may easily be checked that if $\Delta q = 0$, $\varphi(q) = \frac{C_1}{q} + \frac{C_2}{1-q}$ is a solution for all values of C_1 and C_2. Roughly half of the frequency of the subterminal classes $(q = 1/2N,\ q = 1-(1/2N))$ must be lost or fixed respectively in each generation (Poisson distribution) In a steady state these processes must be balanced by mutation from the terminal classes, giving

$$(1/2)\, f(1/2N) = 2Nv\, f(0)$$

(7)

$$(1/2)\, f[(1-(1/2N)] = 2Nu\, f(1)$$

Under the assumption that mutation pressures are negligibly small except for these terminal exchanges, nearly all populations accumulate in the terminal classes with frequencies $f(0) \approx 1-\hat{q} = u/(u+v)$ and $f(1) \approx \hat{q} = v/(u+v)$. The turnover at both boundaries must be the same (approximately $2Nuv/(u+v)$. The steady state solution is thus that in which $C_1 = C_2$, $\varphi(q) = q(1-q)/2[\log 2N + .577]$ excluding the terminal classes.

The solution $\varphi(q) = 4Nv/q$ applies approximately to the case of irreversible mutation from a to A at a negligibly small rate v per generation (excluding the terminal classes). This is not strictly a steady state since there is a slow accumulation of the class at $q = 1$ but the rate v at which the distribution decays is assumed to be extremely small. Similarly $\varphi(q) = 4Nu/(1-q)$ applies approximately to the case with irreversible mutation from A to a at the negligibly small rate u per generation.

It is not surprising that exact algebraic solution for discrete classes in simple cases $(N = 2, 3)$ show some deviation from the estimates from the continuous distributions (Wright 1931, correction in Evolution 9: 105). Fisher (1930) made a general analysis of the deviations near the boundaries in the cases of pure inbreeding and the steady state with $\Delta q = 0$.

I will not go further into details but merely note that by using approximation formulae that permit integration where finite values of Δq are assumed, and expanding $\varphi(q)$ into series, integrating each term and equating with the terms of $\varphi(q_1)$ with the same powers of q and $(1-q)$ it was possible to obtain approximate solution for various cases. The following gives the solution for a fairly general steady state.

$$\Delta q = [v(1-q) - uq] - m[q-Q] + (s+tq)\, q(1-q)$$

(8) $$q^2_{\Delta q} = \frac{1}{2N}\, q(1-q)$$

$$\varphi(q) = Ce^{4Nsq + 2Ntq^2}\, q^{4N(mQ+v)-1}\, p^{4N[mP+u]-1}$$

in which C is a constant such $\int_0^1 \varphi(q)\, dq = 1$. Its value can be estimated by calculating $\varphi(q)$ at suitable intervals over the whole range from 0 to 1 .

Figure 3 shows the steady state distribution for frequencies of a heterotic gene with two values of 4Ns viz. 20 and 200,

$$\Delta q = q(1-q)\,(3q-2), \quad \hat{q} = 2/3$$

(9) $$\sigma^2_{\Delta q} = (1/2N)\, q\,(1-q)$$

$$\varphi(q) = Ce^{2Nsq\,(4-3q)}\, q^{-1}(1-q)^{-1}$$

With 4Ns = 200, there is practically a steady state in the absence of mutation. With 4Ns = 20 there would be fixation at $q = 1$ unless this is prevented by mutation. As most of the populations would have $q = 1$ the ordinates are much exaggerated in this case.

Figure 4 shows the steady state distribution maintained by balance between local selection and immigration with three rates of the latter viz.= .001, .01 and .1 . The values 4Ns = 10 and Q = .25 are assumed.

$$\Delta q = sq\,(1-q) - m\,(q-Q)$$

(10) $$\sigma^2_{\Delta q} = (1/2N)\, q\,(1-q)$$

$$\varphi(q) = Ce^{4Nsq}\, q^{4Nm\,Q-1}\,(1-q)^{4Nm\,(1-Q)-1}.$$

With irreversible mutation and 4Nv not negligible.

(11) $$\varphi(q) = 4Nv\, q^{4Nv-1} \quad \text{(excluding the fixed class)}.$$

The case of steady flux under selection with no dominance and irreversible mutation at a negligible rate is illustrated in figure 2 with four values of 2Ns, viz. 4, 0, 4 and 16

$$\Delta q = sq(1-q)$$

(12) $$\sigma^2_{\Delta q} = (1/2N)\, q(1-q)$$

$$\varphi(q) = \frac{4Nv}{q(1-q)} \frac{1-e^{-4Ns(1-q)}}{1-e^{-4Ns}}$$

This agrees with Fisher (1930) on transformation of his result. The chance of fixation of such a mutation is given by the ratio of the subterminal classes $2s/(1-e^{-4Ns})$ which reduces practically to $2s$ unless $4Ns$ is very small in agreement with Haldane (1927).

The case of selection pressure as above but a finite rate of decay was worked out for comparison with experimental data with good agreement (Wright and Kerr 1954). The rather complicated formulae have been confirmed by Kimura (1957) by another method.

The case of steady flux under selection with any degree of dominance ($\Delta q = (s+tq)\, q(1-q)$ and irreversible mutation at a negligible rate gave the most complicated result obtained by this method. Empirical determination of the rates of fixation of favorable recessives ($s = 0$) at values of t ranging from $4/2N$ to $64/2N$ gave an average of $1.1\sqrt{t/2N}$ which agreed in order of magnitude with a rough estimate obtained by Haldane (1927) $\sqrt{t/N}$ by a wholly different method. Kimura (1957, 62) has since obtained $\sqrt{2t/\pi N}$ or $1.128\sqrt{t/2N}$ by a very elegant method. This result can be confirmed by a formula that I derived in 1945 from the Fokker-Planck equation, but did not apply to this case at that time.

Steady state with respect to all moments

The formula was later obtained for the steady state by identifying the mean and variance before and after the occurrence of any systematic change (Δq) and any random change (δq) (Wright 1937, 38b, 48). The mode of demonstration was later extended to include identity of all moments (Wright 1952). The basic equation is as follows:

(13) $$\sum_{q=0}^{1} \sum_{\delta q=-q}^{1-q} \left\{ [(q-\bar{q}) + (\Delta q + \delta q)]^n f(\delta q)\, f(q) \right\} = \sum_{q=0}^{1} (q-\bar{q})^n f(q) \quad .$$

On expanding the left hand member in powers of $(q-\bar{q})$ and $(\Delta q + \delta q)$, the first term cancels the right hand member. The following hold for random deviations. $\sum \delta q\, f(\delta q) = 0$, $\sum (\delta q)^2 f(\delta q) = \sigma^2_{\delta q} = \sigma^2_{\Delta q}$, $\sum\sum [\delta q (q-\bar{q})\, f(\delta q)\, f(q)] = 0$, $\sum\sum [\delta q\, \Delta q\, f(\delta q)\, f(q)] = 0$.

Unless $\sigma^2_{\Delta q}$ is of the order of Δq or greater, the latter dominates so much that the distribution is practically restricted to the equilibrium value $\hat{q}$. The case of interest is that in which terms in $(\Delta q)^2$, $(\delta q)^3$, $\Delta q(\delta q)^2$ and higher powers may be treated as negligible. With these assumptions, (1) reduces to the following:

$$(14) \qquad \sum_{q=0}^{1} (q-\bar{q})^{n-1} \Delta q \, f(q) + \frac{(n-1)}{2} \sum_{q=0}^{1} [(q-\bar{q})^{n-2} \sigma^2_{\Delta q} f(q)] = 0 \; .$$

It is convenient to substitute integration for summation, $\varphi(q)\,dq$ for $f(q)$ and represent $\Delta q\, \varphi(q)\, dq$ by $d\chi(q)$

$$(15) \qquad \int_0^1 (q-\bar{q})^{n-1} d\chi(q) + \frac{n-1}{2} \int_0^1 (q-\bar{q})^{n-2} \sigma^2_{\Delta q} \varphi(q)\, dq = 0 \; .$$

On integrating the first term by parts it becomes

$$(16) \qquad [\chi(q)(q-\bar{q})^{n-1}]_0^1 - (n-1) \int_0^1 \chi(q)\,(q-\bar{q})^{n-2} dq \; .$$

$$(17) \qquad \text{If } n = 1, \; [\chi(q)]_0^1 = 0, \quad \text{thus } \chi(1) = \chi(0)$$

$$(18) \qquad \begin{aligned} [\chi(q)(q-\bar{q})^{n-1}]_0^1 &= \chi(1)\, [(1-\bar{q})^{n-1} - (-\bar{q})^{n-1}] \\ &= (n-1)\, \chi(1) \int_0^1 (q-\bar{q})^{n-2} dq \; . \end{aligned}$$

Equation (15) now becomes

$$(19) \qquad \int_0^1 (q-\bar{q})^{n-2} [\chi(1) - \chi(q) + (1/2)\, \sigma^2_{\Delta q} \varphi(q)]\, dq = 0 \; .$$

Thus <u>all</u> moments are the same before and after occurrence of Δq and δq if the following holds

$$(20) \qquad \chi(q) - \chi(1) = (1/2)\,\sigma^2_{\Delta q} \varphi(q)$$

$$(21) \qquad \frac{d}{dq} \log [\chi(q) - \chi(1)] = [\frac{d}{dq} \chi(q)] / [\chi(q) - \chi(1)] = 2\Delta q/\sigma^2_{\Delta q}$$

$$(22) \qquad \log [\chi(q) - \chi(1)] = \log(C/2) + 2 \int (\Delta q/\sigma^2_{\Delta q})\, dq$$

(23) $$\chi(q) - \chi(1) = (C/2) \exp\left[2\int(\Delta q/\sigma^2_{\Delta q})\,dq\right]$$

Equating the two expressions for $\chi(q) - \chi(1)$ from (20) and (23)

(24) $$\varphi(q) = (C/\sigma^2_{\Delta q}) \exp\left[2\int(\Delta q/\sigma^2_{\Delta q})\,dq\right].$$

This is the desired formula. All of the steady state solutions, obtained by the first method can be obtained more simply from this and it is possible to deal with random drift due to fluctuations in the coefficients of the directed processes (Wright 1948) while the first method was restricted to the binomial fluctuations.

If $\delta q = (s-\bar{s})\,q(1-q)$; $\sigma^2_{\Delta q} = \sigma^2_s\, q^2 (1-q)^2$

(25) $$\varphi(q) = \frac{C}{q^2(1-q)^2}\left(\frac{q}{1-q}\right)^{(2/\sigma^2_s)[\bar{s}-m(1-2Q)]} \exp\left[(-2m/\sigma^2_s)\left(\frac{Q}{q}+\frac{1-Q}{1-q}\right)\right]$$

If $\delta q = -(m-\bar{m})(q-Q)$; $\sigma^2_{\Delta q} = \sigma^2_m (q-Q)^2$

(26) $$\varphi(q) = C(q-Q)^{(2/\sigma^2_m)[s(1-2Q) - \bar{m} - \sigma^2_m]} \exp\left\{[(-2s/\sigma^2_m(q-Q)]\,[(q-Q)^2 + Q(1-Q)]\right\}$$

If $\delta q = m[Q-\bar{Q}]$; $\sigma^2_{\Delta q} = m^2\sigma^2_Q$

(27) $$\varphi(q) = C \exp\left\{[6m\bar{Q}\,q - 3q^2(m-s) - 2sq^3]/3m^2\sigma^2_Q\right\}.$$

Figures 5 to 7 compare distributions in which the same local selection pressure ($s = .01$) is in all cases balanced by the same amount and kind of immigration ($m = .01$, $Q = .25$), $\Delta q = .0025 - .01q^2$, but with different kinds of fluctuations of gene frequency. The case of sampling fluctuations are given in figure 5, $\sigma^2_{\Delta q} = (1/2N)\,q(1-q)$, $N = 10, 100$ or 1000), of fluctuations in s in figure 6, $\sigma^2_{\Delta q} = \sigma^2_s\, q^2(1-q)^2$, $\sigma_s = .05, .10$ or $.20$), of fluctuations in m or

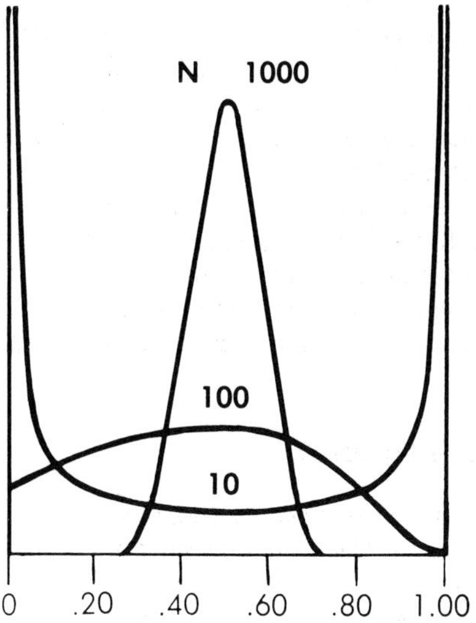

Figure 5

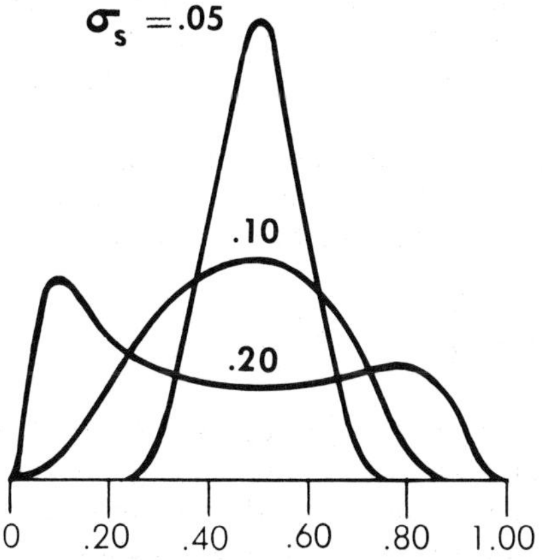

Figure 6

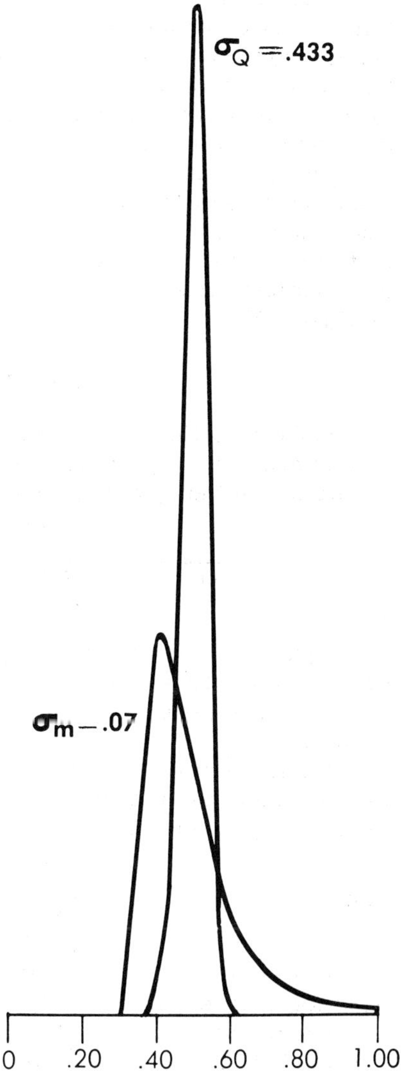

Figure 7

Q in figure 7, $\sigma^2_{\Delta q} = \sigma^2_m (q-.25)^2$, $\sigma_m = .07$ (practically maximum), $\sigma^2_{\Delta q} = .0001\,\sigma^2_Q$, $\sigma_Q = .433$ (maximum).

Both fluctuations due to sampling and ones due to selection can bring about extensive random drift, but while the former can in extreme cases bring about fixation or loss, the latter gives bimodal distribution which theoretically never lead to fixation or loss (cf. Kimura 1954). Fluctuation in amount or especially in quality of immigration can bring about relatively little random drift.

One of the most complicated cases dealt with by this method has been that of self incompatibility alleles (Wright 1939a). The results were questioned by Fisher (1958) who applied his method of 1930. In spite of differences in treatment at every step, it could be shown that all important differences disappeared on correcting errors in his paper (Wright 1960).

Fokker-Planck equation

Fisher's diffusion equation is a special case of the Fokker-Planck equation of physics also known as the Kolmogorov forward equation. In the symbolism used here:

$$\frac{\partial\varphi(q,t)}{\partial t} = \frac{1}{2}\frac{\partial^2}{\partial q^2}\left[\sigma^2_{\Delta q}\,\varphi(q,t)\right] - \frac{\partial}{\partial q}\left[\Delta q\,\varphi(q,t)\right] \tag{28}$$

Kolmogorov (1935) applied this formula in population genetics to the special case $\Delta q = -m(q-Q)$, $\sigma^2_{\Delta q} = (1/2N)\,q(1-q)$ and obtained, as he noted, the same result that I had obtained in 1931 by the integral equation.

I discussed its use in population genetics more generally in 1945. In the case of the steady state (which is the one that is important in the shifting balance theory) the equation reduces to the following:

$$(1/2)\frac{d}{dq}\left[(\sigma^2_{\Delta q}\,\varphi(q)\right] - \Delta q\,\varphi(q) = 0 \;. \tag{29}$$

It may be noted that since $\Delta q\,\varphi(q)$ is the proportion of the distribution that tends to be carried past a specified value of q by the systematic pressure Δq, the other term represents the net proportion that tends to be carried in the opposite direction by random fluctuations, in each generation. The solution is the same as that given by assuming that all moments remain unchanged by systematic and random changes. Equation 28 can readily be derived from these considerations as well as directly.

The case of (almost) steady flux must differ from (8) by a constant term (D), the net proportion of the total (excluding the recipient class q = 1 (or q = 0)) that is carried past each value of q in each generation

$$(30) \quad (1/2)\frac{d}{dq}\left[\sigma^2_{\Delta q}\ \varphi(q)\right] - \Delta q\ \varphi(q) + D = 0$$

$$(31) \quad \varphi(q) = \left\{\exp\left[2\int \Delta q/\sigma^2_{\Delta q}\, dq\right]/\sigma^2_{\Delta q}\right\}\left\{C - 2D\int \exp\left[-2\int(\Delta q\ \sigma^2_{\Delta q})\, dq\right] dq\right\}$$

All of the results obtained for cases of steady flux by the integral equation may be verified by use of this equation.

In cases of constancy of form with decay at a constant rate $\left(K = \frac{1}{-\varphi(q,t)}\frac{\partial\varphi}{\partial t}(q,t)\right)$ the equation reduces to:

$$(32) \quad (1/2)\frac{d^2}{dq^2}\left[\sigma^2_{\Delta q}\ \varphi(q)\right] - \frac{d}{dq}(\Delta q\ \varphi(q)) + k\ \varphi(q) = 0 \ .$$

All of the results obtained for such cases by the integral equation have been verified by use of this equation.

The application of the general formula to the changing forms of successive generations on starting from a single gene frequency is a much more complicated problem. Solutions in several important cases have been presented by Kimura (1954, 55, 56a, 57).

Multigenic distributions of gene frequencies

In accordance with my emphasis on gene interaction, I have looked upon probability distributions for single genes as merely cross-sections of multigenic distributions that involve all of the genes of the interaction system. It is not to be expected that actual steady states of single gene frequencies will be realized in nature. There will be continual shifting. The changes are not the orderly ones represented by the sequence of distributions from a single-gene frequency toward a steady state. Thus the steady-state formulae are to be looked upon as merely presenting in condensed form the current potentialities. Only single-gene distribution were indeed dealt with mathematically in the 1931 paper but these were merely considered to be indications of the sort of thing that is happening in the many dimensions to which the verbal discussion was devoted.

In a later paper (1935a) a formula was given for Δq in cases of multifactorial heredity and an intermediate optimum. This was taken up more generally in 1937 with introduction of the symbol W for selective value of the genotype as a whole, treated in that paper as constant. It was assumed that the local population in question was breeding at random and that it was sufficiently accurate to assume that all loci were combined at random. As brought out later (1952a) this should suffice if deviations from additive effects in selective values for pairs of alleles are of lower order than their recombination rates. Thus the formula is only applicable to small selective differentials. (cf. Kimura 1956b, Lewontin and Kojima 1960). The key formula was as follows:

$$\Delta q = q(1-q) \frac{\partial \overline{W}}{\partial q} / 2\overline{W} \tag{33}$$

in which $\overline{W}$ is the mean selective value ($\overline{W} = \sum Wf$, f being the theoretical genotypical frequency under random association of loci). It was shown (1935a) that in the case of selective value proportional to squared deviation from an optimum (0) and no dominance on the underlying quantitative scale, $\overline{W} = 1-K[2\sum \alpha_i^2 q_i(1-q_i) + (M-0)^2]$ where α_i is a gene effect and $M(=2\sum \alpha_i q_i)$ is the mean on the underlying scale. Thus $\Delta q_i = -Kq_i(1-q_i)[\alpha_i^2(1-2q_i) + 2\alpha_i(M-0)]/2\overline{W}$ is the selective component of change of gene frequency.

The surface, $\overline{W}$, is in this case a very complicated one with multiple selective peaks. For balance between selection and mutation, $\Delta q = [q(1-q)\frac{\partial W}{\partial q}/2\overline{W}] + v(1-q) - uq$. (Wright 1937).

$$\varphi(q_1, q_2 ---) = C\,\overline{W}^{2N}\,\Pi q^{4Nv-1}(1-q)^{4Nu-1} . \tag{34}$$

More important is the case of balance between local selection and immigration in which as brought out later (Wright 1949), the q's may relate to all alleles at all loci.

$$\varphi(q_1, q_2 ---)\ C\,\overline{W}^{2N}\,\Pi q^{4NmQ-1} . \tag{35}$$

Such distributions reflect in exaggerated form the multiple peaks of the "surface" of selection values, $\overline{W}$.

This theory was criticized by Fisher (1941) on the grounds (1) "Apart from technical difficulties of interpretation Wright's formula for natural selection $\Delta p = \frac{pq}{2\overline{W}} \frac{d\overline{W}}{dp}$ seems intended merely to assert the equality of these two quantities for any factor influencing survival" (the two being "average excess" and "average effect") (2) that it is inaccurate to use the finite difference Δp in the same formula as the differential coefficient $\frac{d\overline{W}}{dp}$ and (3) that "Professor Wright here confuses the number of genotypes e. g. 3^{1000} which may be distinguished among individuals with the continuous field of variation of gene frequencies".

I was puzzled as to how Fisher could have supposed that my purpose was to assert the identity of average excess and average effect. As I understood it, Fisher introduced these terms in trying to arrive at a theorem on the rate of increase of "<u>fitness</u>" under natural selection that applies to a species as a whole. My purpose was to obtain a formula for change of <u>gene frequency</u> in a random breeding deme in cases that involve factor interaction and it did not seem necessary to refer to average excess and average effect. The relation to Fisher's theorem was, however, touched on. (Wright 1935b).

With respect to his second criticism it should be noted that Δq is a discrete change in <u>time</u> (one generation) while $\frac{\partial \overline{W}}{\partial q}$ relates merely to the momentary geometry of the field of gene frequencies before this change occurs. The formula for a single factor (that cited by Fisher) is exact, as is the extension later made to multiple alleles (1942, 1949) which requires that frequency (q_i) of an allele other than that (q_x) of the one in question be written $q_i = R_{ix}(1-q_x)$ so that $\frac{\partial q_i}{\partial q_x} = -R_{ix} = -q_i/(1-q_x)$.

With respect to the third criticism I could only have been dealing with the continuous field of gene frequencies ($\overline{W} = \sum Wf$) in obtaining the partial differential coefficient. The summation in the formula for $\overline{W}$ has, however, as many terms as there are kinds of genotypes, 3^{1000} for 1000 pairs of alleles. This, of course, points to a practical difficulty in calculating Δq for more than two or three pairs of interacting factors, unless a regular model is postulated. There was no confusion.

Moran (1962), in contrast with Fisher, states that the formula, which he writes $\Delta P_n = \frac{p_n q_n}{2\overline{W}} \frac{d\overline{W}_n}{dp_n}$, is an important one, but gives no reference. He cites it immediately after a formula for Δp_n as $(p_{n+1} - p_n)$ in which selective values of genotypes had been explicity treated as variable. The correct formula on this assumption is (in my terminology, Wright 1942, 49). $\Delta q = q(1-q)\sum(W\frac{df}{dq})/2\overline{W}$ to which we will return.

Moran goes into detail with respect to the application to multiple alleles (again no reference) but does not give the approximate formula for the case with multiple loci which was the all-important one in my view of evolution.

It is not practicable here to go into various developments from these formula by Li, (1955), Kojima (1959a, b), Mullholland and Smith (1959), Lewontin and Kojima (1960) and others.

Effective values

The most serious criticism of the shifting balance theory has been that local populations are rarely sufficiently small and isolated to permit significant random drift and intrademic selection. It is not, however, necessary that conditions be favorable in all parts of all species all of the time. The theory requires merely that there be a considerable number of demes in which values of s for many interacting genes with slight effects and that of m do not differ from $1/(2N)$ by more than about an order of magnitude.

It may be noted that even selective differention among localities is negligible if s is less than m by an order of magnitude, yet such differences are very common even where s is known to be very small, indicating that m also is often rather small.

I was not unaware in 1931 of this difficulty for the theory. The concept of "effective values" was developed. Effective m would ordinarily be much less than its apparent value (m_0) because immigrants to a particular deme ordinarily came from surrounding ones that differ much less in average gene frequency (Q_0) than does the species as a whole (Q), $m = m_0(q-Q_0)/(q-Q)$.

Effective N would often be less than the apparent number (N_0) for several reasons beside the obvious one that it refers only to mature individuals. Three reasons were listed in 1931 and evaluated in 1938 and 1939. First is a sex ratio effect. With N_m males and N_f females, $N = 4N_mN_f/(N_m + N_f)$ which approaches $4N_m$ if the number of mature females is much greater than that of males.

Second is the variable productivity effect. In a static population (mean number of offspring per pair, $\bar{K} = 2$), N is approximately $4N_0/(2+\sigma_k^2)$ in which σ_k^2 is the variance of the number of offspring per pair that reach maturity. With random (Poisson) variability, $\sigma_k^2 = \bar{k} = 2$ and $N = N_0$ but if most of the mature offspring came from relatively few matings, N may be much less than N_0. Most frequently of importance, however, is the bottleneck effect. If the numbers vary greatly during periods that are too short for selection to be effective, effective N is their harmonic mean which may be much less than the arithmetic mean. Thus if the numbers N_1, $10N_1$, 10^2N_1, 10^3N_1, 10^4N_1, and 10^5N_1, are equally frequent, the arithmetic mean is about $18{,}500N_1$ but effective N is only $5.4N_1$. The most favorable condition for a large amount of sampling drift was described (Wright 1938, '39, '40) as that in which there are many localities in each of which the resident deme is likely to become extinct, to be replaced by a colony founded by a few stray individuals from some other locality. Under such conditions, effective N is exceedingly small. It may readily happen that a large portion of the species may trace its ancestry through a long succession of such bottlenecks.

A mathematical objection to the formulae is that N is treated as a constant although selective value itself (W), defined so that $\bar{W}$ is the ratio of N in successive generation implies that N changes. It would no doubt be an improvement if N were defined as $\bar{W}N'$ where N' is population number of the preceding generation but in this case there would be no steady state distribution. From the biological standpoint, only rough approximation is possible in any case. From this standpoint it appears adequate to take the steady state formulae derived from constant Δq and $\sigma^2_{\Delta q}$ as representing the momentary potentialities for variation of demes.

A simple illustration of the theory

Figure 8 gives a simple example of the theory. Four equivalent factors are assumed to act additively without dominance on a quantitatively varying character but selective value is assumed to fall off with the square of the deviation from the mean $(0=M)$. It is next assumed (figure 9) that there are small additive pleiotropic effects on selective value at two of the loci. Values are chosen so that there are six selective peaks at three levels, a lowest, four intermediate, and a highest. Figure 10 shows two faces of the four-dimensional field of mean selective values involving the lowest selective peak, one of the four intermediate ones and the highest. The arrows show the trajectories of possible populations. As constructed, the population would tend to become fixed at any of the selective peaks but it must be supposed that this is prevented by recurrent mutation at low rates. Figure 11 shows the values of $\bar{W}$ along the course of a population starting near the lowest selective peak. It can only reach a higher selective peak by random processes, whether consisting of accidents of sampling or fluctuations in selection. It is to be noted that the amount of decrease in $\bar{W}$ occurring under random drift need be only a very small fraction of the subsequent increase under strong deterministic selection pressure, once the population has crossed a shallow saddle by random drift. The population is much more likely to cross two of the two-dimensional saddles in succession, in passing from the lowest to the highest peak, than to pass over the four dimensional saddle indicated by the dotted line.

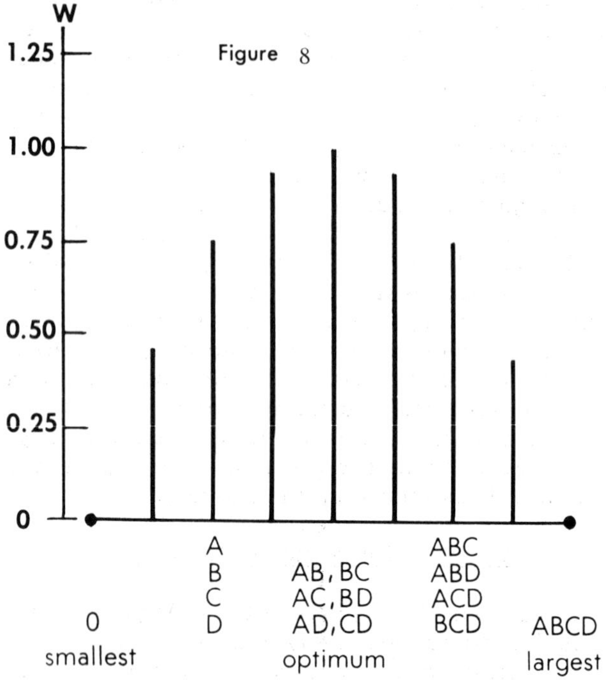

Figure 8

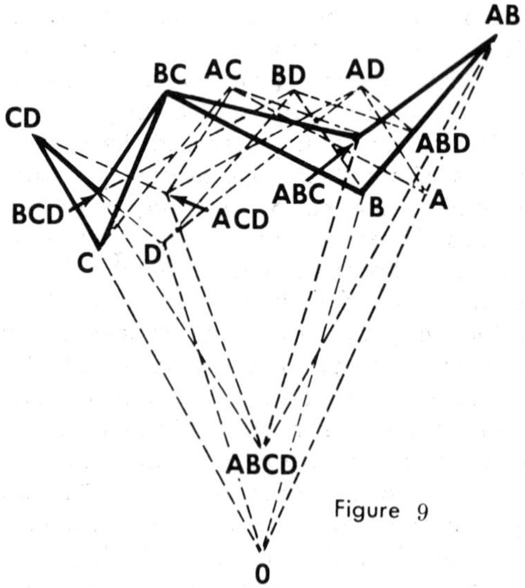

Figure 9

Figure 10

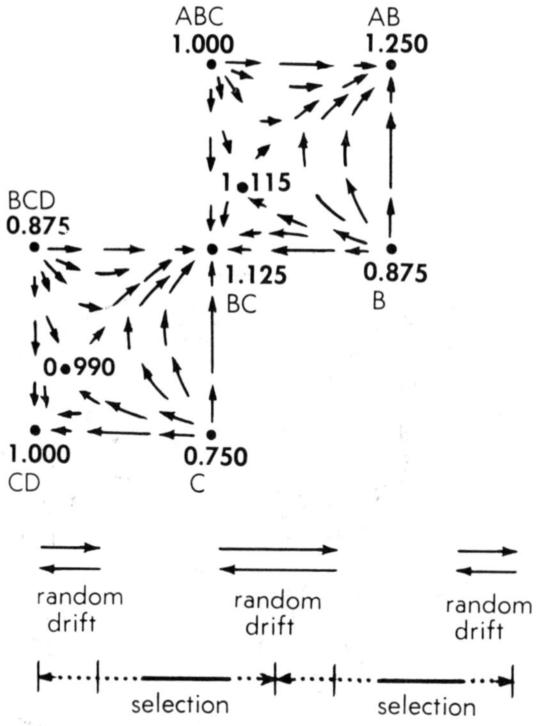

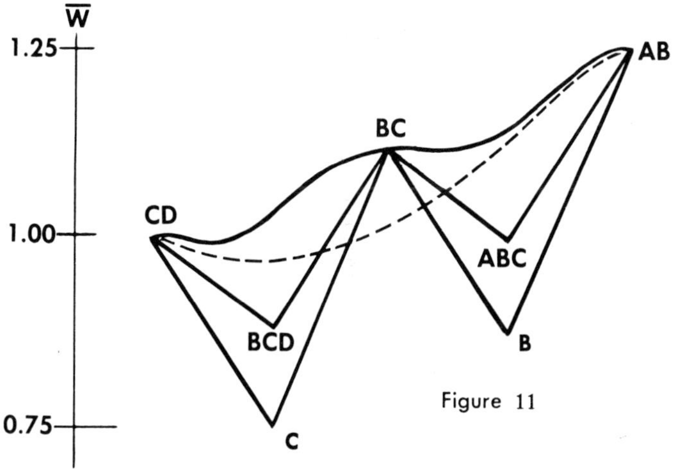

Figure 11

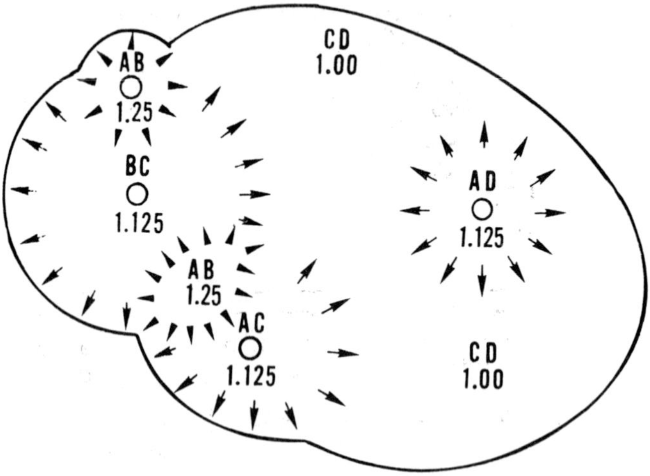

Figure 12

Figure 12 is intended to illustrate an intermediate stage in the process of interdemic selection. Random drift among demes has caused local fluctuation ($\overline{W}$ between .99 and 1.00) in the main body of the species (CD). In three of the demes, however, the saddle leading to a higher selective peak has been passed, intrademic selection has carried $\overline{W}$ to 1.125 in each of these and interdemic selection has brought about spreading, most from the earliest of them (BC), less for AC and least from AD. The area in which BC and AC are characteristic have come to overlap, giving the basis for establishment of the highest selective peak, AB($\overline{W}$ = 1.25) by mass selection. Another population in which the genetic composition is controlled by this highest peak has arisen from a deme within the area characterized by BC that has crossed the threshold to AB. With an indefinitely large number of peaks, the process could go on indefinitely.

The establishment of this "area pattern" (a term coined by Cain and Currey (1963)) has not depended on any environmental differentiation among areas whatever. Yet it is due wholly to selection except for trigger action of random drift in a few of perhaps thousands of demes in each of which there may have been only negligible fluctuations in the sets of gene frequencies for many generations before a saddle was passed and intrademic selection, followed by interdemic selection gave the opportunity to bring about rapid progress.

It should be added that such large selective differences have been assumed in these figures for the purpose of illustration that random drift would be successful only with extremely small effective m and N in bringing about the crossing of a saddle. There would be relatively frequent differentiation of demes in the case of systems in which all selective differences are smaller by one or two orders of magnitude.

It is theoretically possible for very extensive area effects to be brought about without the help of any sort of selection. In a species with a distribution that is as completely continuous as possible over an indefinitely large area but with such limited dispersion that the effective population of "neighborhoods" (areas within which parents may be treated as if drawn at random) is very small, there tends to build up, not only wide differentiation of neighborhoods themselves, but also of larger areas up to a point at which this is prevented by recurrent mutation or by long range dispersal. This is especially the case with merely linear continuity (Wright 1940, '43, '46, '51).

As may be seen from figure 11 and 12 the whole process might well appear under superficial observation to be controlled wholly by mass selection, proceeding according to Haldane's theory. Nevertheless, the stochastic phase, random drift within demes is essential. It is something of a paradox, that random drift is a significant evolutionary process only when there is superficially control by selection.

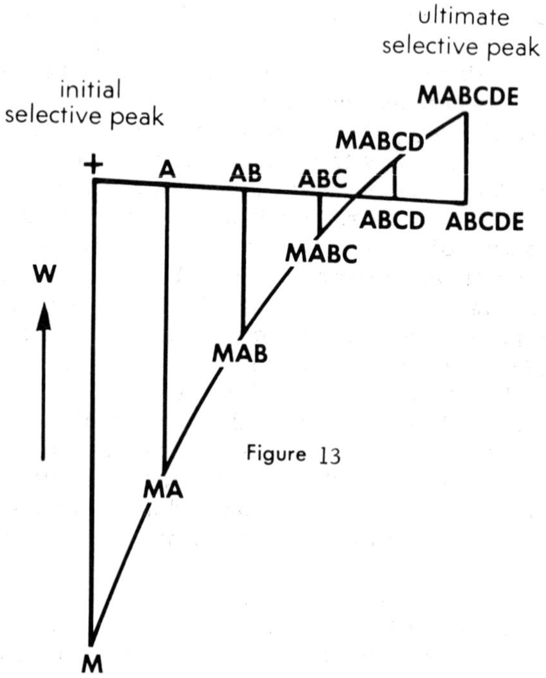
ultimate
selective peak
initial
selective peak
MABCDE
MABCD
+
A
AB
ABC
ABCD
ABCDE
MABC
W
MAB
MA
M

Figure 13

Relatively pure random drift is most conspicuous in laboratory experiments in inbreeding. Distributions of gene frequencies are most easily demonstrated in the case of sharply segregating heterotic pairs of alleles in very small populations (cf. Kerr and Wright 1954a, b, Wright and Kerr 1954, Buri 1956). Random drift is most likely to be conspicuous in nature in the case of heterotic characters but the resulting variation in gene frequencies obviously has little evolutionary significance, unless the locus is associated with others in an interaction system. There is also little evolutionary significance in the case of the degenerative changes that may occur in very small completely isolated natural populations (Wright 1931).

The type of laboratory experiment that simulates most closely the sort of case in which random drift is of evolutionary significance, because coupled with selection, seems to be that in which the amount of differentiation of sub-populations, from a common source, is compared among ones which pass through one or more bottlenecks of small size in contrast with ones that do not (Dobzhansky and Pavlovsky 1956, Dobzhansky and Spassky 1962).

Figure 13 is intended to represent the way in which random drift coupled with both intra- and interdemic selection may lead to the establishment in a species of a major mutation that offers the possibility of a major advance if the usual unfavorable side effects can be overcome by modifiers. There can be no appreciable random drift of the frequency of the major mutation itself because of the postulated strong selection against it, but random drift of the frequencies of nearly neutral modifiers may lead to the establishment in some deme, at some time, of a system of frequencies of these that reverses the selection against the major gene, permitting it and its array of favorable modifiers to become established, first in this deme, but later throughout the species, by differential population growth and dispersion. It is again likely that such a process would be interpreted on superficial observation as involving merely establishment of one of Goldschmidt's fortunate monsters by mass selection even though stochastic processes have actually formed an essential phase.

Variable genotypic selective values

So far it has been assumed that the selective values of total genotypes are constant in a given environment irrespective of their relative frequencies. This is a reasonably satisfactory assumption where there is merely competition in dealing with the environment. It is not a satisfactory assumption if there is selection with respect to social interactions or even with respect to a heterogeneous environment within the range of the deme in question.

In these cases the term $\sum W\frac{\partial f}{\partial q}$ in the approximate formula for selection pressure cannot be written $\frac{\partial \overline{W}}{\partial q}$. It can be written $\left[\frac{\partial \overline{W}}{\partial q} - \left(\overline{\frac{\partial W}{\partial q}}\right)\right]$ which reduces to $\frac{\partial \overline{W}}{\partial q}$ only if all W's are constant, (Wright 1942, '49). It becomes necessary to distinguish the selective peaks, toward which the population tends under selection pressure alone, from the reproductive peaks which are peaks with respect to $\overline{W}$. The actual equilibrium points are, of course, always at deterministic peaks which take account of immigration and mutation pressure as well as selection pressure (Wright 1959).

In certain cases the expression $(\sum W\frac{\partial f}{\partial q})$ can be treated as the gradient, relative to q, of a "surface" of "intrademic selective values" (Wright 1949, '55, '56). In the latter two references, the symbol V_I (or V) was $\int \left[\sum W\frac{\partial f}{\partial q}/\overline{W}\right] dq$. It is probably better to omit $\overline{W}$ in the denominator and define F(W) as $\int \left[\sum W\frac{\partial f}{\partial q}\right] dq$ (where this exists).

With this definition, selection pressure is given by

(36) $$\Delta q = q(1-q)\frac{\partial F(W)}{\partial q}/2\overline{W} .$$

F(W) is, of course, equal to $\overline{W}$ if the genotypic selective values, W, are constant.

F(W) can always be calculated for a single pair of alleles.

If there are multiple alleles or multiple factors, F(W) exists only in special cases, but these are important. It exists, first, if all of the W's are functions of the frequencies (f) of the genotypes to which they pertain. Thus if each W_i is of the type $1+r_i+s_if_i + t_if_i^2$ ---

$$\sum W_i\frac{\partial f_i}{\partial q} = \frac{\partial}{\partial q}\sum\left[f_i + r_if_i + (1/2)\ s_if_i^2 + (1/3)\ t_if_i^3 \text{ ---}\right]$$

(37) $$F(W) = 1 + \bar{r} + (1/2)\sum\left[s_if_i^2\right] + (1/3)\sum\left[t_if_i^3\right] .$$

If in this case, the selective values of genotypes increase with increasing frequency and vice versa, there is a runaway tendency toward fixation of one or another genotype, according to the initial frequencies. This is selection toward conformity as such. If on the other hand (as in figure 17) there is a negative relation between selective value and frequency, there is a tendency toward equilibrium which must be taken into account with other mechanisms of equilibrium

Figure 14

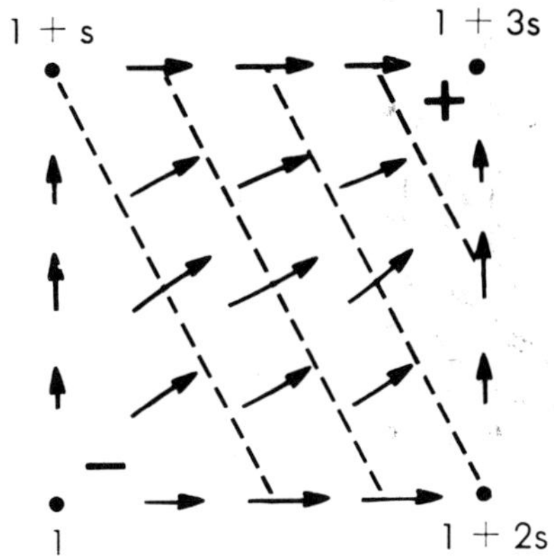

Figure 15

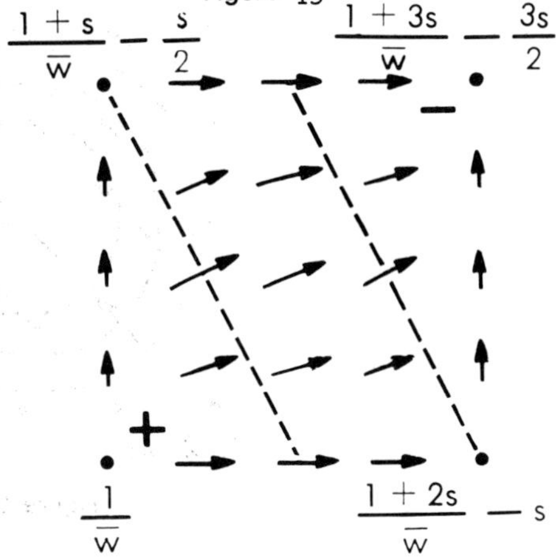

Figure 16

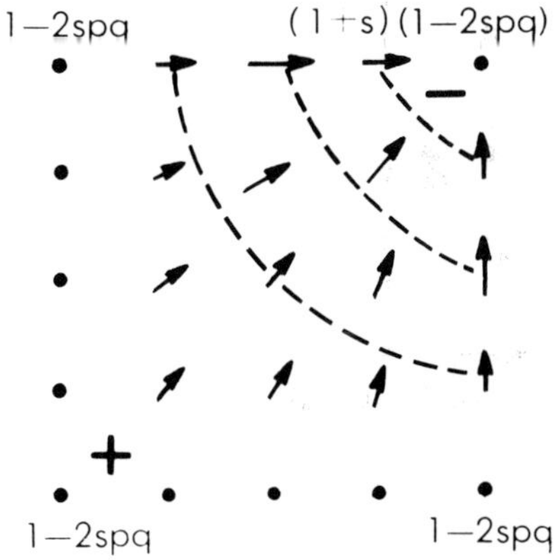

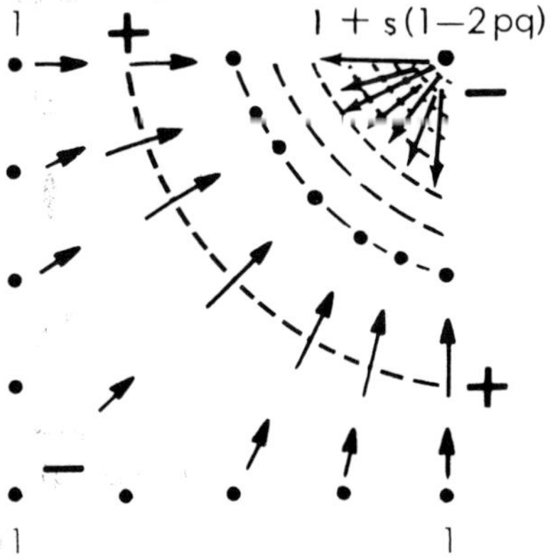

Figure 17

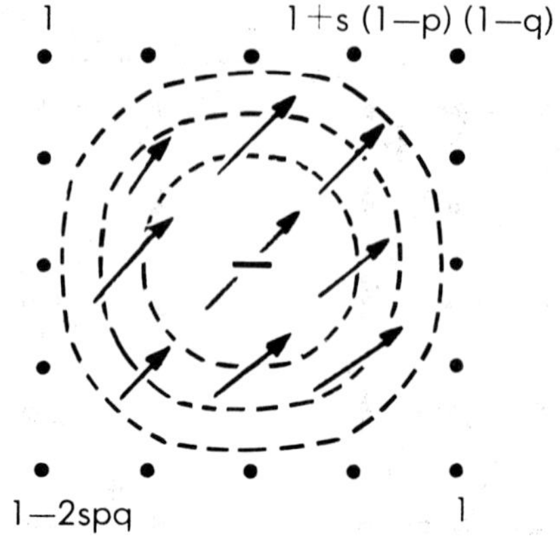

Figure 18

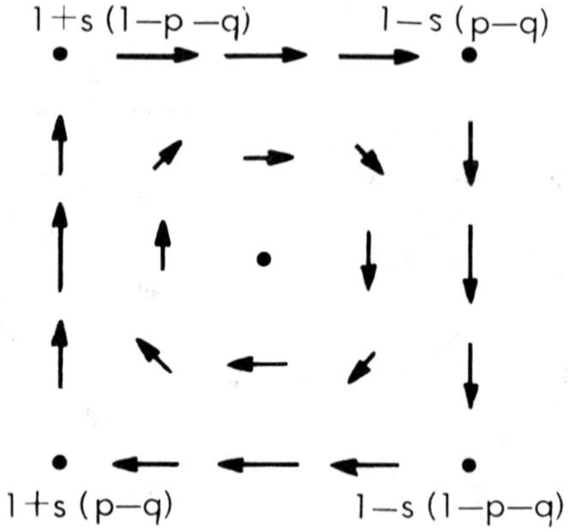

Figure 19

This applies where there is utilization of a heterogeneous environment (Wright 1949), a subject which has been dealt with more explicitly by Levine (1953).

Another important case in which $F(W)$ exists is that in which there is an aspect of selection among genotypes that has no effect on the increase of the population as a whole. Let $W_i = (R_i/\bar{R}) + s_i$ with the R_i's constant. Then $\bar{W} = 1 + \bar{s}$.

(38)
$$\sum W_i \frac{\partial f_i}{\partial q} = \frac{\partial \bar{R}}{\bar{R}\,\partial q} + \frac{\partial \bar{s}}{\partial q} = \frac{\partial[\log \bar{R} + \bar{s}]}{\partial q}$$

$$F(W) = \log \bar{R} + \bar{s}, \quad \Delta q = q(1-q)\frac{\partial F(W)}{\partial q} / 2(1+\bar{s})$$

If the s_i's are all the same, the R's are relative selective values. Selection tends to drive the population to a peak with respect to relative selective value without any change in the absolute selective value, $\bar{W}$, of the population (figure 14 omitting contours). If the s_i's are not the same for all genotypes, the peaks in the two surfaces $F(W)$ and $\bar{W}$ may differ. Individual selection controlled by the former, may bring about continual reduction in $\bar{W}$ and perhaps lead to extinction of the population (figure 15).

The case $W = (R_i/\bar{R}) + s$ with s constant is a special case of that in which the reproductive values all involve the same function ψ of certain genotypic frequencies, but otherwise are independent of the latter. It is convenient here to represent reproductive values as relative to that of some standard genotype, W_{st}, by the symbol $w_i = W_i/W_{st}$. Then $W_i = \psi w_i$, $\bar{W} = \psi \bar{w}$.

(39)
$$\sum W_i \frac{\partial f_i}{\partial q} = \psi \frac{\partial \bar{w}}{\partial q}$$

$$F(W) = \int \left(\psi \frac{\partial \bar{w}}{\partial q}\right) dq$$

(40)
$$\Delta q = q(1-q)\,\psi \frac{\partial \bar{w}}{\partial q} / 2\psi \bar{w} = (1/2)\, q(1-q) \frac{\partial}{\partial q} \log \bar{w}$$

The peak values of $\bar{W}$ are not in general the same as those of $F(W)$ (which are the same as those of $\bar{w}$). Under this head, come cases in which genotypes have effects that are beneficial or injurious to the population as a whole, although they themselves may differ in relative selective values in other respects which are independent of these general effects. Some genotypes may be assets to the population, although tending to extinction themselves because of low relative selective values in competition, while another class of genotypes (social parasites) may increase in relative frequency while forcing the population as a whole toward extinction as in figure 16.

Simple illustrations of cases in which F(W) does not exist can easily be constructed (as in figures 18 and 19) but represent less plausible situations than the preceding cases. On the other hand it is probable that in nature, non-uniform reactions of genotypes to the conditions created by others usually result in more or less departure from the ideal cases in which F(W) exists.

The contributions of local populations to the evolution of the species as a whole depend only in part on their net reproductive rates $(\overline{W}-1)$ since tendency to migrate and specific competitive abilities of the migrants are also involved. Nevertheless $\overline{W}$ is a very important factor in this external sense. The relative fitnesses of genotypes within a deme, in the sense of relative reproductive values (w) may, as noted above, be related negatively to the changes in fitness of the deme in competition with others. If, in a random breeding population, the reproductive value of each genotype is written $W = \sum \alpha + R$ where the α's are the additive contributions from each gene and R is the residual due to dominance and interaction, the relative additive genetic variance, $\sigma_w^2 = \sigma^2 (\sum \alpha/\overline{W})$ is as follows (Wright 1956, Crow and Kimura 1956 by a different method):

$$\sigma_w^2 = \left[\frac{\partial \overline{W}}{\partial t} - \left(\overline{\frac{\partial W}{\partial t}}\right)\right] \Big/ \overline{W} = \frac{1}{\overline{w}} \frac{\partial F(W)}{\partial t} \quad \text{if } F(W) \text{ exists.}$$

If mating is not at random there is an additional term $(\frac{\partial R}{\partial t})$ in the bracket (Wright 1956) which Kimura (1958) has analyzed into terms for dominance deviations and Kempthorne's components of interaction. In these formulae $\overline{W}$ in the denominator can usually be treated as 1.

This equation agrees with Fisher's fundamental theorem if the absolute selective values of genotypes are constants since under this both kinds of fitness agree $F(W) = \overline{W}$. If the absolute selective values are functions of gene frequencies and F(W) exists, Fisher's theorem applies if "fitness" is defined as F(W). If F(W) as defined does not exist, "rate of increase of fitness" can be defined but not fitness itself. Fisher, indeed, compares fitness to entropy, rate of increase of which is more easily defined than it itself.

An approximate formula for the multigenic probability distribution has been given only for the case in which F(W) exists and random drift is restricted to that due to small numbers $(\sigma_{\Delta q}^2 = q(1-q)/2N)$. Assuming, as before, that there is opposition between the pressures of selection and immigration at each locus, $\overline{\Delta q} = (1/2)\, q(1-q) \frac{\partial F(W)}{\partial t} - m(q-Q)$ the distribution in a deme is as follows where there are q's for every allele at every locus in the interaction system (Wright 1956, '59).

(41) $$\varphi(q_1, q_2 --- q_n) = C\, e^{2NF(W)}\, \Pi q^{4NmQ-1}$$

Conclusions

Five major theories of evolution under Mendelian heredity are referred to here. The theory of evolution as a succession of major mutations is rejected except for certain very special cases, involving polyploidy. A succession of even minor mutations is rejected. Evolution as steady progress under selection of multifactorial variation doubtless occurs but is considered too slow to account for the development of extraordinarily detailed adaptations, largely limited as it is by the extremely low rate of occurrence of novel favorable mutations. Evolution of the treadmill sort, due to continued environmental change may be relatively rapid, but under it, species merely hold their own as each new rough adaptation accompanies the undoing of an old one. The shifting balance theory is the one that is advocated as most important.

The premises of the shifting balance theory are (1) the universality of quantitative variability based on multiple minor factors (2) multiple "selective peaks" in the "surface" of selective values relative to the field of gene frequencies, as a result of factor interaction, especially that due to intermediate optima, and pleiotropy (3) subdivision of species into numerous small, partially isolated demes.

A three-phase evolutionary process is deduced from these premises. (1) A phase of random drift of the sets of gene frequencies within demes (2) a phase of intrademic selection following the occasional passage across a saddle in the surface of selective values in a deme and (3) a phase of interdemic selection in which a high selective peak spreads through the species because of a greater surplus population in the successful deme and excess dispersion from it. The importance of ecologic opportunity in determining the long time rate of evolution is stressed.

The mathematical aspects of the theory are principally these of the first two phases. The directed pressures of recurrent mutation, selection and immigration on the gene frequencies of demes in conjunction with random fluctuations due to accidents of sampling, and fluctuations in the coefficients describing the directed process, determine a stochastic distribution instead of a single equilibrium. Three different methods by which the formulae of such distributions have been obtained, are discussed.

These stochastic distributions for single genes are looked upon as merely cross sections of multigenic distributions that involve all genes of an interaction system. These distributions reflect in exaggerated form the multiple peaks of the "surface" of selective values,

$\overline{W}$. "Random drift" is defined by the portion of the distribution surrounding the currently controlling selective peak. Only very shallow saddles between selective peaks have any appreciable chance of being surmounted by random drift. The possibility of passage across saddles is, however, enhanced by the fact that the effective amount of immigration and effective population size may be much smaller than is apparent.

The complications resulting from dependence of selective value on gene frequencies is discussed. In general the direction taken by selection of individuals within demes and that by selection among demes are different. The latter permits three things that are hardly possible at all under deterministic control of evolution by mass selection (1) the exploitation of the virtually infinite field of recombination effects (2) the acquirement of traits that are adaptive for the species even though selected against among individuals (3) the avoidance of social parasitism.

REFERENCES

1. Buri, P. 1956. Gene frequency in small populations of mutant Drosophila. Evolution 10: 367-402.

2. Cain, A. J. and Currey, J. D. 1963. Area effects in Cepaea. Phil. Trans. Royal Soc. London. Series B 246: 1-81.

3. Crow, J. F. and Kimura, M. 1955. Some genetic problems in natural populations. Proc. 3rd. Berkeley Symp. on Math. Statistics and Probability 14: 1-22. Berkeley, University of California.

4. Dobzhansky, Th. and Pavlovsky, O. 1957. An experimental study of inter-action between genetic drift and natural selection. Evolution 11: 311-319.

5. Dobzhansky, Th. and Spassky 1962. Genetic drift and natural selection in experimental populations of Drosphila pseudoobsura. Proc. Nat. Acad. Sci. 48: 148-156.

6. Fisher, R. A. 1922. On the dominance ratio. Proc. Royal Soc. Edinburgh 42: 321-341.

   1928. The possible modification of the response of the wild type to recurrent mutation. Amer. Nat. 62: 115-126.

   1929. The evolution of dominance; reply to Professor Sewall Wright. Amer. Nat. 63: 553-556.

1930. The genetical theory of natural selection 272 pp. Oxford: Clarendon Press.

1941. Average excess and average effect of a gene substitution. Annals of Eugenics 11: 53-63.

1958. The genetical theory of natural selection. Second revised edition 292 pp. New York: Dover Publications.

7. Goldschmidt, R. 1940. The material basis of evolution. 436 pp. New Haven: Yale University Press.

8. Haldane, J. B. S. 1927. A mathematical theory of natural and artificial selection V. Selection and mutation. Proc. Cambridge Phil. Soc. 23: 838-844.

1932. The causes of evolution. London. Harper and Bros. 235 pp.

9. Kerr, W. E. and S. Wright 1954. Experimental studies of the distribution of gene frequencies in very small populations of Drosophila melanogaster I. Forked, Evolution 8: 172-177. III. Aristapedia and spineless. Evolution 9: 293-302.

10. Kimura, M. 1954. Process leading to quasifixation of genes in natural populations due to random fluctuations of selection intensities. Genetics 39: 281-295.

1955. Solution of a process of random genetic drift with a continuous model. Proc. Nat. Acad. Sci. 41: 144-150.

1956a. Stochastic processes and distribution of gene frequencies under natural selection. Cold Spring Harbor Symp. Quant. Biol. (1955) 20: 33-51.

1956b. A model of a genetic system which leads to closer linkage by natural selection. Evolution 10: 278-287.

1957. Some problem of stochastic processes in genetics. Ann. Math. Stat. 28: 882-890.

1958. On the change of population fitness by natural selection. Heredity 12: 145-167.

1962. On the probability of fixation of mutant genes is a population. Genetics 47: 713-719.

11. Kojima, K. 1959. Role of epistasis and overdominance in stability of equilibrium with selection. Proc. Nat. Acad. Sci. 45: 984-989.

1959. Stable equilibria for the optimum model ibid. 45: 989-993

12. Kolmogorov, A. 1935. Deviations from Hardy's formula in partial isolation. C. R. Acad. Sci. URSS 3: 129-132.

13. Levine, H. 1953. Genetic equilibrium when more than one ecological niche is available. Amer. Nat. 87: 331-333.

14. Lewontin, R. C. and Kojima, K. 1960. The evolutionary dynamics of complex polymorphism. Evolution 14: 458-472.

15. Li, C. C. 1955. The stability of an equilibrium and the average fitness of a population. Amer. Nat. 89: 281-295.

16. Moran, P. A. P. 1962. The statistical processes of evolutionary theory. Oxford: The Clarendon Press 200 pp.

17. Morgan, T. H. 1932. The scientific basis of evolution. New York: W. W. Norton and Company 286 pp.

18. Mulholland, H. P. and Smith, C. A. B. 1959. An inequality arising in genetical theory. Amer. Math. Monthly 66: 673-683.

19. Simpson, G. G. 1945. Tempo and mode in evolution. New York Columbia Univ. Press.

20. Wright, S. 1920. Principles of livestock breeding. Bull. No. 905. U. S. Dept. of Agric. 68 pp.

1922b. The effects of inbreeding and crossbreeding on guinea pigs. III. Crosses between highly inbred families. Bull. No. 1121 U. S. D. A. 59 pp.

1923. Mendelian analysis of the pure breeds of livestock. II. The Duchess family of Shorthorns as bred by Thomas Bates. Jour. Hered. 14: 405-422.

1929a. Fishers theory of dominance. Amer. Nat. 63: 274-279.

1929b. The evolution of dominance. Amer. Nat. 63: 556-601.

1931. Evolution in Mendelian populations. Genetics 16: 97-159.

1932. The roles of mutation, inbreeding, crossbreeding and selection in evolution. Proc. 6th. Int. Congress of Genetics 1: 356-366.

1934. Physiological and evolutionary theories of dominance. Am. Nat. 68: 25-53.

1935a. The analysis of variance and the correlations between relatives with respect to deviations from an optimum. J. Genet. 30: 243-256.

1935b. Evolution in populations in approximate equilibrium, ibid. 257-266.

1937. The distribution of gene frequencies in populations. Proc. Nat. Acad. Sci. 23: 307-320.

1938a. Size of population and breeding structure in relation to evolution. Sci. 87: 430-431.

1938b. The distribution of gene frequencies under irreversible mutation. Proc. Nat. Acad. Sci. 24: 253-259.

1939a. The distribution of self-sterility alleles in populations. Genetics 24: 538-552.

1939b. Statistical genetics in relation to evolution. Actualitès scientifiques at industrialle. 802 Paris, Hermann et. Cie. 63 p.

1940. Breeding structure of populations in relation to speciation. Amer. Nat. 74: 232-248.

1942. Statistical genetics and evolution. Bull. Amer. Math. Soc. 48: 223-246.

1943. Isolation by distance. Genetics 28: 114-138.

1945. The differential equation of the distribution of gene frequencies. Proc. Nat. Acad. Sci. 31: 383-389.

1946. Isolation by distance under diverse systems of mating. Genetics 31: 39-59.

1948. On the roles of directed and random changes in gene frequency in the genetics of populations. Evolution 2: 279-294.

1949. Adaptation and selection. Chap. 20 in Genetics, Paleontology and Evolution. Ed. by G. L. Jepson, G. G. Simpson and E. Mayr. Princeton: Princeton U. Press pp. 365-389.

1951a. The genetical structure of populations. Ann. Eugenics 15: 323-354.

1951b. Fisher and Ford on the Sewall Wright effect. Amer. Scient. 39: 452-458.

1952a. The genetics of quantitative variability. In Quantitative Inheritance. London: Her Majesty's Stationery Office 1: 5-41.

1952b. The theoretical variance within and among subdivisions of a population that is in a steady state. Genetics 27: 312-321.

1956. Classification of the factors of evolution. Cold Spring Harbor Symp. on Quant. Biol. (1955) 20: 16-24D.

1959. Physiological genetics, ecology of populations and natural selection. Perspectives in Biol. and Med. 3: 107-151. (Also Evolution after Darwin, Ed. by Sol Tax I: 429-475 Chicago; Univ. of Chicago Press (1960).

1960a. On the number of self-incompatibility alleles maintained in equilibrium by a given mutation rate in a population of given size: a re-examination. Biometrics 16: 61-85.

21. Wright, S. and Kerr, W. E. 1954. Experimental studies of the distributions of gene frequencies in very small populations of Drosophila melanogaster. II. Bar. Evolution 8: 225-240.

FIGURES

Figure 1 Approximate distribution of gene frequencies under inbreeding and a steady rate of decay (1/2N). $\Delta q = 0$, $\sigma^2_{\Delta q} = q(1-q)/2N$, $f(q) = f(o)\, e^{-t/2N}$.

Figure 2 Distribution of gene frequencies under steady flux from selection without dominance. $\Delta q = sq(1-q)$, $\sigma^2_{\Delta q} = q(1-q)/2N$,

$$f(q) = \frac{2v(1-e^{-4Ns(1-q)})}{q(1-q)(1-e^{-4Ns})} \quad \text{rate of fixation } 2s/(1-e^{-4Ns}),$$

$4Ns = -4, 0, 4, 16.$

Figure 3 Steady state distribution for frequencies of a heterotic gene.

$\Delta q = -3sq(1-q)\ [q-(2/3)],\ \sigma^2_{\Delta q} = q(1-q)/2N,$

$$\varphi(q) = Ce^{2Nsq(4-3q)}/q(1-q)$$

4Ns = 20 (with steady state permitted by some mutation, or 4Ns = 200.

Figure 4 Steady state distribution for gene frequencies maintained by balance between local selection and immigration.
$\Delta q = sq(1-q) - m(q-Q),\ \sigma^2_{\Delta q} = q(1-q)/2N,$

$\varphi(q) = Ce^{4Nsq}\, q^{4NmQ-1}\, (1-q)^{4Nm(1-Q)-1},\ N = 100,\ Q = .25,$

$s = .025,\ m = .1,\ .01$ or $.001$.

Figure 5-7 Steady state distributions for gene frequencies varying about $q = .50$, under balance between local selection and immigration because of four different kinds of random drift, $\Delta q = sq(1-q) - m(q-Q),\ s = .01,\ m = .01,\ Q = .25$.

Figure 5 $\sigma^2_{\Delta q} = q(1-q)/2N,\ N = 10,\ 100,\ 1000$.

Figure 6 $\sigma^2_{\Delta q} = \sigma^2_s q^2 (1-q)^2,\ \sigma_s = .05,\ 10$ or $.20$.

Figure 7a $\sigma^2_{\Delta q} = \sigma^2_m (q-.25)^2,\ \sigma_m = .07$ (practically maximum)

Figure 7b $\sigma^2_{\Delta q} = .0001\sigma^2_Q,\ \sigma_Q = .433$ (maximum)

Figure 8 Selective values (W) according to squared deviations from optimum in case of quantitative variability due to four equivalent additive pairs of alleles, no dominance. Symbols refer to homozygotes. Note existence of six equal selective peaks.

Figure 9 Selective values in same systems as in figure 1 except for additive pleiotropic increments to W, 0625 for each A or B with no dominance. Note existence of selective peaks at three levels. W = 1 for CD, 1.125 for BC, AC, BD, and AD and 1.25 for AB .

Figure 10 Trajectories of gene frequency system under selection on two of the faces of the 4-dimensional system of gene frequencies implied by figure 9. Note shallow saddles at $\overline{W} = .99$ and $\overline{W} = 1.115$

Figure 11 Values of $\overline{W}$ along path of least depression from lowest peak CD, ($\overline{W}$=1) through saddle ($\overline{W}$ = .99) to intermediate peak BC ($\overline{W}$ = 1.125) and thence through saddle ($\overline{W}$ = 1.115) to highest peak AB ($\overline{W}$ = 1.25). The values of $\overline{W}$ along the path through the 4-dimensional saddle ($\overline{W}$ = .973) is indicated in dotted line.

Figure 12 Differentiation of areas in the absence of environmental differences as described in the text.

Figure 13 M is a major mutation with drastic net unfavorable effect in the presence of five type modifiers that are only very slightly favored over their alleles (A, B, C, D, E) in the absence of M. Unfavorable effects of M are partially overcome by presence of one or more of A, B, C, D and E, resulting in net favorable effects of combinations of M with four or five of these.

Figure 14-19 Trajectories of gene frequencies in cases of selection involving two pairs of alleles, with no dominance in genotypic values so that selective values may be assigned haploid genotypes.

$$\Delta q = q(1-q) \sum W \frac{\partial f}{\partial q'}, \quad \Delta q = q(1-q) \sum W \frac{\partial f}{\partial q} .$$

The surfaces of mean selective values, $\overline{W} (= \sum Wf)$ are indicated by contour lines, the trajectories by arrows of length proportional to rate of change.

Figure 14 Absolute selective values additive, one gene with twice the effect of the other. The population moves toward peak $\overline{W}$. With the same relative selective values (w) but selection without effect on population size ($W = kw/\overline{w}$) $\overline{W}$ would be constant. There would be no contours, no peak value but movement would be the same as in figure 14.

Figure 15 Assuming competition without effect on population size as above in one respect, it is here assumed that there is a proportional absolute effect in the opposite direction on a second character. If this is not too great selection carries the population toward low $\overline{W}$.

Figure 16 Genotype AB (upper right), a social parasite, has a constant selective advantage over all others but has a uniform deleterious effect on the population, proportional to its frequency which if great enough again carries the population to low $\overline{W}$. Reversal of all signs and of the direction of the arrows would illustrate the case in which AB is a social asset but at a disadvantage itself and thus doomed to extinction.

Figure 17 Genotype AB is at an advantage when rare, but disadvantage when abundant. Movement is toward a curved line of intermediate gene frequencies ($pq = 1/2$) which is not the line of maximum $\overline{W}$ ($pq=1/4$) .

Figure 18 Genotype AB benefits at the expense of genotype ab . There is a low value of $\overline{W}$ at (1/2, 1/2) and equal high $\overline{W}$ along edges but movement is toward fixation of A or B . In contrast with figures 15-17, there is no surface F(W) .

Figure 19 This represents a very implausible cyclic system of selective values in which again F(W) does not exist. $\overline{W}$ is constant. The trajectories spiral out from (1/2, 1/2) . With slight changes in the postulated selective values of the haploid genotype, $\overline{W}$ may be either a maximum or a minimum at (1/2, 1/2) . If the former there may be either a divergent or convergent spiral movement.

This study was conducted under grant No. 9-11336 from the National Science Foundation.

Paper No. 950 from the Department of Genetics, University of Wisconsin.

DISCUSSION PARTICIPANT

Robert Coifman
Research Assistant, Department of Medical Genetics
Genetics Building, The University of Wisconsin
Madison, Wisconsin

DISCUSSION

Robert Coifman. Your description of your polyallelic multiple factor model with multiple selective peaks brought to my mind the heterosis hypothesis of Dr. Bruce Wallace, in which the number of alleles at any locus is of appreciable size with respect to the number of individuals in any (interbreeding) segment of the population[1]. Is it only this extreme local polyallelism, which seems to me to be an allowable but extreme case within the set defined in your model, that precludes the application of your gene-diffusion computational methodology and leads Dr. Wallace to conclusions that are not generally accepted by yourself?

Sewall Wright. As Mr. Coifman implies, Dr. Wallace's heterosis hypothesis agrees with the view that I have maintained (since 1931) that there is a virtually infinite array of possible genotypes within any natural species because of the occurrence of multiple alleles at many or all loci. There is a difference in emphasis with respect to the mechanisms by which heterozygosis is maintained. Wallace seems to restrict this almost wholly to the effect of selective advantage of heterozygotes over homozygotes. I recognized this as important in my 1931 paper but gave varying weights to all kinds of balance. I have, perhaps, given most weight to the consequences of selective advantages of different sets of gene frequencies in different localities, in shifting balance in each locality with the effects of diffusion from the others.

The most important difference in our views, however, seems to be that I have stressed the inevitable existence of a vast number of discrete peaks in the "surface" of mean selective values of sets of gene frequencies as a result of factor interactions (especially that due to the usual intermediacy of the optimum grade of quantitative characters) and of pleiotropy (which insures that these peaks be of widely different heights), which Wallace has not done.

1 B. Wallace: Heterotic mutations. Molecular Genetics and Human Disease, L. I. Gardner, ed., C. Thomas, Springfield, Illinois (1961) pp. 212-230.

The principal model that I discussed here was necessarily a highly oversimplified one, designed to exhibit the sort of evolutionary process to be expected in the presence of several (six) selective peaks, with as few extraneous complications as possible. With multiple alleles at all loci in multiple interlocked reaction systems (instead of merely pairs at four loci) there would be an enormously greater number of peaks and an evolutionary process of the sort described could continue indefinitely. My formulae for selection pressure and for multidimensional stochastic distributions apply in principle to such systems. Detailed computation is, of course, precluded by the number of terms in the case of extensive irregular interaction systems but the mathematical forms of the formulae themselves bring out important general properties.

Perhaps the basic differences in viewpoints is that Wallace has been concerned primarily with the genetic basis for current adaptation while I have been concerned primarily with the dynamics of evolution as a process.

SAMUEL KARLIN and JAMES McGREGOR

On Some Stochastic Models in Genetics

The fluctuations in the genetic composition of populations subject to mutation and selection have been studied by Fisher, Wright, Haldane, Kimura, Moran and numerous other investigators. We are interested here in stochastic models. Most of the models which have been used deal with a population of fixed size in which there are individuals of several genetic constitutions. One wishes to study the progression in time of the numbers of individuals of the various types or of the gene frequencies. Ideally one should like to obtain the distributions of the gene frequencies at an arbitrary time, but in practice the models have not yielded to such detailed analysis. In simple cases it has been possible to find the rate of approach to statistical equilibrium, and occasionally also the form of the equilibrium distribution. Such information, while quite valuable and interesting, is nevertheless very meager. In more complicated cases, and especially in models involving selection, even these simple results are no longer available.

In the limit as the population size $N \to \infty$ the models frequently pass over formally into continuous diffusion models which have been found somewhat more susceptible to analysis. Computations based on the continuous diffusion models have been taken to give approximations valid for the discrete models with large N. The nature of such approximations has never been fully analyzed. For an excellent discussion of some of the problems involved in developing such diffusion approximations we refer the reader to [22].

Recently Moran has devised discrete models with fixed population size which, at least in the simpler cases, permit much more detailed analysis. Our object is to discuss some of the results obtained for these models.

In section 1 some earlier one-locus two allele models of Wright and Fisher are described for purposes of comparison with the Moran models. In section 2 the analogous Moran models are set forth and the type of results which we obtained are indicated. Section 3 is devoted to a discussion of limiting cases of the Moran model as $N \to \infty$. It turns out that there is a somewhat wider variety of limiting diffusion processes than has previously been suspected. Moreover for the Moran models the limit procedures permit a rigorous analysis. The interpretations and relevance of the various limiting processes in different biological contexts are discussed briefly in section 4. In section 5 we briefly describe a related simpler model well known in statistical mechanics. In section 6 we indicate the extension of the results to many allele versions of the Moran model.

1. Wright models.

We first discuss some stochastic models introduced by S. Wright and R. Fisher for investigating the effects of mutation, selection, migration and random drift on the fluctuations of gene frequencies. There is a population of N haploid individuals each of which may be either of two types $\underline{A}$ or $\underline{a}$. The system is in state ℓ if there are ℓ individuals of type $\underline{A}$ and $n-\ell$ of type $\underline{a}$. The next generation is formed by selecting, with replacement, N individuals from the parent generation according to rules which embody the forces of mutation, selection, etc.

In the simplest case there is random mating but no mutation, selection, or migration. If the parent generation has exactly ℓ individuals of type $\underline{A}$ then each selection results in an A-type individual with probability $p_\ell = \ell/N$ and in an a-type individual with probability $q_\ell = 1 - p_\ell = (N-\ell)/N$. The probability that the next generation has exactly m individuals of type $\underline{A}$ is therefore

$$P_{\ell,m} = \binom{N}{m} \left(\frac{\ell}{N}\right)^m \left(\frac{N-\ell}{N}\right)^{N-m} \tag{1.1}$$

Let X_k, $k = 0, 1, 2, \ldots$ be the number of A-individuals in the kth generation. Then X_k is a discrete Markoff process whose possible states are $0, 1, \ldots, N$ and for which (1.1) is the one-step transition probability. The k-step transition probability

$$P^{(k)}_{\ell,m} = \Pr\{X_k = m | X_0 = \ell\} \tag{1.2}$$

can be found, in principle, as follows. The eigenvalues of the matrix $P = (P_{\ell,m})$, $\ell, m = 0, 1, \ldots, N$ have been found by the method of generating functions (Feller [6]) to be

$$\lambda_\nu = \binom{N}{\nu}\frac{\nu!}{N^\nu} \qquad \nu = 0, 1, 2, \ldots, N . \tag{1.3}$$

These are of the form $1 = \lambda_0 = \lambda_1 > \lambda_2 > \lambda_3 > \ldots > \lambda_N > 0$. There are left eigenvectors $Q_\nu = (Q_{\nu,0}, Q_{\nu,1}, \ldots, Q_{\nu,N})$ satisfying $Q_\nu P = \lambda_\nu Q_\nu$ and right eigenvectors R_ν satisfying $PR_\nu = \lambda_\nu R_\nu$ which together form a biorthonormal system

$$\sum_{\ell=0}^{N} Q_{\nu\ell} R_{\mu\ell} = \delta_{\nu,\mu} = \begin{cases} 1 & \nu = \mu \\ 0 & \nu \neq \mu \end{cases} .$$

The transition probabilities (1.2) have the representation

$$P^{(k)}_{\ell,m} = \sum_{\nu=0}^{N} \lambda_\nu^k R_{\nu\ell} Q_{\nu m} . \tag{1.4}$$

Corresponding to the repeated eigenvalue $\lambda_0 = \lambda_1 = 1$ there are two trivial left eigenvectors $Q_{0,\ell} = \delta_{0,\ell}$ and $Q_{1,\ell} = \delta_{N,\ell}$. Unfortunately, the other left eigenvectors are not known explicitly and virtually nothing is known about their properties. (The right eigenvectors are slightly more tractable. They can be computed recursively, in terms of certain polynomial systems although no analytic form is discernible. It seems likely that the eigenvectors cannot be expressed in terms of classical functions and ultimately numerical methods will have to be employed). Because of this analytic impasse the results available for the model are meager and consist primarily of approximations valid when N is large, and evaluation of rates of convergence for fixed N as $k \to \infty$. (The same remarks apply to the mutation version of the model, which we describe in the next paragraph.) In the above model the homozygous states $\ell = 0, N$ are absorbing states, i.e., if $X_k = 0$ for some k then $X_t = 0$ for $t \geq k$. Since $0 < \lambda_\nu < 1$ for $\nu = 2, 3, \ldots, N$ we see that in (1.4) the terms with $\nu = 0$, $\nu = 1$ predominate when k is large. The next largest term ($\nu = 2$) decreases like $(1 - 1/N)^k$ as $k \to \infty$, and this is the rate of approach to homozygosity. (See Moran [19] for a more detailed discussion.)

In the mutation model it is assumed that when the next generation is formed each new individual may or may not mutate to the other type. If α_2 is the probability for an individual of type A to mutate to a and α_1 is the probability for an individual of type a to mutate to A then (1.1) is to be replaced by

$$P_{\ell,m} = \binom{N}{m} (p_\ell)^m (q_\ell)^{N-m} . \tag{1.5}$$

where

$$p_\ell = \frac{\ell(1-\alpha_2) + (N-\ell)\,\alpha_1}{N} ,$$

$$q_\ell = \frac{\ell\alpha_2 + (N-\ell)(1-\alpha_1)}{N} = 1 - p_\ell .$$

The eigenvalues in this case (Feller, loc. cit.) are

$$\lambda_\nu = (1 - \alpha_1 - \alpha_2)^\nu \binom{N}{\nu}\frac{\nu!}{N^\nu} , \qquad \nu = 0, 1, \ldots, N .$$

We assume $\alpha_1 > 0$, $\alpha_2 > 0$ and $\alpha_1 + \alpha_2 < 1$. The eigenvalues are then distinct $1 = \lambda_0 > \lambda_1 > \ldots > \lambda_N > 0$. As in the model without mutation the left eigenvectors are not known explicitly and consequently a detailed analysis of the properties of the process is not available. In this model there are no absorbing states, but there is a limiting distribution $\lim_{k\to\infty} \Pr\{X_k = m \mid X_0 = \ell\} = \pi_m$. The difference between $P_{\ell m}^{(k)}$ and π_m decreases like $\lambda_1^k = (1 - \alpha_1 - \alpha_2)^k$, i.e., the rate of convergence does not depend on N . On the other hand the fluctuations about the equilibrium are of order $\sqrt{N}$, i.e., the variance is of order $\sqrt{N}$. If one sets $\alpha_i = \gamma_i/N$ and let $N\to\infty$ with γ_1, γ_2 fixed it has been shown heuristically that the process X_t/N approximates the diffusion process with (backward) Fokker-Planck equation $(0 < x < 1,\ t > 0)$

$$\frac{\partial u}{\partial t} = \frac{1}{2}x(1-x)\,\frac{\partial^2 u}{\partial x^2} + [(\gamma_1 - x(\gamma_1 + \gamma_2)]\frac{\partial u}{\partial x} .$$

Various quantities associated with the diffusion process, for example the limiting stationary distribution, can be computed exactly with comparative ease, and have been used as approximations for the discrete case with large N .

A version of the model incorporating selection has also been considered. If the A-type is to have a selective advantage $s > 0$ over the a-type we assume the offspring of A and a are produced in numbers proportional to $1 + s$ and 1 respectively. The new generation is chosen by selecting N individuals from a large pool of offspring of the individuals from the parent generation. The one-step transition probability is then (1.5) where

$$p_\ell = \frac{\ell(1+s)}{\ell(1+s)+N-\ell} = \frac{\ell(1+s)}{N+\ell s} ,$$

$$q_\ell = \frac{N-\ell}{N+\ell s} .$$

As in the model without mutation the homozygous states are absorbing and $\lambda_0 = \lambda_1 = 1$ is a repeated eigenvalue. The other eigenvalues are unknown and the eigenvectors are not known, and correspondingly the information available about the process is even more sketchy than in the earlier cases. There is a diffusion approximation heuristically motivated as before. Generally, taking account of the influence of selection presents formidable open problems.

2. Moran's models.

Moran devised continuous time Markoff chain models to study the same phenomena. An event consists of the death of a single individual and the birth of a single new individual, and these events occur at random times. Consequently the generations overlap in these models.

There is a population of N individuals each of which may be of type $\underline{A}$ or $\underline{a}$ as before. The system is in state ℓ if there are ℓ of type $\underline{A}$ and $N-\ell$ of type $\underline{a}$.* When an event occurs an individual, chosen at random, duplicates and produces a progeny which replaces a second (possibly the same) individual chosen at random from the population. When the system is in state ℓ and an event occurs, the subsequent state will be $\ell-1$, ℓ, $\ell+1$ with probabilities $q_\ell, 1-p_\ell-q_\ell$, p_ℓ which will depend on assumptions concerning mutation, migration, and selection. For the simplest random mating model

$$p_\ell = (N-\ell)\ell/N^2, \quad q_\ell = \ell(N-\ell)/N^2 . \tag{2.1}$$

The quantity $(N-\ell)/N$ represents the probability of an a-gene dying and ℓ/N is the probability of replacing it with an A-gene. In the case of mutation it is assumed that the progeny, immediately on being formed, may mutate. If the mutation $\underline{a} \to \underline{A}$ occurs with probability α_1 and $\underline{A} \to \underline{a}$ with probability α_2 then we have

---

* The set up and notation differs in two respects from the treatment of [11]. In [11] the state variable was the number of a-genes while in the present context the state variable is the number of A-genes. The reader can pass from the formulas of [11] to those here by replacing γ_2, γ_1 by α_1, α_2 respectively and N for $N-1$ throughout.

$$q_\ell = \ell[\ell\alpha_2 + (N-\ell)(1-\alpha_1)]/N^2 ,$$

(2.2)

$$p_\ell = (N-\ell)[\ell(1-\alpha_2) + (N-\ell)\alpha_1]/N^2 .$$

The time intervals between successive events are identically distributed independent random variables $T_1, T_2, \dots$ all with the same exponential distribution

$$\Pr\{T > t\} = e^{-N\mu t} ,$$

and $1/\mu$ is the expected lifetime of an individual. The state $X(t)$ at time t is then a continuous time parameter Markoff chain. The transition probability matrix $P(t) = (P_{\ell,m}(t))$, defined by

$$P_{\ell,m}(t) = \Pr\{X(t+s) = m \mid X(s) = \ell\} ,$$

satisfies the system of differential equations

$$\frac{dP_{\ell,m}}{dt} = N\mu[q_\ell P_{\ell-1,m} - (p_\ell + q_\ell) P_{\ell,m} + p_\ell P_{\ell+1,m}] \tag{2.3}$$

$$\ell, m = 0, 1, \dots, N$$

or in matrix form $dP/dt = AP$ where A is the Jacobi matrix

$$A = N\mu \begin{bmatrix} -(q_0+p_0) & p_0 & 0 & \cdot\ \cdot\ \cdot & 0 \\ q_1 & -(q_1+p_1) & p_1 & & \\ \cdot & \cdot & \cdot & \cdot & \cdot \\ \cdot & \cdot & \cdot & \cdot & \cdot \\ \cdot & \cdot & \cdot & \cdot & \cdot \\ 0 & & & -(q_{n-1}+p_{n-1}) & p_{n-1} \\ 0 & \cdot\ \cdot\ \cdot & & q_n & -(q_n+p_n) \end{bmatrix}$$

In [11] the authors have found the eigenvalues and the eigenvectors of the matrix A for both of the cases (2.1), (2.3). It turns out that the eigenvectors are easy to express in terms of the Hahn polynomials

$$Q_n(x) = Q_n(x; \alpha, \beta, N) = {}_3F_2(-n, -x, n+\alpha+\beta+1; \alpha+1, -N; 1)$$

whose properties are known in great detail [10] . The resulting formula for the transition probabilities we record for the case of the mutation model with $\alpha_1 > 0$, $\alpha_2 > 0$, $\alpha_1 + \alpha_2 < 1$:

$$(2.4) \quad P_{\ell,m}(t) = \pi_m \sum_{\nu=0}^{N} \exp\left\{-\frac{\mu(1-\alpha_1-\alpha_2)\,\nu(\nu+\alpha+\beta+1)}{N} t\right\} Q_\nu(\ell)\, Q_\nu(m)\, \psi_\nu$$

where

$$\alpha = \frac{N\alpha_1}{1-\alpha_1-\alpha_2} - 1, \qquad \beta = \frac{N\alpha_2}{1-\alpha_1-\alpha_2} - 1,$$

$$\pi_m = \frac{\binom{\alpha+m}{m}\binom{\beta+N-m}{N-m}}{\binom{N+\alpha+\beta+1}{N}}$$

$$\psi_\nu = \frac{\binom{N}{\nu}\binom{\alpha+\nu}{\nu}\binom{\alpha+\beta+\nu}{\nu}}{\binom{N+\alpha+\beta+1+\nu}{\nu}\binom{\beta+\nu}{\nu}} \cdot \frac{2\nu+\alpha+\beta+1}{\alpha+\beta+1} .$$

The eigenvalues of A are

$$\lambda_\nu = -\frac{\mu(1-\alpha_1-\alpha_2)\,\nu(\nu+\alpha+\beta+1)}{N}, \quad \nu = 0, 1, 2, \ldots, N ,$$

and the rate of convergence to the limiting distribution is now like

$$(2.5) \qquad e^{-\lambda_1 t} = e^{-\mu(\alpha_1+\alpha_2)t} .$$

To compare this with the result for the Wright model it is natural to take $t = 1/\mu$ as comparable to one generation time and we have, as for the Wright model, the rate of convergence $e^{-(\alpha_1+\alpha_2)} = 1-(\alpha_1+\alpha_2)$ approximately, per generation. However from the explicit formula (2.4) much more detailed information can be obtained. For example an explicit formula for the distribution of the time starting from a homozygous population ($\ell = 0$), to first reach the state $\ell = N/2$ can be given. Similarly in the model without mutation, not only can the rate of approach to homozygosity (absorption) be found, but the distribution of the time of absorption is known, and the conditional distribution of $X(t)$ given that absorption has not occurred at time t is explicitly known. Thus the analytic results for the Moran models (with no selection) are much more extensive than for the Wright models

Selection may be incorporated in the Moran model in several ways, all of which lead to such difficulties that neither the eigenvalues nor the eigenvectors can be determined. In this respect the situation is similar to that with the Wright models. However it seems not unlikely that further analysis of Moran models with selection should prove fruitful.

3. Limit processes.

As with the Wright models, the Moran model possesses limiting diffusion processes as $N \to \infty$. We make a list which is not complete but which indicates the enormous wealth of limit processes for the Moran model. Each of these limit processes is appropriate for different situations. The first example examines the fine fluctuations of the population size of A genes about the mean equilibrium level. The second example is the standard diffusion associated with gene frequency studied by Fisher and Wright. The next limit process corresponds to the case of a rare gene. The following example treats a situation intermediate between that of examples (ii) and (iii). A further discussion of the implications and relevance of these limit processes and the other examples is given in Section 4. The examples of Table 1 all involve mutation while Table 2 lists three examples of limit processes for the Moran model without mutation. We indicate the formalities of the limit processes, rigorous details and the further analysis will be set forth in [12].

(i) In the classical deterministic model of the gene frequencies in an infinite haploid population with two alleles at one locus and mutation rates α_1, α_2 per birth, there is an equilibrium frequency for A genes of $\alpha_1/(\alpha_1+\alpha_2)$. In the Moran model one should therefore expect the states near $\ell = N\alpha_1/(\alpha_1+\alpha_2)$ to be favored, and indeed from (2.2) we see that $p_\ell > q_\ell$ or $p_\ell < q_\ell$ according as $\ell < N\alpha_1/(\alpha_1+\alpha_2)$ or $\ell > N\alpha_1/(\alpha_1+\alpha_2)$, so there is an attraction toward the special value. When N is large the system tends to spend long times in the neighborhood of the pseudo-equilibrium state $\ell = N\alpha_1/(\alpha_1+\alpha_2)$. The study of fluctuations about the pseudo-equilibrium leads to consideration of the following limit procedure.

With α_1, α_2 fixed we assume the initial population is

$$\ell = \left[N\frac{\alpha_1}{\alpha_1+\alpha_2} + x\sqrt{Nc} \right] = \sigma(x)$$

where $c = 2\alpha_1\alpha_2/(\alpha_1+\alpha_2)^3$, x is a fixed real number and $[u]$ denotes the greatest integer $\leq u$. Then we can show that as $N \to \infty$, for any fixed real y

$$(3.1)\qquad \lim_{N\to\infty} \sum_{m\le\sigma(y)} P_{\sigma(x),m}(\tau) = \int_{-\infty}^{y} p(\tau,x,y')\,\rho(y')\,dy'$$

where the limit is the transition probability of the diffusion process on $-\infty < x < \infty$ governed by the backward diffusion equation

$$(3.2)\qquad \frac{\partial P}{\partial\tau} = \mu\left[\frac{1}{2}\frac{\partial^2 P}{\partial x^2} - x\frac{\partial P}{\partial x}\right]$$

The limit can be expressed in terms of Hermite polynomials [12],

$$p(\tau,x,y) = \sum_{\nu=0}^{\infty} \exp\{-\mu(\alpha_1+\alpha_2)\,\nu\tau\}\,\frac{H_\nu(x)\,H_\nu(y)}{\nu!\,2^\nu},$$

$$\rho(y) = \pi^{-1/2}\,e^{-y^2}.$$

Moveover the system of differential equations (2.3) passes over formally into the diffusion equation (3.2).

We interpret the existence of the limit (3.1) in more picturesque language as follows. When the population is large the gene frequencies are appropriately found by a deterministic model, since the fluctuations in ℓ, the number of A individuals, are only of order $\sqrt{N}$ and hence do not affect the gene frequencies. To study the fluctuations in ℓ the above diffusion process should give a "reasonable" approximation.

The diffusion process governed by (3.2) is well known and has an extensive literature, [1], [6], [8]. It is called the Ornstein-Uhlenbeck process or sometimes Brownian motion of an elastically bound particle.

The following table outlines some further examples of limit procedures for the Moran mutation model. The examples are discussed in a formal way below, and detailed analysis is given in [12]. In all cases γ_1, γ_2 denote fixed positive constants, and d is a constant, $0 < d < 1$.

(ii) It was shown in [11] that under this limit procedure

$$(3.3)\qquad \lim_{N\to\infty} \sum_{\substack{m\le Ny_1 \\ \ell=[Nx]}} P_{\ell,m}(N\tau) = \int_0^{y_1} p(\tau,x,y)\,\rho(y)\,dy, \qquad 0 < y_1 < 1$$

Example	α_1	α_2	t	ℓ	Limit Process
(i)	fixed	fixed	τ	$N\frac{\alpha_1}{\alpha_1+\alpha_2} + x\sqrt{Nc}$ $-\infty < x < \infty$	Diffusion on $(-\infty, \infty)$ Ornstein-Uhlenbeck process
(ii)	$\frac{\gamma_1}{N}$	$\frac{\gamma_2}{N}$	$N\tau$	xN, $0 < x < 1$	Jacobi diffusion on $(0, 1)$ x = gene frequency
(iii)	$\frac{\gamma_1}{N}$	fixed	τ	fixed	Birth and death process linear growth with immigration
(iv)	$\frac{\gamma_1}{N}$	$\frac{\gamma_2}{N^d}$ $0 < d < 1$	$N^d\tau$	xN^d $0 < x < \infty$	Laguerre diffusion on $(0, \infty)$ linear growth with immigration
(v)	$\frac{\gamma_1}{N}$	$\frac{\gamma_2}{N}$	τ	fixed	Birth and death process linear growth with immigration
(vi)	$\frac{\gamma_1}{N}$	$\frac{\gamma_2}{N}$	$N^d\tau$ $0 < d < 1$	xN^d	Bessel diffusion on $(0, \infty)$

TABLE 1

where the limit is the transition probability belonging to the backward diffusion equation

$$(3.4) \qquad \frac{\partial P}{\partial \tau} = \mu \left[x(1-x) \frac{\partial^2 P}{\partial x^2} + \{\gamma_1 - (\gamma_1 + \gamma_2) x\} \frac{\partial P}{\partial x} \right]$$

on $0 < x < 1$. More precisely

$$p(\tau, x, y) = \sum_{\nu=0}^{\infty} \exp\{-\mu\nu(\nu + \gamma_1 + \gamma_2 - 1)\tau\} P_\nu(1-2x)\, P_\nu(1-2y)\, w_\nu ,$$

where $w_\nu = \Gamma(\nu + \gamma_1)\, \Gamma(\nu + \gamma_1 + \gamma_2 - 1)/\Gamma(\nu + \gamma_2)\, \Gamma(\nu + 1)$ and P_ν is expressed in terms of the Jacobi polynomials [20],

$$(3.5) \qquad P_\nu(1-2x) = \frac{P_\nu^{(\gamma_1 - 1, \gamma_2 - 1)}(1-2x)}{P_\nu^{(\gamma_1 - 1, \gamma_2 - 1)}(1)} ,$$

and

$$\rho(y) = \frac{y^{\gamma_1 - 1}(1-y)^{\gamma_2 - 1}}{\int_0^1 z^{\gamma_1 - 1}(1-z)^{\gamma_2 - 1}\, dz} .$$

Moreover, the system of differential equations (2.3) passes over into the diffusion equation (3.4). The diffusion equation (3.4) has been used by Fisher, Wright, Kimura and others to obtain approximations for the Wright model with mutation.

The existence of the limit might be interpreted as follows. If the population N is large and mutation probabilities are small (of order $1/N$) and if the gene frequencies are observed over long periods of time--one unit of τ equals N units of t--then the gene frequencies behave like sample functions of the diffusion process.

(iii) In the third limit procedure the mutation $a \to A$ has small probability compared to the mutation $A \to a$. We study a large population containing a small number ℓ of A individuals. In the limit we get a birth and death process for ℓ:

$$(3.6) \qquad \lim_{N \to \infty} P_{\ell m}(\tau) = P^*_{\ell m}(\tau) ,$$

where

$$(3.7)\qquad \frac{dP^*_{\ell m}}{d\tau} = \mu\left[\ell P^*_{\ell-1,m} - \{(2-\alpha_2)\ell + \gamma_1\} P^*_{\ell m} + \{(1-\alpha_2)\ell + \gamma_1\} P^*_{\ell+1,m}\right]$$

Thus $P^*_{\ell m}$ is the transition probability if a birth and death process of linear growth type in which the death rate $\mu\ell$ exceeds the birth rate $\mu(1-\alpha_2)\ell$ but there is a compensating immigration rate $\mu\gamma_1$ representing mutations $a \to A$ from an infinite external population of a-individuals.

(iv) In this example we have a family of limit procedures depending on a parameter d, $0 < d < 1$. The mutation $A \to a$ is rare compared to the mutation $a \to A$ and the relative rarity depends on the parameter d. The cases $d = 0$, $d = 1$ correspond to (iii), (ii) respectively.

The pseudo equilibrium value of ℓ is now

$$\ell = N\frac{\alpha_1}{\alpha_1 + \alpha_2} = N^d \frac{\gamma_1}{\gamma_2 + \frac{\gamma_1}{N^{1-d}}} \sim N^d \frac{\gamma_1}{\gamma_2}$$

and the fluctuations in ℓ are of the same order of magnitude N^d. The limit process is the diffusion on $(0,\infty)$ governed by the equation

$$(3.8)\qquad \frac{\partial P}{\partial \tau} = \mu\left[x\frac{\partial^2 P}{\partial x^2} + (\gamma_1 - \gamma_2 x)\frac{\partial P}{\partial x}\right] .$$

One unit of τ-time now corresponds to N^d units of t-time.

(v) This example stands in sharp contrast with example (ii). The population is large and the mutation probabilities are small as in (ii). However, the periods of successive observation are shorter. The number ℓ of A individuals is observed and this remains small as $N \to \infty$. The limit process is the birth and death process governed by the equations

$$(3.9)\qquad \frac{dP^*_{\ell m}}{d\tau} = \mu\left[\ell P^*_{\ell-1,m} - (2\ell + \gamma_1) P^*_{\ell m} + (\ell + \gamma_1) P^*_{\ell+1,m}\right] .$$

It is of linear growth type with immigration and the birth rate exceeds the death rate only by virtue of the immigration.

(vi) In this example we have a family of limit procedures depending on a parameter d, $0 < d < 1$ with $d = 0, 1$ corresponding to examples (v) and (ii) respectively. The limit process is a diffusion on $(0, \infty)$ governed by the equation

$$(3.10) \qquad \frac{\partial P}{\partial \tau} = \mu \left[x \frac{\partial^2 P}{\partial x^2} + \gamma_1 \frac{\partial P}{\partial x} \right] .$$

Limit processes with no mutation.

We close this section by listing three limiting processes associated with the Moran model involving no mutation, i.e., $\alpha_1 = \alpha_2 = 0$. As in the case of Table 1, each limit process is valid and appropriate for different time scales. (See our more elaborate discussion in Section 4.)

TABLE 2

Example	t	ℓ	Limit Process
I	$N\tau$	xN, $0 < x < 1$	Jacobi diffusion on $(0,1)$ absorbing boundaries at 0 and 1
II	τ	finite	Birth and death process with absorbing barrier at 0
III	$N^d\tau$ $0 < d < 1$	xN^d $0 < x < \infty$	Bessel diffusion $(0,\infty)$ absorbing boundary at 0

(I) Here the time between successive observations is long, $t = N\tau$. The relevant variable is x = gene frequency whose sample functions are governed by stationary transition probabilities $P(\tau; x, y)$ satisfying the backward diffusion equation

$$\frac{\partial P}{\partial \tau} = \mu\, x(1-x) \frac{\partial^2 P}{\partial x^2} .$$

The endpoints 0 and 1 act as absorbing barriers. The density function of the absorption time for the loss of A genes from the population where the initial A gamete gene frequency is x, is

$$(3.11) \qquad \phi(x,\tau) = \mu\, x(1-x) \sum_{n=1}^{\infty} e^{-\mu n(n+1)\tau} P_{n-1}(1-2x; 1, 1)\, n(n+1)\,(2n+1)$$

and $P_{n-1}(1-2x; 1, 1)$ is the function (3.5) for $\gamma_1 = \gamma_2 = 2$. For details on the derivation of (3.11) the reader may consult [11] or [15].

(II) When the number of A-genes is very rare, then the limiting process is a birth and death process analogous to that of example (v). The state of the limit process is represented by an integer ℓ = number of A-genes in an infinite population. The backward equation of the process is

$$\frac{dP_{\ell m}(\tau)}{d\tau} = \mu[\ell P_{\ell-1,m} - 2\ell P_{\ell,m} + \ell P_{\ell+1,m}] , \tag{3.12}$$

$$\ell, m = 0, 1, \ldots$$

The state 0 acts as an absorbing barrier in the sense that whenever $\ell = 1$, then with probability $\mu h + o(h)$, the A-gene dies during the following h units of time. The transition probability is explicitly given for $\ell, m \geq 1$ by

$$P_{\ell m}(\tau) = \frac{1}{m}\int_0^\infty e^{-\mu\xi\tau} L_{\ell-1}^{(1)}(\xi)\, L_{m-1}^{(1)}(\xi)\, e^{-\xi}\, 2\xi\, d\xi \tag{3.13}$$

where $L_m^{(\alpha)}(\xi)$ denotes the classical Laguerre polynomials of parameter α. A complete discussion of this process can be found in [9], see also [6]. For any initial state $\ell \geq 1$, absorption at $\ell = 0$ takes place with probability 1, however, the mean absorption time is infinite. The density function of the time of absorption (disappearance of the A gene) for the initial state ℓ is

$$\phi_\ell(\tau) = \mu \int_0^\infty e^{-\mu\xi\tau} e^{-\xi}\, \xi L_{\ell-1}^{(1)}(\xi)\, d\xi = \frac{\ell\, \mu^\ell\, \tau^{\ell-1}}{(1+\mu\tau)^{\ell+1}} .$$

This model shows that a newly introduced mutant A gene, in general, cannot become established. However since the expected time until absorption is infinite, it is possible by a change of environment for the A gene to increase.

(III) In this example, $t = N^d\tau$, $0 < d < 1$ so the time scale is intermediate between I and II. When the A gene population is established of the order of magnitude $\ell = xN^d$ then the transition density of the fluctuations of x (as $N \to \infty$) satisfies the backward diffusion equation

$$\frac{\partial P}{\partial \tau} = \mu\, x \frac{\partial^2 P}{\partial x^2} \qquad 0 < x < \infty$$

and 0 is an absorbing boundary. This is in sharp contrast to (3.11) which refers to gene frequencies. For any initial specification of x, absorption at the origin is certain, the mean absorption time again is infinite.

4. Discussion of biological interpretations of limit processes.

The multiplicity of limit processes listed in the preceding section pose the challenge as to the relevance of each. This problem is related partly with the meaning of the time scale of observation and partly with the concept of rare mutant.

1. The parameter $1/\mu$ associated with Table 1 represents the expected lifetime of an individual in units of t time. If the population is scrutinized only after N complete renewals, which some argue is appropriate from an evolutionary standpoint, then we find ourselves in the situation of Case (ii) Table 1, in the presence of mutation, and in Case I of Table 2 when there are no mutation pressures. Here in the limit process one unit of τ time corresponds to N renewals of the population. Of course, it should be realized that Case (ii) only treats fluctuations of gene frequency. This is meaningful provided both types A and a are sufficiently abundant of the order of magnitude of the full population size.

If $\tau = 1$ corresponds to one renewal of the population then the relevant limit process is one of Cases (ii), (iii), (v) of Table 1 or Case II of Table 2 depending on whether the mutation forces are nonzero or not.

The observation time and meaning of τ in Cases (iv) and (vi) and III is of an intermediate character.

2. As pointed out earlier, Case (iii) corresponds to a situation where the A-type is very rare. Its relative frequency is essentially zero. The mutation rate of $\underline{A}$ to $\underline{a}$ is large compared to the rate at which individual $\underline{a}$ types mutate into $\underline{A}$ types. However, the a-gene population is very numerous and therefore a balance is maintained consisting of a finite number ℓ of A genes surrounded by a virtually infinite population of a-genes. The actual fluctuations of ℓ are governed by the birth and death process (3.7). This process possesses a stationary distribution given by

$$\Pr\{\ell=z\} = \frac{(1-\alpha_2)^z\left(\frac{\gamma_1}{1-\alpha_2}\right)\left(\frac{\gamma_1}{1-\alpha_2}+1\right)\left(\frac{\gamma_1}{1-\alpha_2}+2\right)\cdots\left(\frac{\gamma_1}{1-\alpha_2}+z-1\right)}{z!\,(\alpha_2)^{\gamma_1/(1-\alpha_2)}}$$

$$z = 0, 1, 2, \ldots$$

3. It is interesting to compare the situation of Case (v) with that discussed in paragraph 2 above. Here, the mutation rates in

both directions are γ_1/N and γ_2/N. The quantities γ_1 and γ_2 can be interpreted as the intensity of mutation from a to A and A to a respectively, in the sense of the parameter of a Poisson process. Again if the initial size of the A-gene population is small while that of the a-gene population is large and if the process is examined ofter per generation time then the fluctuations in the A-gene size obey the laws of the birth and death process (3.9). This process is transient if $\gamma_1 > 1$ and null recurrent when $0 < \gamma_1 \leq 1$. This means that for $\gamma_1 > 1$ the A-gene population tends to infinity as $\tau \to \infty$. On the other hand if $0 < \gamma_1 \leq 1$ there does not exist any stationary distribution although all states are recurrent. The property that the A-gene population becomes infinite could be interpreted to the effect that the relevant approximation passes from that of (v) to one of the others as t becomes large.

4. The Case of (vi) is applicable when the initial A-gene population is of the order xN^d, the process is observed after long times, in fact, of the order of time of N^d renewals of the population and the mutation rates are comparably small. The gene frequency of A is again virtually zero but the actual A gene population size fluctuates of the order xN^d $(0 < x < \infty)$. The variations in x obey the laws of a stochastic process of Bessel diffusion type (3.10). When $0 < \gamma_1 \leq 1$, the process is null recurrent. For $\gamma_1 > 1$, x tends to infinity with probability 1 as $t \to \infty$. For $1 \leq \gamma_1$, x can never reach zero. On the other hand, when $\gamma_1 < 1$ then the origin becomes a regular boundary and the proper boundary condition is that of a reflecting barrier.

The discussion of Case (iv) is similar. We trace the fluctuations of the A population of the order xN^d. The transition density satisfies the Laguerre diffusion process (3.8). This process is null recurrent when $0 < \gamma_1 \leq 1$ and weakly transient for $\gamma_1 > 1$.

5. The cases of Table 2 with no mutation can be interpreted similarly. When the A-gene pool is small then the correct process to determine its rate of disappearance from the population (this event is certain) is Case II. We emphasize again that this is a situation where the frequency of the A-gene is essentially zero and it is the changes in the actual number of A-gene that are under study. Only when it is meaningful to consider bona fide frequencies for A and a-types is it appropriate to apply Case I. This entails that the population size of A and a-gene are each of the order of N. The intermediate case corresponds to Case III.

6. The existence of the limit processes, their properties as listed in Tables 1 and 2 and further analysis for the Moran model will be elaborated in [12]. It is of interest to point out now that the Wright mutation model as formulated in Section 2 also appears to possess a multiplicity of limit processes under the same kinds of normalizations

for the time and space scale as enumerated in Tables 1 and 2. The limit diffusions of examples (i), (ii), (iv) and (vi) can formally be obtained by direct considerations of the conditional expected displacement and expected variance of the one step transition law. In place of a limit birth and death (example iii) we now can deduce a limit branching process whose progeny probability distribution function is Poisson. The results of Table 2 can also be imitated in the case of Wright's model of random drift with no mutation. Actually there is a general theory involving direct product branching processes which subsumes the case of Wright's model and other important biological examples (see [13] for details). These all possess families of limit processes with corresponding interpretations.

5. The Ehrenfest urn model. A significant simplification occurs in the Moran mutation model when $\alpha_1 > 0$, $\alpha_2 > 0$, $\alpha_1 + \alpha_2 = 1$. Such a choice of the mutation rates would appear to be of negligible interest in genetics, but is noteworthy because the model is then equivalent to the Ehrenfest urn model, well known in statistical mechanics, and for which an extensive literature exists [1], [8], [9].

When $\alpha_1 = p = 1 - \alpha_2$, $0 < p < 1$ we have in place of (2.2)

$$q_\ell = \frac{\ell}{N} q , \qquad p_\ell = \frac{N-\ell}{N} p \tag{5.1}$$

and these are linear in ℓ rather than quadratic. The role of the Hahn polynomials is now taken over by the simpler Krawtchouk polynomials [4], [10], [20]

$$K_n(x) = {}_2F_1(-n, -x; -N; \frac{1}{p}) \qquad n = 0, 1, \ldots, N \tag{5.2}$$

which are orthogonal with respect to the binomial distribution

$$\sum_{x=0}^{N} K_i(x)\, K_j(x) \binom{N}{x} p^x q^{N-x} = \frac{\delta_{ij}}{\binom{N}{i} \left(\frac{p}{q}\right)^i}$$

The formula for the transition probability is

$$P_{\ell,m}(t) = \binom{N}{m} \left(\frac{p}{q}\right)^m \sum_{\nu=0}^{N} e^{-\mu\nu t} K_\nu(\ell) K_\nu(m) \binom{N}{\nu} p^\nu q^{N-\nu} . \tag{5.3}$$

The urn description of the model is as follows. There are N balls distributed in two urns, an A-urn and an a-urn. The system is in state ℓ when there are ℓ balls in the A-urn. Events occur at random times as in the Moran model. When an event occurs a ball is chosen at random, any one of the N balls having probability $1/N$ to be chosen. The chosen ball is removed from its urn and then placed in the A-urn with probability p, in the a-urn with probability q.

While the Ehrenfest model is immensely simpler analytically than the Moran model it nevertheless exhibits some of the same general features. There is an attraction to a pseudo-equilibrium state $\ell = Np$ and there is a limiting relation with the Ornstein-Uhlenbeck process (section 3, example (i)). There is also a limiting birth and death process analogous to example (iii) of section 2. But on the other hand there is no limiting diffusion on $(0, 1)$ as in example (ii) of section 2.

There is also an Ehrenfest model with absorbing states corresponding to the Moran model (2.1) with no mutation. In [13] we describe an urn model equivalent to the general Moran mutation model and give a detailed discussion of Ehrenfest models, including multi-urn versions analogous to multi-allele mutation models (see section 6).

6. Multi-allele Moran models.

Versions of the Wright models with diploidy, two sexes, and several alleles at the locus of interest have been investigated by a number of authors [16], [17], [19]. In general the results are somewhat less extensive even than in the simple haploid two allele case. Moran has described analogous generalizations of his models and our purpose here is to indicate how the methods and results of section 3 can be carried over to certain multi-allele haploid Moran mutation models. We give the details for the case of 3 alleles.

Consider a population of N individuals each of which is of one of the types A_1, A_2, A_3. The system is said to be in state (ℓ, m, n) if there are ℓ of the A_1-type, m of the A_2-type and n of the A_3-type, where $\ell + m + n = N$. The set of all possible states (ℓ, m, n) can be identified with lattice points in the equilateral triangle $\{(x, y, z);\ x \geq 0,\ y \geq 0,\ z \geq 0,\ x + y + z = N\}$. A state (ℓ, m, n) interior to the triangle has six neighboring states $(\ell-1, m+1, n)$, $(\ell-1, m, n+1)$, $(\ell, m-1, n+1)$, $(\ell+1, m-1, n)$, $(\ell+1, m, n-1)$, $(\ell, m+1, n-1)$. Events occur at random times as in the two allele model. When an event occurs two individuals, possibly the same, are chosen at random from the population. The first chosen individual duplicates producing a progeny. The progeny may mutate and then replaces the second chosen individual. Thus the state either remains unchanged or else moves to a neighboring state.

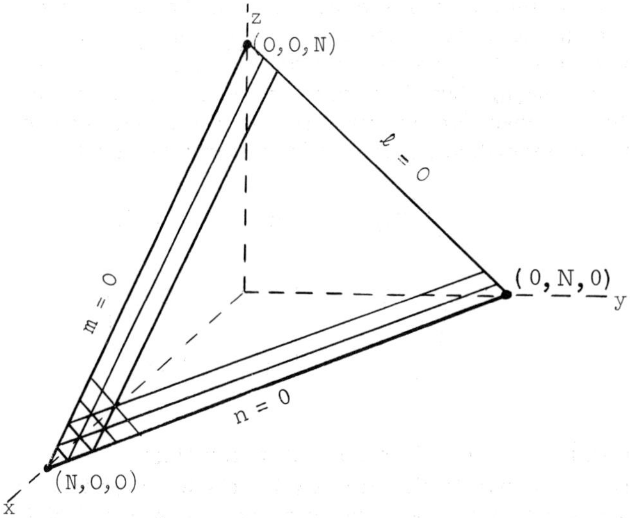

In the case when there are no mutations, changes of state result only from random sampling. If the state is (ℓ, m, n) and an event occurs the probabilities for the possible subsequent states are

New state	Probability
$(\ell-1,\ m+1,\ n)$	$\ell m/N^2$
$(\ell-1,\ m,\ n+1)$	$\ell n/N^2$
$(\ell,\ m-1,\ n+1)$	mn/N^2
$(\ell+1,\ m-1,\ n)$	$m\ell/N^2$
$(\ell+1,\ m,\ n-1)$	$n\ell/N^2$
$(\ell,\ m+1,\ n-1)$	nm/N^2
(ℓ, m, n)	$1 - [\ell(m+n) + m(n+\ell) + n(\ell+m)]/N^2$

If mutations occur, let α_{ij} be the probability that the progeny of an A_i individual is of type A_j after mutation. Then $\alpha_{ij} \geq 0$ and $\alpha_{i1} + \alpha_{i2} + \alpha_{i3} = 1$. The probabilities in the above table must now be replaced by quantities depending on the α_{ij}, for example $\ell m/N^2$ in the first row is replaced by $\ell(\ell\alpha_{12} + m\alpha_{22} + n\alpha_{32})/N^2$.

Analysis of the resulting model seems to be extremely complicated in general, but there are a number of special cases of interest for which a complete analysis is possible. We mention two of these, which are described in terms of the mutation matrix

$$\begin{pmatrix} \alpha_{11} & \alpha_{12} & \alpha_{13} \\ \alpha_{21} & \alpha_{22} & \alpha_{23} \\ \alpha_{31} & \alpha_{32} & \alpha_{33} \end{pmatrix}$$

which in the general case has six parameters.

If this matrix is the identity matrix we have the no mutation model described above. The homozygous states $(N, 0, 0)$, $(0, N, 0)$, $(0, 0, N)$ are absorbing, and there are three absorbing sets corresponding to the three edges $\ell = 0$, $m = 0$, $n = 0$ of the triangle. That is if a state with $\ell = 0$ is reached (the A_1-allele is lost from the population) then all subsequent states have $\ell = 0$. For this model a completely explicit formula for the transition probabilities can be given (using Hahn polynomials again). In [13] we give not merely the rate at which absorption occurs, but also the distribution of the time of absorption. The rate at which one allele is lost from the population is also known. We also obtain the joint distribution of the time and place at which one of the absorbing sets ($\ell = 0$, $m = 0$, $n = 0$) is reached. Finally a rigorous discussion of a limiting diffusion process on the triangle $\{(x, y, z);\ x \geq 0,\ y \geq 0,\ z \geq 0,\ x+y+z=1\}$ is presented.

We will now describe in somewhat greater detail the results when the mutation matrix has the special form

$$\begin{pmatrix} 1-\alpha_2-\alpha_3, & \alpha_2 & \alpha_3 \\ \alpha_1 \quad , & 1-\alpha_1-\alpha_3, & \alpha_3 \\ \alpha_1 \quad , & \alpha_2 & 1-\alpha_1-\alpha_2 \end{pmatrix}$$

Here the mutation probabilities depend on the end products of mutation but not on the initial condition, and the matrix has three rather than six parameters. Explicit formulas for the transition probabilities of the process and various related distributions are given in [13] . For this exposition we will assume that $\alpha_1 > 0$, $\alpha_2 > 0$, $\alpha_3 > 0$ and $\alpha_1 + \alpha_2 + \alpha_3 < 1$. (There is a simplification to a three urn Ehrenfest model when $\alpha_1 + \alpha_2 + \alpha_3 = 1$.) The transition probabilities $P(t; (\ell, m, n), (\ell', m', n'))$ of the process form a matrix $P(t)$ indexed by the set of states (ℓ, m, n), and they satisfy a system of differential equations like (2.3) . We write the differential equations in matrix form

$$(6.1) \qquad \frac{dP(t)}{dt} = AP(t), \qquad P(0) = I ,$$

where A is a matrix indexed by the set of states, $A = (a((\ell, m, n), (\ell', m', n'))$. Explicitly,

$$(6.2) \quad a((\ell, m, n), (\ell', m', n'))$$

$$= \frac{\mu(1-\alpha_1-\alpha_2-\alpha_3)}{N} \begin{cases} \ell(m+\beta+1) & \text{if } (\ell', m', n') = (\ell-1, m+1, n) \\ \ell(n+\gamma+1) & (\ell-1, m, n+1) \\ m(n+\gamma+1) & (\ell, m-1, n+1) \\ m(\ell+\alpha+1) & (\ell+1, m-1, n) \\ n(\ell+\alpha+1) & (\ell+1, m, n-1) \\ n(m+\beta+1) & (\ell, m+1, n-1) \end{cases}$$

$$a((\ell, m, n), (\ell, m, n))$$

$$= -\frac{\mu(1-\alpha_1-\alpha_2-\alpha_3)}{N}[(\ell+m)(n+\gamma+1) + (m+n)(\ell+\alpha+1) + (n+\ell)(m+\beta+1)] .$$

$a((\ell, m, n), (\ell', m', n')) = 0$, otherwise,

where

$$(6.3) \quad \alpha = \frac{N\alpha_1}{1-\alpha_1-\alpha_2-\alpha_3} - 1, \quad \beta = \frac{N\alpha_2}{1-\alpha_1-\alpha_2-\alpha_3} - 1, \quad \gamma = \frac{N\alpha_3}{1-\alpha_1-\alpha_2-\alpha_3} - 1 .$$

We introduce the set of positive weights

(6.4) $$\pi_{\ell,m,n} = \binom{\ell+\alpha}{\ell}\binom{m+\beta}{m}\binom{n+\gamma}{n}\Big/\binom{N+\alpha+\beta+\gamma+2}{N}$$

relative to which A is Hermitian in the following sense. For vectors $f = (f(\ell, m, n))$ whose (complex) components are indexed by the set of states we define the inner product

$$(f, g) = \sum f(\ell, m, n)\, \overline{g(\ell, m, n)}\, \pi_{\ell, m, n} .$$

Then if $Af = h$ is defined by

$$h(\ell, m, n) = \sum_{(\ell', m', n')} a((\ell, m, n), (\ell', m', n'))\, f(\ell', m', n')$$

we have the Hermitian property $(Af, g) = (f, Ag)$. The vector space has dimensions $d = (N+1)(N+2)/2$ so A has d eigenvalues $\lambda_1 \leq \lambda_2 \leq \cdots \leq \lambda_d$ and a corresponding orthonormal set of d eigenvectors $f_1, f_2, \ldots, f_d$:

$$Af_i = \lambda_i f_i ,$$

$$\sum f_i(\ell, m, n)\, f_j(\ell, m, n)\, \pi_{\ell, m, n} = \delta_{ij} .$$

The solution of (6.1) is

(6.5) $$P(t; (\ell, m, n), (\ell', m', n')) =$$

$$= \pi_{\ell', m', n'} \sum_{\nu=0}^{d} e^{\lambda_\nu t} f_\nu(\ell, m, n)\, f_\nu(\ell', m', n')$$

To find the eigenvalues and eigenvectors we proceed in the spirit of the method of separation of the variables. We look for solutions f of $Af = \lambda f$ of the form

$$f(\ell, m, n) = Q(\ell+m, \lambda)\, \varphi(\ell, m, n)$$

where Q does not depend on ℓ and m separately. The procedure is rather complicated, and we refer to [13] for details. The results are as follows. The eigenvalues are conveniently parametrized by pairs of integers (ξ, η) with

$$0 < \xi, \eta, \quad \xi + \eta \leq N .$$

To the pair (ξ, η) corresponds the eigenvalue

$$(6.6) \qquad \lambda(\xi, \eta) = -\frac{\mu(1-\alpha_1-\alpha_2-\alpha_3)}{N}(\xi+\eta)(\xi+\eta+\alpha+\beta+\gamma+2)$$

and the eigenvector

$$(6.7) \quad f(\ell, m, n; \xi, \eta) = \frac{\binom{N-\xi}{n}}{\binom{N}{n}} Q_\eta(\ell+m-\xi; \alpha+\beta+1+2\xi, \gamma, N-\xi)\, Q_\xi(\ell; \alpha, \beta, \ell+m)$$

where the Q's are Hahn polynomials. These eigenvectors form a complete orthogonal system and the normalizing constants are explicitly known. Thus we have all the ingredients of (6.5).

The eigenvalues are not all distinct, in fact there are only N+1 distinct eigenvalues,

$$\lambda_\nu = -\frac{\mu(1-\alpha_1-\alpha_2-\alpha_3)}{N}\nu(\nu+\alpha+\beta+\gamma+2), \qquad \nu = 0, 1, \ldots, N,$$

and λ_ν occurs with multiplicity $\nu+1$. The rate of convergence to the limiting distribution is

$$(6.8) \qquad e^{-\lambda_1 t} = \mu^{-\mu(\alpha_1+\alpha_2+\alpha_3)t}$$

much like (2.5). For a more extensive discussion and similar results relating to the multi-allele model without mutation we refer to [13].

Limiting procedures for the 3-allele mutation model exist in great profusion. Not only are there two dimensional versions of each limit procedure described in section 2, leading to two dimensional diffusion processes or two dimensional birth and death processes, but there are also cases in which the limit process may be a mixed birth and death and diffusion process. We describe a few examples, again indicating only the formalities involved and referring to [13] for details and further examples.

(i) Let $\alpha_1 = \gamma_1/N$, $\alpha_2 = \gamma_2/N$, $\alpha_3 = \gamma_3/N$, $t = N\tau$, where $\gamma_1, \gamma_2, \gamma_3$ are positive constants. If $N\to\infty$, $\ell/N \to x$, $m/N \to y$ where $0 < x, y, x+y < 1$ then, much as in example (i) of section 2, we get a limiting diffusion on the triangle $0 < x, y, x+y < 1$. The eigenfunction (6.7) converges to the function

(6.9) $\varphi(x, y; \xi, \eta)$

$$= (x+y)^{\xi} F\left(\begin{matrix} -\xi, & \xi+\gamma_1+\gamma_2-1 \\ & \gamma_1 \end{matrix} \middle| \frac{x}{x+y}\right) F\left(\begin{matrix} -\eta, & \eta+\gamma_1+\gamma_2+\gamma_3-1+2\xi \\ & \gamma_1+\gamma_2+2\xi \end{matrix} \middle| x+y\right)$$

($F\left(\begin{matrix} a, b \\ c \end{matrix}\middle| x\right)$ is another notation for the hypergeometric function ${}_2F_1(a, b; c; x)$) which is a polynomial of degree $\xi+\eta$ in the two variables x, y. This system of polynomials ($\xi, \eta = 0, 1, 2, \ldots$) is (as one may easily verify) a complete orthogonal system on the triangle $0 < x, y, x+y < 1$ with respect to the weight function

$$(6.10) \qquad \rho(x, y) = \frac{\Gamma(\gamma_1 + \gamma_2 + \gamma_3)}{\Gamma(\gamma_1)\,\Gamma(\gamma_2)\,\Gamma(\gamma_3)}\, x^{\gamma_1-1}\, y^{\gamma_2-1}\, (1-x-y)^{\gamma_3-1} .$$

This solves a problem raised in [4] (vol. 2, p. 271). The system of differential equations (6.1) passes over into the diffusion equation

$$(6.11) \qquad \frac{\partial P}{\partial \tau} = \frac{\mu}{\rho(x, y)} \left\{ \left(\frac{\partial}{\partial x} - \frac{\partial}{\partial y}\right) \left[xy\, \rho(x, y) \left(\frac{\partial P}{\partial x} - \frac{\partial P}{\partial y}\right)\right] + \frac{\partial}{\partial x}\left[x(1-x-y)\,\rho(x, y)\,\frac{\partial P}{\partial x}\right] + \frac{\partial}{\partial y}\left[y(1-x-y)\,\rho(x, y)\,\frac{\partial P}{\partial y}\right]\right\}$$

$$= \mu \left\{ x(1-x)\frac{\partial^2 P}{\partial x^2} - 2xy\frac{\partial^2 P}{\partial x\,\partial y} + y(1-y)\frac{\partial^2 P}{\partial y^2} + \left[\gamma_1-1-(\gamma_1+\gamma_3-2)\,x\right]\frac{\partial P}{\partial x} + \left[\gamma_2-1-(\gamma_2+\gamma_3-2)\,y\right]\frac{\partial P}{\partial y}\right\}$$

and the transition probabilities converge to the transition probabilities of a diffusion on the triangle governed by this equation.

(ii) If we set $\alpha_1 = \gamma_1/N$, $\alpha_2 = \gamma_2/N$, $\alpha_3 = \gamma_3$, $t = \tau$ and let $N \to \infty$ with ℓ, m fixed then the transition probabilities of the mutation process converge to the transition probabilities of a two dimensional birth and death process. (Here the mutations $A_i \to A_1$, $A_i \to A_2$ are rare compared to the mutations $A_i \to A_3$.) A state of the limiting two dimensional process is denoted by a pair of non-negative integers

(ℓ, m), which can be interpreted as the number of rare A_1, A_2 mutants in an infinite population. The system of differential equations (4.1) passes over into the infinite system for the two dimensional birth and death process,

(6.12)

$$\frac{dP}{d\tau}(\tau, (\ell, m), (\ell', m'))$$

$$= \mu\{\ell P(\tau, (\ell-1, m), (\ell', m')) + [\ell(1-\gamma_3) + \gamma_1] P(\tau, (\ell+1, m), (\ell', m'))$$

$$+ mP(\tau, (\ell, m-1), (\ell', m')) + [m(1-\gamma_3) + \gamma_2] P(\tau, (\ell, m+1), (\ell', m'))$$

$$- [(\ell+m)(2-\gamma_3) + \gamma_1 + \gamma_2] P(\tau, (\ell, m), (\ell', m'))\} .$$

The limit process is a direct product of two one dimensional processes of the same type as the limit in example (ii) of section 2.

(iii) Consider the case

$$\alpha_1 = \frac{\gamma_1}{N}, \qquad \alpha_2 = \text{fixed}, \qquad \alpha_3 = \text{fixed} .$$

If we let

$$\ell = \ell$$

$$m = \frac{N\alpha_2}{\alpha_2 + \alpha_3} + x\sqrt{Nc} \qquad c = \frac{2\alpha_2\alpha_3}{(\alpha_2 + \alpha_3)^3}$$

$$n = \frac{N\alpha_3}{\alpha_2 + \alpha_3} - x\sqrt{Nc} - \ell$$

and let $N \to \infty$, the transition probability function $P(t; (\ell, m, n), (\ell', m', n'))$ converges to the direct product probability

$$R(\tau; x, y)\, \widetilde{R}(\tau; \ell/\ell')$$

where $R(\tau; x, y)$ is the transition probability function of the Ornstein-Uhlenbeck process (3.2) with parameter $\mu(\alpha_2 + \alpha_3)$ in place of μ and $\widetilde{R}(\tau; \ell/\ell')$ is the transition probability function of the limit process of example (iii) with birth rate $(1-\alpha_2-\alpha_3)\,\ell + \gamma_1$ and death rate ℓ .

REFERENCES

1. R. Bellman and T. E. Harris, Recurrent times for the Ehrenfest model, Pac. J. Math. 1 (1951), 184-188.

2. J. Crow and M. Kimura, Some genetic problems in natural populations, 4 (1956), 1-22, Proc. Third Berkeley Symp. Math. Statis Prob., University of California Press.

3. J. L. Doob, The Brownian movement and stochastic equations, Annals of Math., 40 (1942), 351-69.

4. A. Erdélyi, Higher Transcendental Functions, Vol. II, McGraw-Hill, New York, 1953.

5. W. Feller, Two singular diffusion problems, Ann. of Math. 54 (1951), 173-182.

6. ____________, Diffusion processes in genetics (1951), 227-34, Proc. Second Berkeley Symp. Math. Statis. Prob., University of California Press.

7. R. A. Fisher, The Genetical Theory of Natural Selection, Oxford University Press, Oxford, 1930.

8. M. Kac, Random walk and the theory of Brownian motion, Amer. Math. Monthly 54 (1947), 369-391.

9. S. Karlin and J. McGregor, Linear growth, birth and death processes, J. Math. and Mech. 7, No. 4 (July 1958), 643-662.

10. ____________, The Hahn polynomials, formulas and an application, Scripta Math. 26, Spring Issue, Nov. 1961, 33-46.

11. ____________, On a genetics model of Moran, Proc. Camb. Philos. Soc. 58, (1962), 299-311.

12. S. Karlin and J. McGregor, Limit diffusion approximations of stochastic processes occurring in population genetics, to be published.

13. ____________, On a multiallelic gene frequency stochastic process, to be published.

14. M. Kimura, Stochastic processes and distribution of gene frequencies under natural selection 20 (1955), 33-53; Cold Spring Harbor Symp. on Quantitative Biology, Biological Lab. Cold Spring Harbor, L.I.

15. ____________, Some problems of stochastic processes in genetics. Ann. Math. Statist. 28 (1957), 882-901.

16. P. A. P. Moran, Random processes in genetics, Proc. Camb. Philos. Soc. 54 (1958), 60-72.

17. ____________, The distribution of gene frequency in a bisexual diploid population. Proc. Camb. Philos. Soc. 54 (1958), 468-474.

18. ____________, A general theory of the distribution of gene frequencies. I. Overlapping generations. Proc. Roy. Soc. London Ser. B, 149 (1958), 102-112.

19. ____________, The Statistical Processes of Evolutionary Theory, Clarendon Press, Oxford, 1962.

20. Szego, G., Orthogonal Polynomials, Amer. Math. Soc. Coll. Pub. 23 (1939).

21. S. Wright, The genetical structure of populations. Ann. Eugenics, 15 (1951), 323-354.

22. G. A. Watterson, Some theoretical aspects of diffusion theory in population genetics, Ann. Math. Stat. 33, No. 3, Sept. 1962, 939-956.

Prepared under auspices of the
National Institutes of Health
GM 10452-01A1

DISCUSSION PARTICIPANTS

Dr. Alice M. Brues
University of Oklahoma School of Medicine,
Oklahoma City, Oklahoma

Dr. James F. Crow
Professor of Medical Genetics and Acting Dean,
School of Medicine, University of Wisconsin
Madison, Wisconsin

Dr. Walter T. Federer
Biological Statistics, Biometrics Unit,
Cornell University
Ithaca, New York

Dr. Donald L. Iglehart
Upson Hall, Cornell University
Ithaca, New York

Professor Sewall Wright
Department of Genetics
University of Wisconsin
Madison, Wisconsin

DISCUSSION

Alice M. Brues. Is it true of the Moran model and other continuous models, that an individual is placed in the population as a "parent" immediately upon birth? This tends to increase the speed of drift. The length of time an individual is held in a non-reproductive stage is a factor to be included.

Samuel Karlin. We know of no stochastic two stage population growth model that has been formulated to take account of a nonreproductive and reproductive state of an individual. Such a model would certainly be worth studying.

It is true that the Moran model treats each new individual as an immediate potential parent which is somewhat unrealistic. In this respect it is possible to modify the model by associating to each new birth a probability p that the individual will mature and be capable of producing offspring and with probability $1-p$ of no progeny. Analytically this has only the effect of adjusting the intensity of the rate of events (birth-death events).

James F. Crow. I should like to say that, as a population geneticist who uses mathematical methods but who is really not a mathematician, I am very pleased that mathematicians are getting interested in these problems. As in many previous instances in the history of science the mathematical rigor comes some time after the rough and ready methods of the applied mathematician. The diffusion models are so powerful and useful that it is important that their underlying assumptions be understood and their range of applicability known.

Samuel Karlin. We certainly agree with Dr. Crow that it is important to understand the relevance, range of applicability, similarities, and contrasting implications of various models used to derive qualitative conclusions concerning physical or biological phenomena. We also believe that one purpose of any theoretical investigation is to point out logical inconsistencies as well as new possibilities in interpretation and analysis. We hope that the wealth of limit processes for the Wright and Moran model uncovered in this paper serve to clarify to some extent the nature of each separate approximation as well as the relevance of each. This problem is not at all settled and we urge that further analysis of these approximations in conjunction with computation be done. We ourselves are contemplating some program of this kind.

Walter T. Federer. Aren't there many choices of α_1, α_2, t, and ℓ which will give rise to a Fokker-Planck equation? Since there appears to be fairly substantial genetic evidence that α_1 and α_2 should be fixed, would it be more fruitful of research time to investigate all cases where α_1 and α_2 are fixed and which lead to the six limit processes (or more) described in your lecture?

Samuel Karlin. In introducing the diffusion approximation one usually says that the possible values of the gene frequency x are $0, \frac{1}{N}, \frac{2}{N}, \frac{3}{N}, \ldots$ and when N is large x can be treated as a continuous variable. On this basis one could expect the diffusion to be obtained as a limit when $N \to \infty$. Unfortunately if the mutation rates per gene are fixed and $N \to \infty$ the limiting diffusion equation which has been most widely used is not obtained as the correct limit. For more details on this we refer to our answer to Professor S. Wright's second question.

Donald L. Iglehart. I would like to ask the speaker two questions. The first deals with the two allele case which leads to the one-dimensional birth and death process. You have implied that if one considers selection as well as mutation, it is still possible to obtain limiting diffusion processes. Can you tell me in that case if it is also possible to obtain explicit expressions for the probability transition functions which describe the transient part of the process?

Secondly, in the multi-dimensional birth and death processes which arise when you consider multi-allelic models, are the Markov chains reversible and if so, can explicit self-adjoint representations be obtained?

Samuel Karlin. The standard limit diffusion of gene frequency (Wright's diffusion process) involving a selection factor possesses a solution expressible in terms of spheroidal wave functions. In contrast, the usual diffusion process corresponding to mutation and migration without selection can be analyzed in terms of the much simpler hypergeometric functions. This fact was pointed out by Kimura and shows the intrinsically more complicated nature of the selection model. In the case of finite population stochastic selection model, it is not known as yet how to obtain explicitly solutions. Even adequate approximations appear to be unknown.

The multiallelic haploid gene frequency version of the Moran model leads to a reversible process. An explicit time dependent solution is indicated in the last section of this paper. Diploid models present non-reversible birth and death processes whose solutions are unknown as yet. The whole problem of analyzing the structure of multi-dimensional birth and death processes of nonreversible type, is one of the important directions of future research. Models of this kind occur not only in population genetics but also in epidemic theory, ecological models and general population growth problems.

Sewall Wright. I do not understand the pertinance for population genetics of the various alternatives for mutation rate per gene that you present (γ/N, γ/N^d, fixed), without questioning the desirability of such exploration from the standpoint of pure mathematics. Observation indicates that mutation rates vary specifically from gene to gene, are affected by temperature and of course by the presence of mutagens, but there is no reason to suppose that they are functions of population size. It would seem better to assign single symbols such as u and v of my formulae to the specific mutations of particular genes and treat the number of mutations of the corresponding sorts in a population of size N as $2Nu$ and $2Nv$ rather than by single symbols such as γ_1 and γ_2 .

Samuel Karlin. The diffusion equations for gene frequencies which have been widely and successfully used as approximations are those of case (ii) in table 1 and case I in table 2. These diffusion equations do not arise by passage to the limit with the mutation rates per gene fixed, but only, so far as we know, when the mutation rates approach zero like $1/N$. (In this connection, see also references [6] and [22] of our paper.)

The result does not imply that the usual diffusion approximation is not useful but it does imply that if the mutation rates are fixed and the population size N increases then the accuracy of the approximation will not improve. On the contrary the limit process when $N \to \infty$ with the mutation rates fixed, as indicated in case (i) of table I, exhibits fluctuations which are too small to affect the gene frequencies. Under these circumstances the gene frequency behaves in a deterministic way. This fact is rather surprising at first but appears more natural in view of the following. The presence of mutation rates tends to stabilize the gene frequency at an equilibrium value $\alpha_1/(\alpha_1 + \alpha_2)$. Random sampling on the other hand results in random fluctuations of the gene frequency and the magnitude of these fluctuations approaches zero as $N \to \infty$. It is not unreasonable then that, for larger N, smaller mutation rates are appropriate to balance the random sampling effects.

The cases with mutation rates of order γ/N^d and appropriate time scales have been recorded because they are of an intermediate character between the usual diffusion approximation and the deterministic case.

Sewall Wright. Another matter that I would like to take up is the interpretation of the stochastic distribution of gene frequencies. It can be looked upon as the distribution over an adequate period of time. In the case of the complete absence of systematic pressure on gene frequency ($\Delta q = 0$) but sampling variance $\sigma^2_{\Delta q} = q(1-q)/(2N)$ the rate of decrease in heterozygosis and ultimately the rate of fixation is just $1/(2N)$ (under random union of genetes). This suggests that a number of generations equal to a small multiple of population size is adequate. In my theory, N nearly always refers to the effective number in a local population that may be treated as panmictic (a deme) and thus is usually rather small. It is also possible to look at the distribution as that which would be exhibited by a large number of similar demes at a single moment and this is what I have usually had in mind.

Samuel Karlin. This seems to check with our table 1 case (ii) in which a unit of diffusion time, $\Delta\tau = 1$, corresponds to $\Delta t = N$, i.e. a number of generations equal to the population size. The other limiting cases in table 1 correspond to quite different choices of the time scale.

The choice of the time scale of observation is certainly important in determining the appropriate limit process. In deriving approximating diffusion processes it is always essential to properly relate the time scale with the state variable (cf. [6], [22]). Some confusion occurring in the literature on population genetics bears on this problem.

Sewall Wright. A third question is the closeness of approximation of the continuous model of stochastic distributions to the discrete model. In using the continuous model in 1931 I was not worried about the closeness in the major portion of the range in which there could hardly be any difference of biological significance under the conditions assumed in setting up the integral equation that I used at that time. I was concerned, however, about the terminal exchanges between loss and mutation. It is a simple matter to determine algebraically the exact steady state frequencies in populations of 2 or 3 with random union of gametes. I did this for the steady state under very small reversible mutation rates ($\varphi(q) = C/q(1-q)$, for a very small rate of irreversible mutation ($\varphi(q) = C/q$) and for complete absence of mutation ($\varphi(q) = 1$) . In the case of 3 monoecious individuals, the results were as follows, using here corrected values published later in the case of irreversible mutation.

	Steady State		Irreversible Mutation		Steady Fixation		
Exchange	$\varphi(q) = C/c(1-q)$	exact	$\varphi(q) = C/q$	exact		$f(q) = \frac{1}{2N-1}$	exact
$\frac{2N-1}{4N}f(\frac{1}{2N}) =$	11.0	10.8	18.25	16.31	$\frac{1}{4N} =$ loss of A	8.33	8.33
1A: 5a	26.3	27.5	43.8	42.40		20.0	18.3
2A: 4a	16.4	15.4	21.9	21.07		20.0	21.0
3A: 3a	14.6	14.1	14.6	15.54		20.0	21.4
4A: 2a	16.4	15.4	10.9	11.99		20.0	21.0
5A: 1a	26.3	27.5	8.8	9.00		20.0	18.3
Total unfixed	100.0	99.9	100.0	100.00		100.0	100.0
exchange	11.0	10.8	loss of a 3.65	4.34	loss of a	8.33	8.33

These results indicated that even in this very extreme case, the continuous distribution gives a fairly good approximation. After correspondence with R. A. Fisher in 1929 in the course of which the manuscript of the 1931 paper was sent to him, he accepted my formulae in place of ones that he had published in 1922 and he calculated the exact distributions for large N . These appeared in his book in 1930.

	Steady State			Steady Fixation	
	approximate	exact		approximate	exact
Exchange	1.000 (2/q)	1.000	loss of A	.500	.500
1A:(2N-1)q	2.000	2.241		1.000	.818
2A:(2N-2)q	1.000	.954		1.000	.917
3A:(2N-3)q	.667	.672		1.000	.945
4A:(2N-4)q	.500	.501		1.000	.958
5A:(2N-5)q	.400	.400		1.000	.967
6A:(2N-6)q	.333	.333		1.000	.972

The terminal exchanges and all class frequencies except those of populations with only one to three representatives of the gene are given satisfactorily by the approximate solution in the case of the steady state. The agreement is less satisfactory in the case of steady fixation (except for the rate of fixation) but are not very seriously in error except for very small numbers of representatives. There can be no problem where the steady state solution is i-shaped. Thus the approximate formulae seem reasonably satisfactory from the biological standpoint in extremes in population size and in form of the distribution.

Samuel Karlin. We are planning to do some numerical computations to compare the various continuous diffusion models with the discrete model, but have not done so as yet. Our results indicate that although mutation rates should be regarded as fixed, it is important to consider the relation between the order of magnitude of mutation rates and population size.

The relative initial frequencies of the two types of genes is also a determining factor for the appropriate approximating process. In the case of a rare mutant the relevant approximating process is a branching process for discrete time processes and a birth and death in the corresponding continuous version. It is meaningless to talk about gene frequency since it is essentially zero and remains so. There are several gradations of zero frequency depending whether the population of the rare mutant is finite and small, or large, but of a smaller order of magnitude thanthe wild type, etc. These considerations are relevant in determining the correct continuous approximation.

Because of the different forms of the solutions we do not believe that the probabilistic quantity like rate of fixation, conditional steady state distributions, etc. can be robust with respect to the various diffusion approximations.

The computations in your first table are interesting. In the case at hand because $N = 3$ all measurements indeed reflect bona fide frequencies. However, in order to properly obtain boundary effects, N would have to be much larger.

We do not understand the basis of the computation of the second table. So far as we know the exact solutions of the model with large N have never been found. The standard limit theorems for branching processes (due to Yaglom) shows that the distribution of the population of mutant genes, properly normalized and conditioned that no fixation has occurred is an exponential distribution. The conclusions derived from this limit theorem do not agree with the figures of Table 2.

WILLIAM G. COCHRAN and MILES DAVIS

Stochastic Approximation to the Median Effective Dose in Bioassay

INTRODUCTION

When a stimulus is applied in some types of experimentation, all that we can observe is whether a certain type of response does or does not take place. With explosive powders, an impact applied to the powder may or may not explode it. An insect or animal may die or may survive when given a specific dose of a toxic agent or a virus inoculum. For practical purposes, what we would probably like to know in such experiments is the largest amount of stimulus that can be given without any of the subjects responding, and the smallest amount that will cause all the subjects to respond; e. g. the largest shock that an explosive can stand without any risk of an explosion and the smallest shock that is certain to ignite the powder. But a little reflection, assisted by some attempts to conduct experiments, soon shows that these amounts of stimulus are almost impossible to determine experimentally. Instead, the common practice is to estimate the amount of stimulus that will cause half the subjects to respond. This may be called the median effective dose (ED50) or, in toxicology, the median lethal dose (LD50) .

This paper describes some recent work in which the ideas of stochastic approximation are used in the hope of developing experimental methods for estimating the median effective dose that are more economical and convenient in certain situations than the standard methods in current use. Although the mathematical theory of stochastic approximation has some fascinating aspects, the orientation here is applied, and questions of rigor and generality will not be stressed. Further, the possible experimental plans based on stochastic approximation have by no means been thoroughly explored as yet, so that the present account is of the nature of an interim report.

Mathematical background

Suppose that we could determine for each subject in a population the amount X of the stimulus that would just produce the response in that subject. Over a population of subjects, the variate X would follow a frequency distribution, sometimes called the <u>tolerance</u> distribution. Let $\phi(X)$ be the frequency function. If now a fixed amount x is applied to every subject in the population, the proportion P of subjects who respond is given by

$$P = \int_{-\infty}^{x} \phi(t)\,dt \ .$$

Similarly, if the dose x is applied to a random sample of m subjects, the proportion p who respond in the sample will be distributed as a binomial variate with mean P and sample size m, assuming that the population is very much larger than the sample.

Write $y = (t - \mu)/\sigma$, where μ is the median and σ the standard deviation of the tolerance distribution. Suppose that $\phi(t)\,dt$ becomes $f(y)\,dy$. Then

(1) $$P = \int_{-\infty}^{(x-\mu)/\sigma} f(y)\,dy = \int_{-\infty}^{\beta(x-\mu)} f(y)\,dy$$

where $\beta = 1/\sigma$. In biological assay the quantity β, called the <u>slope</u>, is a commonly used term. The name arises because a standard method of analyzing the data is to transform the p values to variates z where

(2) $$p = \int_{-\infty}^{z} f(y)\,dy \ .$$

By comparison with (1) it is clear that if the binomial errors can be neglected, the variate z will plot against x as a straight line with slope β.

In practice some simplifying assumptions are made about the tolerance distribution $\phi(X)$. By a suitable choice of the scale in which X is recorded (usually the log dose scale in bioassay), it is assumed that $\phi(X)$ is symmetrical about its mean and median, and depends only on the parameters μ and σ. Most commonly, $\phi(X)$ is taken to be either the normal or the logistic frequency distribution. These two assumptions usually give closely similar results, the logistic being in some respects easier to work with.

One important consequence of these assumptions may be noted. Suppose that the reduced form of the tolerance frequency function $f(y)$ is the same for two different stimuli and that σ is also the same, only the means μ, μ' being different. It follows that the plots of z against x for the two stimuli should be, apart from binomial errors, two parallel straight lines. This fact is used in practice to provide a test of significance of the null hypothesis that the two σ's are equal. Further, the dose x of one stimulus that produces a specified proportion P of responders is $\mu + Z\sigma$, where Z is the transform of P as in equation (2). It follows, and this is the important point, that the difference in dosages required to produce any specified P has the constant value $\mu - \mu'$. If x is measured on a log scale so that μ and μ' are the logs of the actual dosages, this means that the ratio of the doses required to produce any specified P for the two stimuli is a constant. This constant, inverted, is called the relative potency of the two stimuli. For stimuli that have similar modes of action, there is a good deal of evidence, although most of it is based on small samples, that the hypothesis of parallelism (i.e. $\sigma = \sigma'$) can often be supported.

Non-sequential experiments

When an experiment is being planned, the investigator does not of course know the values of μ and σ. As will appear later, his degree of ignorance about these quantities plays an important role both in the choice of an experimental strategy and in determining the precision of the experiment that he decides to conduct. In practice the accuracy of initial guesses about μ and σ varies greatly from one situation to another. In bioassay, a standard agent on which much previous research has been done is frequently compared with a new agent thought to have a similar mode of action. The values of both μ and σ should be fairly well known for the standard. For the new agent, σ' will be fairly well known if it can be assumed that σ' is approximately equal to σ, but μ may be known only poorly. However, if essentially nothing can be guessed about μ for the new agent, the investigator is likely to start with a small pilot experiment, perhaps involving only one subject at each dose, from which he makes a rough initial estimate x_0 of the ED50. In the absence of a standard agent, neither μ nor σ may be at all well known initially. With inanimate "subjects", such as explosives or plastic water pipe, Wetherill (1963), the material may be more uniform so that μ and σ can be guessed fairly successfully in advance from previous results on similar material.

In the calculations that we have made, the properties of stochastic approximation methods have been investigated for starting values out to $\pm 8\sigma$ away from μ. This is probably a wider range than is needed for any practical application. The value of σ, with x measured on a log scale, is assumed known initially to within a 4 to 1 ratio. Although this range may be too narrow for some biological research, it appeared reasonable from inspection of data collected by Gaddum (1933) and Bliss and Cattell (1943). These workers summarized the estimated values of σ found in bioassays on several different experimental animals with death as the response. The calculations of Brownlee, Hodges and Rosenblatt (1953) and Wetherill (1963), who also considered this problem, amount to assuming that σ is known within a 2 to 1 ratio.

The usual method of experimentation is illustrated in Figure 1, which sketches the relation between P and X, for a large range of values of X, on the assumption of a normal tolerance distribution. (For a smaller value of σ, the curve would be steeper in the rising part.) Given an initial guess at μ, the practice is to test at a number of different levels of the stimulus centered about this initial guess. The levels are illustrated by the points x_1, x_2, x_3, x_4 in Figure 1. The number of levels may vary from 2 to about 8: they are often equally-spaced on the x (log dose) scale. The idea is to obtain at least two levels like x_2 and x_3 that are in the rising part of the curve and straddle the ED50. Levels like x_1 and x_4 which give zero or 100% response contribute little or nothing in the analysis.

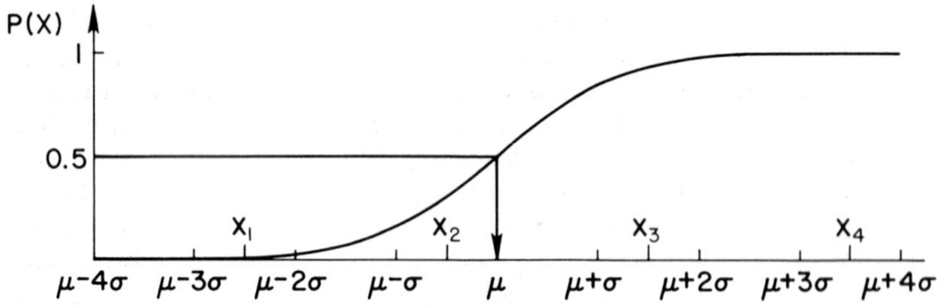

Fig.1. Relation between P(X) and X.

Estimation of the ED50 from the results of such an experiment has been extensively studied. The more sophisticated methods depend on transforming to the z scale already mentioned, estimating μ by fitting the linear regression of z on x. Relatively little advice is available in the literature on the planning of such experiments, except when μ and σ are well known in advance. The problem of planning is complex. Decisions have to be made about the number of levels, the distances between them, and the numbers of subjects to be tested at the different levels. Part of the problem is that the exact distributions of the maximum likelihood (M.L.) estimate and of other commonly used estimates of μ have been worked out only for the asymptotic case in which the number of animals tested at each level is large. Bross (1950) and Berkson (1955), who worked the M. L. estimate for specific small experiments, both encountered a number of troublesome cases in which the estimate either did not exist or appeared ridiculous.

In attempting to give positive advice for experiments using around 50 subjects, Finney (1951) worked out the effective variances of the ED50, assuming that the asymptotic formula remains valid, for different numbers and spacings of levels. The calculations were made for both normal and logistic tolerance distributions. To illustrate, his recommendation for an experiment with four levels in that equal numbers of subjects be tested at levels expected to give 15%, 35%, 65% and 85% responses. With a normal tolerance law, this amounts to selecting the levels $x_0 - 1.04\sigma_0$, $x_0 - 0.38\sigma_0$, $x_0 + 0.38\sigma_0$, $x_0 + 1.04\sigma_0$, where x_0, σ_0 are the preliminary guesses at μ and σ. However, if x_0 is likely to be in error by more than one standard deviation, this set of levels can scarcely be recommended. For instance, if x_0 is actually at $\mu + 1.2\sigma$ while σ_0 is correct, the lowest level of stimulus is set at $\mu + 0.16\sigma$. The expected response at this level is 56% and the four levels do not straddle the ED50 at all. If x_0 is correct but $\sigma_0 = \sigma/2$, the actual effective variance from the asymptotic formula is about double the value obtained when σ_0 is correct. There appears to be no available discussion of satisfactory plans for experiments of modest size in which the investigator has only a rough idea initially of the values of μ and σ.

The Up and Down method

The two stochastic approximation methods that will be considered differ from the standard plan in that the experiment is conducted sequentially. The Up and Down method, Dixon and Mood (1948), was first suggested in connection with the testing of explosives by dropping weights on the powder from different heights. In its original form a single subject is tested at any given time. If at the nth step in the process the stimulus is at level x_n, the sequential rule is that the $(n + 1)$th test be made at level

$$x_{n+1} = \begin{cases} x_n + d & \text{if there is no response at } x_n \\ x_n - d & \text{if there is a response at } x_n, \end{cases}$$

where d is a constant. When the experiment is terminated at some chosen value $n = N$, Dixon and Mood give a graph by which the M. L. estimate of μ is obtained, assuming a normal tolerance distribution.

From the asymptotic theory they recommend that the step size $\underline{d}$ should be approximately equal to σ .

The performance of this process in small samples was studied by Brownlee, Hodges and Rosenblatt (1953) . As a simpler alternative to the M. L. estimate they suggest taking $\hat{\mu}$ as the mean of the levels x_i at which the tests were conducted, omitting the starting level x_1 but including the level x_{N+1} at which the next test would have been made had the experiment not stopped at X_N .

The requirement that subjects be tested one at a time severely restricts the utility of this method, since the verdict (response or no response) must be known almost at once if the experiment is not to last an undesirable length of time. In this paper we wish to consider plans that will be feasible if the response is known within an hour or less. This implies that an experiment with $N = 8$ takes up to a day to perform. To meet this situation and still amass a reasonable size of sample, Brownlee, Hodges and Rosenblatt suggest that several processes be run simultaneously with the same starting value x_1 . As an estimate $\bar{\hat{\mu}}$ they propose the mean of the estimates $\hat{\mu}_i$ obtained from the different runs. Thus if a sample size of 48 is wanted, six runs with $N = 8$ each might be made. This method is not as accurate as a run of 48 single subjects, because the estimates $\hat{\mu}_i$ are biased unless x_1 happens to equal μ, and their average $\bar{\hat{\mu}}$ is subject to the same bias. (The estimate for 48 single subjects is also biased, but the bias is in general smaller.)

Although less efficient, this plan has one possible advantage for estimating the standard error of $\bar{\hat{\mu}}$. If the bias in $\bar{\hat{\mu}}$ is negligible relative to its standard error, the quantity $\sqrt{\Sigma(\hat{\mu}_i-\bar{\hat{\mu}})^2/k(k-1)}$ is an almost unbiased estimate of s. e. $(\bar{\hat{\mu}})$, where k is the number of repetitions. Dews and Berkson (1954) have produced evidence to suggest that the customary estimates of the standard error of the ED50, computed from the internal results of a single trial, may seriously overrate the precision of the estimate as judged from its stability in repeated experiments of the same type. Their tentative opinion is that the discrepancy is due primarily to an "error of dosage" i. e., to a group of factors that may influence the constancy of the effective administration of the dose. A standard error computed from the observed variability in the $\hat{\mu}_i$ will contain a contribution due to this "error of dosage." On the other hand the number of available degrees of freedom may be scanty.

The Robbins-Monro process (1951)

This is a general process for estimating the value of X for which a monotonic function $M(X)$ of X attains some specified value α , in situations in which the available estimate $Y(X)$ of $M(X)$ is subject to error. The process has also been adapted by Kiefer and Wolfowitz (1952) to the estimation of the turning value of a regression function. In its application to the estimation of the ED50 the sequential rule may be stated as follows. At the _n_th step let m_n subjects be tested at level x_n and let the proportion dying be p_n. Then

(3) $$x_{n+1} = x_n - a_n(p_n - \frac{1}{2})$$

where the a_n are a sequence of positive numbers such that Σa_n diverges and Σa_n^2 converges. When the experiment is stopped at the Nth step, the estimate $\hat{\mu}_{RM}$ of the ED50 is simply the level x_{N+1} at which the next test would have taken place.

From consideration of the asymptotic distribution of x_{N+1}, Hodges and Lehmann (1956) recommend that $a_n = c/n$, where c is a constant. The rule then becomes

(4) $$x_{n+1} = x_n - \frac{c}{n}(p_n - \frac{1}{2}) .$$

Note that, unlike the Up and Down method, the steps become shorter as n increases. The step size also depends on how close the observed proportion of responders p_n is to 1/2.

With this choice of the a_n it has been shown that for any of the tolerance distributions likely to be encountered in practice, $\hat{\mu}_{RM}$ is asymptotically normally distributed with mean μ. If m subjects are tested at each step, the asymptotic variance after N steps is

(5) $$V(\hat{\mu}_{RM}) = \frac{c^2}{4mN(2c\beta f_0 - 1)}$$

where $f_0 = f(0)$ is the ordinate of the tolerance distribution at the ED50. This result requires that $c > 1/2\beta f_0$. The value of c that minimizes (5) is $c = 1/\beta f_0$. The minimum variance is

(6) $$V_{min}(\hat{\mu}_{RM}) = \frac{1}{4mN\beta^2 f_0^2} = \frac{\sigma^2}{4mNf_0^2} .$$

For the normal tolerance distribution $f_0 = 1/\sqrt{2\pi}$ and the minimizing value of $c = c_0 = \sqrt{2\pi}\,\sigma = 2.506\sigma$. (Note that the largest step size that can be taken, which happens when all subjects respond or fail to respond at the first test, is $\frac{1}{2}c_0$ or 1.25σ). The minimum variance is $\pi\sigma^2/2mN$.

The small-sample behavior of the Up and Down and RM processes

The results to be discussed here are for experiments with $mN = 12$, 24 or 48 subjects, involving not more than 12 steps. We supposed that the investigator who guesses that σ lies between known values σ_L and σ_H will use as his estimate $\sigma_1 = \sqrt{\sigma_L \sigma_H}$. Thus if $\sigma_H/\sigma_L = 2$ and if the true σ actually lies between these limits, the estimate σ_1 will lie somewhere between $\sigma/\sqrt{2} = 0.71\sigma$ and $\sqrt{2}\,\sigma = 1.41\sigma$. If $\sigma_H/\sigma_L = 4$, then σ_1 lies between $\sigma/2$ and 2σ.

For the Up and Down process, Brownlee, Hodges and Rosenblatt give recurrence relations by which the mean and mean square error (MSE) of their estimate $\hat{\mu}$, and hence of $\hat{\bar{\mu}}$, can be calculated. From these relations they computed values for $\sigma_1 = 2\sigma/3$, σ, $3\sigma/2$ and for a range of starting values x_1. For the RM process the mean and MSE of $\hat{\mu}_{RM}$ were programmed for the IBM 704 (later for the 7090) for $\sigma_1 = \sigma/2, 2\sigma/3, \sigma, 3\sigma/2$, and 2σ. Both calculations assume a normal tolerance distribution. In both cases it is supposed that the investigator tries to use the recommended optimum step size. That is, he takes $d = \sigma_1$ for the Up and Down process and $c = \sqrt{2\pi}\,\sigma_1$ for the RM process.

The MSE of the estimate will be used to gauge the accuracy of the process. Our immediate interest is in the values of the MSE for different starting values and guesses at σ. Except in minor details, the effects of different values of x_1 and σ_1 on the MSE were the same for the different combinations of m and N that were studied. Figures 2a (Up and Down) and 2b (RM) show the values of MSE/σ^2 for an experiment with 24 subjects having $m = 3$, $N = 8$ Each figure shows the plot of MSE/σ^2 against x_1 for $\sigma_1 = 2\sigma/3$, σ and $3\sigma/2$.

In every curve the MSE remains approximately constant for a range of starting values near μ. Thereafter it begins to rise, soon climbing very steeply. When $\sigma_1 = 2\sigma/3$, the range in which the MSE is constant is quite short, only out to about 0.7σ. As σ_1 increases this 'stable range' also increases in length. On the other hand, if the start is near the ED50, short steps perform better than long steps. In fact for $\sigma_1 = 2\sigma/3$ the constant value of MSE/σ^2 is about 0.06 for both processes, slightly below the optimum asymptotic value of $\pi/48 = 0.065$.

In general, the RM process is somewhat more accurate than the Up and Down process. For instance, with $\sigma_1 = 3\sigma/2$ the stable value of MSE/σ^2 is about 0.078 for the RM process as against 0.089 for the Up and Down process. Further, MSE/σ^2 does not rise above 0.1 for the RM process until x_1 is out at 3.9σ, as compared with 2.2σ for the Up and Down process. The differences in performance, however, are not in any sense sensational.

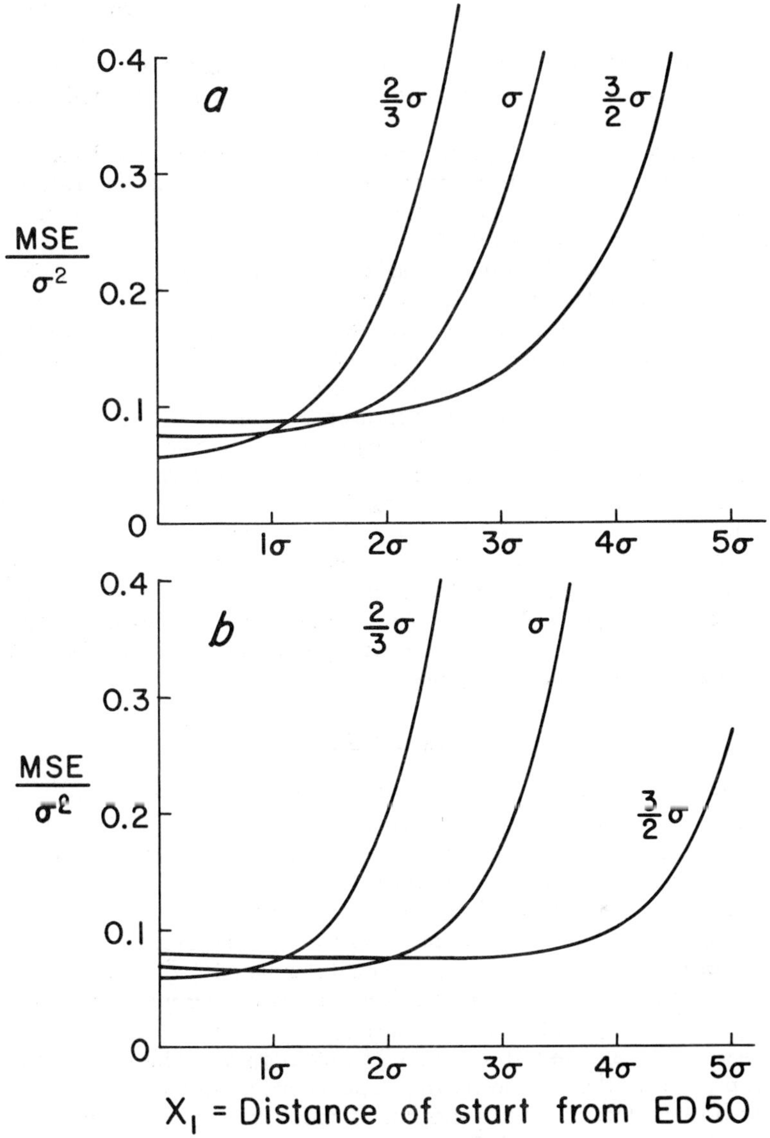

Fig. 2. MSE for Up and Down process *(a)* and MSE for RM process *(b)*. m = 3, N = 8.

The stable ranges become larger if more steps are used for the same number of subjects, for instance $m = 2$, $N = 12$ as against $m = 3$, $N = 8$, or if m is increased, for instance $m = 6$, $N = 8$ versus $m = 3$, $N = 8$. But in both cases the increases are usually small, the size of the stable range being determined primarily by the ratio σ_1/σ.

The explanation of the rapid rise in the MSE is an obvious one. When the starting value is distant from μ, several steps are needed to bring the test levels near to the neighborhood of μ. By the time the experiment is terminated, the test levels still lie mostly on the same side of μ as the starting value, so that the estimate is biased. In fact if we start far enough away on the positive side, then with a limited number of steps all subjects are practically certain to respond at all test levels. Thus the variance of the estimate tends to zero and the MSE is composed entirely of bias.

To summarize from the experimenter's point of view, the original Up and Down and RM processes can scarcely be recommended unless <u>either</u> μ or σ is well known in advance. If the starting guess is certain to lie within $\pm\sigma$ of μ and if σ is known within a 2 to 1 ratio, the experimenter might choose σ_1 slightly higher than $\sqrt{\sigma_L \sigma_H}$ to guard against underestimating σ by more than say 20%. This should keep him within the stable range. If σ is well known but μ is not, taking $\sigma_1 = 3\sigma/2$ should keep him in the stable range for starts out to 3σ. There is, however, need for plans that are more robust than the original processes.

Some variants

Numerous variants can be suggested in an attempt to make the MSE less dependent on a good initial guess at μ. For Up and Down runs with single subjects Brownlee, Hodges, and Rosenblatt considered omitting any initial run of levels at which the responses are all the same when computing $\hat{\mu}'$, the mean of the levels at which tests were conducted. For the RM process we investigated a 'delayed' version in which the factor $1/n$ is not introduced so long as p_n remains at 0 or at 1. We also examined two different choices for the a_n factors, namely $a_n = 2c/(n+1)$ and $a_n = 3c/(n+2)$. Both changes in the a_n have the effect of slowing down the rate at which the step size is diminished as the experiment proceeds.

As an illustration of the effects of these variants of the RM process, Table 1 shows MSE/σ^2 for each variant for a range of starting values out to 5σ. The experiment has $m = 3$, $N = 8$ and $\sigma_1 = \sigma$.

Table 1. Values of MSE/σ^2 for variants of the RM process.

Starting value x_1	Original process	Delayed process	$2c/(n+1)$	$3c/(n+2)$
0	.070	.070	.083	.104
$.62\sigma$	.067	.068	.083	.104
1.25σ	.065	.068	.082	.104
1.88σ	.070	.079	.083	.104
2.51σ	.102	.099	.085	.105
3.13σ	.206	.113	.096	.106
3.76σ	.516	.129	.132	.112
4.39σ	1.242	.140	.241	.123
5.01σ	2.697	.159	.570	.211

The delayed process is the most successful of the three RM variants. It gives about the same results as the original process out to $x_1 = 2.5\sigma$. Thereafter the MSE/σ^2 climbs, but much less drastically than with the original process. The two alternative choices of the a_n also extend the stable range as anticipated, but have the disadvantage that they give in general less precision than the original process if x_1 happens to be within $\pm 2\sigma$ of μ.

Summarizing for the whole range of calculations that we have carried out with these variants, it appears that no process of this type is entirely satisfactory for the investigator whose initial x_1 may lie far from μ.

A two-stage process

These considerations led us to examine a two-stage process. The first stage is conducted with single subjects and a step length of constant size. Its objective is to reach quickly a starting point for the second stage that is reasonably sure to be near the ED50. The plan has much flexibility, particularly with respect to how the first stage is conducted and how much effort is put into it. For instance, the first stage might be conducted non-sequentially by a simultaneous test of a subject at each of a set of six to ten levels, from which a quick estimate of a starting point for the second stage is made. This is in fact what is commonly done when work is started with a relatively unknown agent.

The type of first stage plan on which we have worked is as follows. A single animal is tested at level x_0. Thereafter the level is moved up or down by steps of length $1.25\sigma_1$ until a reversal in results is obtained. Stage 2 is started at the midpoint x_1 of the two levels at which the reversal occurs.

For given step size $1.25\sigma_1$ it turns out that the frequency distribution of x_1 depends very little on the original starting point x_0, no matter how far away x_0 is from μ. Since an animal started at or beyond $+4\sigma$ is practically certain to respond, it follows that x_1 has practically identical distributions for $x_0 = 2.75\sigma$, 4σ, 5.25σ, etc., the only difference being that different numbers of subjects are required to reach a reversal. The distribution of x_1 is not the same for $x_0 = 4\sigma$ as for $x_0 = 4.27\sigma$ (say) or $x_0 = 4.82\sigma$, but these distributions have closely similar means, shapes and MSE's. For example, when $\sigma_1 = \sigma$ and x_0 is far out, the mean of x_1 varies only between 0.11σ and 0.15σ and its MSE between $0.59\sigma^2$ and $0.62\sigma^2$.

We have already seen that if σ is underestimated, it is particularly important to ensure that the second stage RM or UP and Down process starts near μ. An advantage of the two-stage plan with steps that are some multiple of σ_1 is that if σ_1 is too small, the initial steps are short and the first stage gives a somewhat more precise estimate of μ than it does with long steps. Our choice of $1.25\sigma_1$ for the first stage step size is arbitrary, except that it is suggested by the RM process.

The average number $\bar{n}_1$ of subjects required to reach a reversal is not large. For starting points x_0 beyond $\pm 3.75\sigma$, the following equations give the averages approximately.

$$\sigma_1 = \sigma/2 \qquad \bar{n}_1 = 0.9 + 1.6x_0/\sigma$$

$$\sigma_1 = \sigma \qquad \bar{n}_1 = 1.4 + 0.8x_0/\sigma$$

$$\sigma_1 = 2\sigma. \qquad \bar{n}_1 = 1.8 + 0.4x_0/\sigma$$

The second stage starts at x_1 and consists either of the RM process with $c = \sqrt{2\pi}\,\sigma_1$ or the Up and Down process with step size σ_1. Examination of the MSE's at the end of stage 2 showed that while generally satisfactory they were still undesirably inflated by a bad underestimate of σ, as when $\sigma_1 = \sigma/2$. To improve this defect, we suggest that the reversal be checked by testing a second subject at each of the two levels. To show how this goes, suppose that $x < x'$ and that the first stage gives 0 at x and 1 at x', so that $x_1 = (x + x')/2$. If the two tests give $(0,0)$ at x and $(1,1)$ at x', or $(0,1)$ at x and $(1,0)$ at x', we keep x_1 unchanged. But we take $x_1 = x$ if the results are $(0,1)$ and $(1,1)$, and $x_1 = x'$ if they are $(0,0)$ and $(0,1)$. This change does not help if $\sigma_1 \geq \sigma$, but is useful insurance against an underestimate.

With this version of stage 1, Table 2 shows MSE/σ^2 for the estimate of μ at the end of stage 2 for experiments with 24 subjects requiring 8, 6 or 4 steps in the second stage. (Results for the Up and Down process were not available for $\sigma_1 = \sigma/2$ or $\sigma_1 = 2\sigma$).

Table 2. MSE/σ^2 for a two-stage plan

$\sigma_1 =$		$\sigma/2$	$2\sigma/3$	σ	$3\sigma/2$	2σ
k	N	Second stage: RM process				
3	8	.092	.070	.068	.079	.094
4	6	.099	.070	.067	.079	.096
6	4	.115	.075	.067	.082	.101
k	N	Second stage: Up and Down process				
3	8	---	.071	.073	.089	---
4	6	---	.080	.070	.088	---
6	4	---	.090	.069	.128	---

Considering the RM process first, the results are satisfactory if N = 6 or 8 steps are used in the second stage and if σ_1 lies between $2\sigma/3$ and $3\sigma/2$. The MSE's obtained under these conditions all lie within 20% of the asymptotic value of 0.0655 for 24 subjects. For $\sigma_1 = \sigma/2$ or $\sigma = 2\sigma$, the MSE's exceed the asymptotic value by 40% to 50% . If only four steps are used at stage 2, results are in general slightly worse than those for N = 6 .

Except when $\sigma_1 = \sigma$, the Up and Down process does not perform as well as the RM process in the second stage. There is a hint that the Up and Down process is more sensitive to errors in estimating σ, and perhaps requires more steps to appear at its best.

Concluding notes

The extent to which plans of this type become used in practice will of course depend on whether there are situations in which experimenters find the plans convenient and economical of resources. The plans are simple to execute and the estimates of the ED50 are very easily computed. Moreover, as illustrated by the two-stage plan, they offer the prospect of giving estimates whose accuracy is not vitiated by poor initial guesses at the values of μ and σ . Their chief limitation, at least for much experimental work, is that the stepwise method of doing the experiment may not fit the conditions of measurement of the responses. It is for this reason that we have concentrated on plans involving no more than 12 steps.

A second limitation is that we do not at present have a reliable method of computing the standard error of the estimate of μ. For the two-stage RM process one might contemplate using the asymptotic formula $\pi\sigma^2/2mN$ for the variance of $\hat{\mu}_{RM}$, increased by perhaps 25% in line with the results of Table 2. The trouble is that our estimate of σ^2 may be poor. For the Up and Down process the procedure already mentioned of calculating the standard error of $\hat{\bar{\mu}}$ from the observed variability among the $\hat{\mu}_i$ may be used. The disadvantage is that this standard error does not allow for the bias in $\hat{\bar{\mu}}$ and is rather weak in number of degrees of freedom.

An alternative approach is to analyze the results at the second stage, as if the experiment were non-sequential, by one of the classical methods that provides an estimate of the standard error. Although some preliminary work has been done, this may not be a practical solution except in special circumstances with larger experiments. The chief trouble is that, as previous workers have pointed out, these processes are not designed to give a good estimate of σ, so that the estimated s.e. $(\hat{\mu})$, which depends on σ, may be rather an unstable quantity. Further, the statistical analysis of the results will become more involved, since we will be using a more complex estimate of μ. One advantage of research of this type is that we may learn whether the simple estimates used in this paper for the two processes are fully efficient. Wetherill (1963) suggests that the "average level" estimate of μ for the Up and Down process may be inefficient unless the start is near μ. Similarly, with the RM process it is natural to ask whether use of the results at levels previous to x_N may not improve the estimate of μ.

Since a very poor guess at σ inflates the MSE even with the two stage process, the question has been asked whether it may be possible to make an estimate of σ, say about half-way through the experiment, using this estimate to determine the step size in the last half. With small experiments this proposal is likely to be defeated by the inability of the process to furnish good estimates of σ. It might turn out to be feasible in an experiment with 12 steps at the second stage and 96 subjects, although this has not yet been investigated.

The present investigation has assumed a normal tolerance distribution. It will be of considerable interest to discover how much the results are changed under a different tolerance distribution, particularly since both processes are essentially non-parametric. Some work on this question is underway by the second author.

For experiments in which it is feasible to test single subjects and use many steps, the paper by Wetherill (1963) should be consulted. Many forms of the Up and Down process are investigated in order to seek a plan of high efficiency even if μ and σ are not well known. His recommendation is that the original Up and Down process be used, with step size σ_1, until five changes in response type have occurred. Thereafter the step size is halved, continuing the process as long as is necessary to attain a desired accuracy in the estimate. His investigations assume a logistic tolerance distribution and were made by experimental sampling. In line with this approach, investigation of a longer stage 1 in our process might be fruitful.

For the investigator who could use a sequential plan, although he finds a standard non-sequential plan more convenient, it would be informative to compare these two-stage plans with an alternative in which our first stage is followed by one of the standard plans with, say, four or five fixed levels. The only comparison in the literature that is partially relevant was made by Brownlee, Hodges and Rosenblatt. They compared the original Up and Down process (with estimate $\hat{\mu}$) and their variant (with estimate $\hat{\mu}'$) with a five-level non-sequential plan, assuming that the asymptotic formula for the variance of the latter remains valid in small experiments. Their results indicated that if the start x_1 is near μ, the non-sequential plan requires 30% more observations as compared with $\hat{\mu}'$ and 50% more as compared with $\hat{\mu}$ for equal accuracy. For starts out beyond 2σ the relative accuracy of the non-sequential plan declines rapidly.

Summary

This paper discusses the performance of two sequential methods of estimating the median effective dose (ED50) in biological assay - the Up and Down method of Dixon and Mood and the stochastic approximation method of Robbins and Monro. The study was made for experiments using from 12 to about 60 subjects, and was restricted to plans that require not more than 12 sequential steps. This restriction should make the plans operationally feasible for experiments in which the response (death or survival) to the stimulus becomes known within an hour or less. The performance of any plan was judged by the mean square error (MSE) of the resulting estimate of the ED50 .

In order to start any experiment for estimating the ED50, some initial guess is needed about the value of the ED50 and about the standard deviation σ of the tolerance distribution. Our calculations show that the original Up and Down or Robbins-Monro plans can be relied on to give satisfactory precision only if either the ED50 or σ is well known in advance.

For situations in which this does not not hold we investigated a two-stage plan. In the first stage, subjects are tested singly by the Up and Down method until a reversal occurs. As a check, another subject is tested at each of the two levels involved in the reversal.

The second stage is started at the estimate x_1 of the ED50 given by the results at these two levels. The frequency distribution of x_1 turns out to be practically independent of the original guess x_0 at the ED50 . Further, if at least six steps are used in the second stage, the MSE of the final estimate with the RM process is close to the asymptotic minimum provided that σ is known within a 2 to 1 ratio (on a log scale) . Even if σ is known initially only within a 4 to 1 ratio, use of the RM process in the second stage gives final estimates whose MSE's are not more than 50% higher than the asymptotic minimum.

REFERENCES

1. Berkson, J., (1955). Maximum likelihood and minimum χ^2 estimates of the logistic function, Jour. Amer. Stat. Assoc. Vol. 50. pp. 130-161.

2. Bliss, C. I. and Cattell, Mc K. (1943). Biological assay. Annual Rev. Phys. 5, 489.

3. Bross, I. (1950). Estimates of the LD50: a critique. Biometrics, 6, 413-423.

4. Brownlee, K. I., Hodges, J. L., and Rosenblatt, M. (1953). The up-and-down method with small samples. Jour. Amer. Stat. Assoc. 48, 262-277.

5. Dews, P. B., and Berkson, J. (1954). On the error of bioassay with quantal responses. "Statistics and Mathematics in Biology" The Iowa State College Press, Ames, Iowa.

6. Dixon, W. J. and Mood, A. M. (1948). A method for obtaining and analyzing sensitivity data. Jour. Amer. Stat. Assoc. 43, 109-126.

7. Finney, D. J. (1951). Statistical Method in Biological Assay. Hafner Publishing Company, New York.

8. Gaddum, J. H. (1933). Methods of biological assay depending on a quantal response. British Med. Res. Council. Special Report No. 183.

9. Hodges, J. L. and Lehmann, E. L. (1956). Two approximations to the Robbins-Monro process. Proc. Third Berkeley Symposium. Vol. I, 95-104. University of California Press.

10. Kiefer, J. and J. Wolfowitz. (1952). Stochastic estimation of the maximum of a regression function. Ann. Math. Stat., Vol. 23, pp. 462-466.

11. Robbins H. and Monro S. (1951). A stochastic approximation method. Ann. Math. Stat. 22, 400-407.

12. Wetherill, G. B. (1963). Sequential estimation of quantal response curves. Jour. Royal Stat. Soc. B, 25, 1-48.

This work was assisted by Contract Nonr 1866(37) with the Office of Naval Research, Navy Department. Reproduction in whole or in part is permitted for any purpose of the United States Government. The calculations were done in part at the Computation Center at MIT, Cambridge, Massachusetts.

DISCUSSION PARTICIPANTS

Dr. Walter T. Federer
Biological Statistics, Biometrics Unit,
Cornell University
Ithaca, New York

Dr. Marvin A. Schneiderman
Biometry Branch, National Cancer Institute,
National Institutes of Health
Bethesda, Maryland

Dr. Donald T. Searls
Statistical Research Division, Research Triangle Institute
Box 490, Durham, North Carolina

DISCUSSION

Walter T. Federer. What is your advice on the selection of X_i to estimate the median when the active part of the curve is very steep?

In order to increase the precision of the estimated variance why not add two observations at the end of experimentation and locate these two observations at the points of inflection? Also, it might be advisable to discard the first two observations of your preliminary trial for variance computations.

William G. Cochran. I'm not sure that I grasp the particular difficulty caused by a very steep curve (small σ), unless it means that our initial guess x_1 is likely to be very far out, or that there is difficulty in giving the exact dose level that the sequential technique calls for. If x_1 is expected to be a poor guess, an approach like that suggested by Dr. Searls may be worthwhile for the first stage.

We have had in mind Dr. Federer's suggestion about additional observations whose purpose is to improve the estimate of s.e. $(\hat{\mu})$, but have no results on the best number and placement of these observations.

Donald T. Searls. To avoid wasting a lot of animals for a bad choice of starting point, why not double the distance between levels until a reversal is reached. At this point the distance between levels could be halved until the original distance between levels was attained.

Example:

start

0 1 1 11

←

Now change direction

→

0 0 1

↓

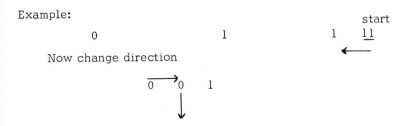

William G. Cochran. For the first stage of our two-stage process, this method is certainly an improvement over the use of a fixed step size when the value of σ is underestimated and we start far out. To cite one calculation, suppose that our guessed value, σ_1, is actually $\sigma/2$ and that the start is at $+10\sigma$. Dr. Searls's method requires about 9.5 animals to complete his first stage, as against about 17 with a fixed step size of $1.253\sigma_1$ (0.625σ). Also, somewhat to my surprise, his method gives a smaller MSE in this case for the estimate $\hat{\mu}$ made at the end of stage 1. With better initial guesses at σ and μ there is less to be gained. With $\sigma_1 = \sigma$ and a start at $+4\sigma$, for instance, the fixed size takes on the average only about 4.5 animals for stage 1.

Marvin Schneiderman. Often we are not interested in the LD50 -- but rather something like the LD05 (in a therapeutic trial). What advice have you for handling this problem? Fixed schemes? Sequential schemes?

William G. Cochran. Estimation of LD05 is a challenging problem on which I know of no thorough study. Wetherill (loc. cit.) made some empirical sampling trials to estimate LD75 and LD95 by the Robbins-Monro process. He was very disappointed with the results, the estimate being subject to a substantial bias that appeared to be an inevitable feature of the method. I think his conclusions may be too pessimistic. His sample sizes were only 15, 25 and 35. Since one cannot expect good precision in this problem without large sample sizes, I would like to see some work done on modifications of the RM or Up and Down process with big samples.

ANATOL RAPOPORT

A Stochastic Model for the Prisoner's Dilemma

The nickname Prisoner's Dilemma was derived from an anecdote used to illustrate a certain non-zero-sum game (cf. Luce and Raiffa, 1957, p. 95).

The pay-offs of this game are the entries of Matrix 1, the first of each pair being the pay-offs to the row-chooser

	C_2	D_2
C_1	R_1, R_2	S_1, T_2
D_1	T_1, S_2	P_1, P_2

Matrix 1.

The pay-offs satisfy the following conditions:

(1) $$S_i < P_i < R_i < T_i \quad (i = 1, 2) \quad .$$

Thus the game is determined by eight parameters subject to the above restrictions. If the pay-offs are to be invariant with respect to the permutation of the players, we must have $R_1 = R_2$; $S_1 = S_2$; $T_1 = T_2$; $P_1 = P_2$. The number of parameters is then reduced to four. On the other hand, to satisfy inequalities (1), we must have at least two numerical values to represent the parameters, hence essentially two independent parameters. In its simplest form, then, Prisoner's Dilemma is exemplified by Matrix 2.

	C_2	D_2
C_1	1, 1	-2 2
D_1	2, -2	-1, -1

Matrix 2.

The "dilemma" can be clearly seen from the fact that for each player strategy D "dominating strategy" C, that is, strategy D is preferable to C regardless of what the other player does. Yet both players lose a unit if both choose C.

We shall refer to C as the cooperative choice and to D as the defecting choice. The letters chosen for the pay-offs (cf. Matrix 1) symbolize reward (R) for the double cooperative choice; temptation (T), the pay-off to the single defector; sucker's pay-off (S) to the single cooperator; and punishment (P) for the double defecting choice. These designations point to the obvious motivation pressures expected to be operating in this game.

The pressures can be assumed to operate in both directions. On the one hand, there is a pressure to choose D, because (1) of the tempting largest pay-off T and because (2) of the fear of receiving the smallest pay-off S, if one is the lone cooperator. On the other hand, there is a pressure to choose C, because the double cooperative choice CC, is rewarded, while the double defecting choice DD is punished.

Each choice is therefore supported by a rationale and one can conclude nothing about which strategy will in fact be chosen by the "rational player."

On the other hand, experimental data show certain regularities in the behavior of human subjects playing Prisoner's Dilemma games (with communication disallowed) many times in succession. These regularities emerge only from "massive" data, i.e., from data gathered in experiments involving scores of subjects and hundreds of choices per session. This is to be expected simply on the basis of individual differences among subjects. Indeed, differences in performance in the Prisoner's Dilemma game have been found to be correlated with certain independently assessed personality differences (e.g., Deutsch, 1960; Lutzker, 1960).

There is, however, another possible source of variance which may be important in repeated plays of the Prisoner's Dilemma game, having nothing to do with personality differences. Assume both players to be psychologically identical and characterized by certain initial propensity (probability) of choosing cooperatively. If they happened to choose C on the first play of the game, the result (which is announced to them) reinforces the conviction of each that "it pays to cooperate," i.e., that the other is willing to go along. In this case the cooperative choices may continue and so reinforce further continuation. Suppose, on the other hand, that on the initial play, one player happened to choose C while the other happened to choose D. The "betrayed" cooperator may conclude that "it doesn't pay to cooperate," while the defector may conclude that it pays to defect. Accordingly the next pair of choices may well be DD.

This is punishing to both. However, in order to escape from the DD trap, a risk must be taken to start cooperating even in the face of the possibility that the other, instead of going along will take advantage of the largest pay-off, T . Initially, both players had a certain propensity for taking this risk. But the (accidental) "bad start," may have reduced these propensities, because the initial cooperator was "burned" and the initial defector may be scared of retaliation by the other. In this case, although initially the pair may have had a considerable propensity to cooperate, they may nevertheless "lock in" on the DD response instead of on the CC response. The accidentally determined initial conditions rather than inherent propensities may well be the determining factors of a pair's performance. In other words, we may be dealing with a characteristically unstable system.

Experimental evidence, to be discussed below, indicates that such "instability" is likely to be indeed characteristic of the situation. We are thus led to the conjecture that a stochastic model with a built-in unstable equilibrium may well be appropriate as the basis of a theory underlying the behavior in Prisoner's Dilemma games. In what follows, we shall assume that the two players are psychologically entirely alike. Let each be characterized by the following four propensities:

x: the probability of cooperating on the next play, given that on a given play the player has cooperated and has been rewarded (i. e., that the last outcome was CC) ;

y: the probability of cooperating on the next play, given that the player has cooperated and has been punished (CD) ;

z: the probability of cooperating on the next play, given that the player has defected and has been rewarded (DC) ;

w: the probability of cooperating on the next play, given that the player has defected and has been punished (DD) .

Assume these propensities constant and the chances of the players on any <u>particular</u> play independent of each other (as they must be in the absence of communication). The two players now constitute a system passing through a sequence of states: CC, CD, DC, and DD. The above assumptions determine the following Markov process:

$$p'_{CC} = x^2 p_{CC} + yz\, p_{CD} + zy\, p_{DC} + w^2\, p_{DD}$$

$$p'_{CD} = x\tilde{x}\, p_{CC} + y\tilde{z}\, p_{CD} + \tilde{y}z\, p_{DC} + w\tilde{w}\, p_{DD}$$

(2)

$$p'_{DC} = \tilde{x}x\, p_{CC} + \tilde{y}z\, p_{CD} + y\tilde{z}\, p_{DC} + \tilde{w}w\, p_{DD}$$

$$p'_{DD} = \tilde{x}^2\, p_{CC} + \tilde{y}\tilde{z}\, p_{CD} + \tilde{y}\tilde{z}\, p_{DC} + \tilde{w}^2\, p_{DD}\,,$$

where the p's are the probabilities of the states denoted by their subscripts, the primes refer to the probabilities on the next plays and the complements of x, y, z, and we are denoted by $\tilde{x}$, $\tilde{y}$, $\tilde{z}$, and $\tilde{w}$ respectively.

If we are dealing with psychologically identical players, we must have $p_{CD} = p_{DC}$, hence $p_{DD} = 1 - 2p_{CD} - p_{CC}$. Equations (2) then reduce to the following two independent equations:

$$p'_{CC} = x^2 p_{CC} + 2yz\, p_{CD} + w^2(1-2p_{CD} - p_{CC})$$

(3)

$$p'_{CD} = x\tilde{x}\, p_{CC} + (y\tilde{z}+\tilde{y}z)\, p_{CD} + w\tilde{w}(1-2p_{CD}-p_{CC})$$

If, in addition, we assume that the process is ergodic, we can obtain the asymptotic distribution of the probabilities of the states, namely

$$p_{CC}(\infty) = \frac{w^2(1-y\tilde{z}-\tilde{y}z+2w\tilde{w}) - 2w\tilde{w}(w^2-yz)}{(1-y\tilde{z}-\tilde{y}z+2w\tilde{w})(1-x^2+w^2)-2(w^2-yz)(w\tilde{w}-x\tilde{x})}$$

(4)

$$p_{CD}(\infty) = \frac{w\tilde{w}(1-x^2+w^2) - w^2(w\tilde{w}-x\tilde{x})}{(1-y\tilde{z}-\tilde{y}z+2w\tilde{w})(1-x^2+w^2)-2(w^2-yz)(w\tilde{w}-x\tilde{x})}$$

The formulas are bulky and hardly suggestive. It is instructive, however, to examine some very simple special cases.

Case 1: Two Simpletons

The simplest case is one where $x=w=1$, $y=z=0$. The case may be thought of as representing two subjects with the crudest discriminatory faculties and decision rules. They distinguish punishing pay-offs from rewarding ones and choose accordingly: following a rewarded choice, they choose the same on the next play; following a punished choice, they choose the opposite.

It is easily seen that the two "simpletons" will do very well, since they will reach CC on the first, second, or third play at the latest and will persist in that state indefinitely thereafter.

Case 2: The Simpletons are Tempted

The next simplest case is one where $x < 1$; $w = 1$; $y = z = 0$. We may suppose here that the simpletons are subject to temptation, when they are in the CC state, namely a temptation to defect and so get the bigger pay-off T . Here $\tilde{x} = 1 - x$ represents the probability of such defection. Substituting these values into equations (4), we observe that these equations reduce to

$$(5)\quad p_{CC} = \frac{1}{2 + 2x - 3x^2}, \qquad p_{CD} = \frac{x\tilde{x}}{2 + 2x - 3x^2}$$

From equations (5) we can calculate the "cost of temptation." For instead of the average pay-off, R, which accrues to the two untempted simpletons, we now have each of the tempted simpletons receiving an average pay-off

$$(6)\quad R' = \frac{R}{2 + 2x - 3x^2} + \frac{P(1 - x^2)}{2 + 2x - 3x^2}$$

If say, $P = -R$, this amounts to

$$(7)\quad R' = \frac{Rx^2}{2 + 2x - 3x^2},$$

and we have the attenuation factor of the expected reward, as a function of x, namely,

$$(8)\quad \frac{R'}{R} = \frac{x^2}{2 + 2x - 3x^2}$$

The rate of change of (R'/R) with respect to x is obtained by differentiation:

$$(9)\quad \frac{d}{dx}\left(\frac{R'}{R}\right) = \frac{4x + 2x^2}{(2 + 2x - 3x^2)^2},$$

which equals 6 at $x = 1$. In other words a slight temptation (deviation of x from unity) costs our simpletons six times that fraction in reduced reward.

Turning now to equation (4) and solving for x in terms of p_{CC}, we have

$$(10)\quad x = \frac{1 \pm \sqrt{7 - 3/p_{CC}}}{3}.$$

We conclude that $p_{CC} > 3/7$ is an absolute restriction on this model. From our data to be examined below (cf. Table 1) we observe $p_{CC} < 3/7$ in two of the seven types of Prisoner's Dilemma games, which disposes of this model, a conclusion not unexpected because of the extreme simplicity of the model.

Case 3: Temptation and Distrust

If $\tilde{x} = 1 - x$ can be viewed as an index of temptation, $\tilde{w} = 1 - w$ can be viewed as an index of distrust. For $\tilde{w}$ is the reluctance of trying to escape from the punishing DD state. This reluctance can be attributed to the apprehension that in switching to C, one will be alone and stuck with the lowest pay-off, S.

A Two-parameter Model

Let now $x < 1$; $w < 1$; $y = z = 0$. Then equations (3) become

$$p_{CC} = \frac{w^2}{(1-x^2+w^2)(1+2w\tilde{w}) - 2w^2(w\tilde{w}-x\tilde{x})}$$

(11)

$$p_{CD} = \frac{w\tilde{w}(1-x^2+w^2) - w^2(w\tilde{w}-x\tilde{x})}{(1-x^2+w^2)(1+2w\tilde{w}) - 2w^2(w\tilde{w}-x\tilde{x})}$$

Formally, equations (11) could be solved for x and w in terms of p_{CC} and p_{DD}. It would appear, then, that any pair of observed values p_{CC} and p_{DD} could be accounted for by a pair of theoretically inferred values of x and w, in which case the two-parameter model would be sufficient to explain at least asymptotically any observed distribution of states (assuming $p_{CD} = p_{DC}$). It turns out, however, that the two-parameter model still implies some restriction on the asymptotic distribution, as will now be shown.

We replace the pair of independent variables p_{CC} and p_{CD} by another pair, namely $p = p_{CC}$ and $r = p_{CC}/p_{CD}$. Since $p_{CC} + 2p_{CD} \leq 1$, we must have

$$p_{CD} = \frac{p_{CC}}{r} \leq \frac{1-p_{CC}}{2}$$

(12)

$$p_{CC} = p \leq \frac{r}{r+2}$$

However, this limitation on p does not concern us, since it follows from definitions. We are concerned with possible restrictions on p and r, which are consequences of equations (11) and which, if violated, would preclude the solution of equations (11) for w and x in terms of observed values of p and r . If there are such restrictions, this model too must be discarded.

From (11), we obtain*

$$r = \frac{w}{1 - x^2 - x + wx} \tag{13}$$

Solving for w, we obtain

$$w = \frac{r(1-x^2)}{1 + r - rx} \tag{14}$$

In turn, substituting (14) into (11), we obtain, after rearrangements

$$p = \frac{r^2(1-x^2)}{1 + 4r + 2r^2 - 2rx - 2r^2x - 2rx^2} \tag{15}$$

Finally, solving for x ,

$$x = \frac{r(r+1)p \pm Q}{r^2 - 2rp} \tag{16}$$

where

$$Q^2 = p^2(r^4 + 6r^3 + 9r^2 + 2r) - p(2r^4 + 6r^3 + r^2) + r^4 . \tag{17}$$

We know that $0 \leq x < 1$. We ask whether any conditions must be imposed on p and r to insure this. These conditions are

$$Q^2 \geq 0 , \tag{18}$$

to insure that x is real, and either

$$r(r+1)p - Q < r^2 - 2rp \text{ and } Q \leq r(r+1)p \tag{19}$$

or

$$r(r+1)p + Q < r^2 - 2rp \tag{20}$$

---

* We have disregarded the uninteresting case when $w = 0$ and hence DD is an absorbing state.

to insure that there exists a value of x, $0 \leq x < 1$ to satisfy (16).

Let us examine (20) first. Suppose first that $r^2 - r^2p - 3rp \geq 0$, i.e., that $p \leq r/(r+3)$, which is somewhat stronger than (12). Then for (20) to hold, it is sufficient that

$$Q^2 \leq (r^2 - r^2p - 3rp)^2 \tag{21}$$

Expanding the right side of (21) and comparing with (17), we see that the inequality holds if $p \leq r/2$. But this obviously holds in view of (12), and so (20) is satisfied, provided only $p \leq r/(r+3)$

Let us now turn to (18). The value of Q^2 depends on p. It is positive for $p = 0$, but may change sign as p increases from 0 to its maximum theoretical value, namely $r/(r+2)$. To see where such a change of sign may occur, we solve the quadratic equation $Q^2 = 0$ for p and obtain

$$p = \frac{2r^3 + 6r^2 + r \pm r(2r+1)}{2r^3 + 12r^2 + 18r + 4} \tag{22}$$

Therefore for values of p between the two values given by the right side of (22), inequality (18) cannot be satisfied. Consider first the larger root. This is

$$\frac{2r^3 + 8r^2 + 2r}{2r^3 + 12r^2 + 18r + 4} = \frac{r}{r+2} \tag{23}$$

But this is the upper bound of p. Hence the excluded region for p is the entire region above the smaller of the two roots of p, given by (22). In other words, we must have

$$p \leq \frac{2r^3 + 4r^2}{2r^3 + 12r^2 + 18r + r} = \frac{r^3 + 2r^2}{r^3 + 6r^2 + 9r + 2} \tag{24}$$

Note that

$$\frac{r^3 + 2r^2}{r^3 + 6r^2 + 9r + 2} \leq \frac{r}{r+3} \tag{25}$$

Therefore if (24) is satisfied, (20) is automatically satisfied, and (24) remains as the only restriction on p and r. The restriction is the more stringent the smaller the value of r. If r is very large (it has no natural upper bound), p can range virtually to its theoretical upper bound. However, already for $r = 1$, p is restricted to values smaller than 1/6. Hence, in particular we could not account for a uniform distribution $p_{CC} = p_{CD} = p_{DC} = p_{DD} = 1/4$ in terms of the two parameter model. In examining our data (cf. Table 1 below), we find that in one game of the seven we have used, Game II, condition (24) was violated.

A Three-Parameter Model Suffices

We will now show that a three parameter model frees p and r from all restrictions and so suffices to account for any observed pair of values. Let the third parameter be z, as defined above, so that now z can vary from 0 to 1 . We still suppose $y = 0$. Then equations (4) lead by the same reasoning as in the preceding section to the following solution for x in terms of p, r, and $\tilde{z}$.

$$x = \frac{pr(r + \tilde{z}) \pm Q}{p^2 - 2pr} \tag{26}$$

where

$$Q^2 = (r^2 - pr^2 - 2pr - pr\tilde{z})^2 + \tilde{z}^2(2p^2r - pr^2) \quad .$$

We note that Q^2 can be always made positive by taking z sufficiently small. Also, setting $z = 0$ (i.e., $z = 1$), we have

$$x = \frac{pr^2 \pm (r^2 - pr^2 - 2pr)}{r^2 - 2pr} \tag{27}$$

Taking the value of x determined by the plus sign, we obtain $x = 1$. This makes (CC) an absorbing state.

But now making $\tilde{z} < 1$, regardless of what values p and r assume, we can satisfy (26) with a value of $x < 1$.

A Test of the Markov Model

We have now shown that three independent parameters, say x, z, and w are sufficient to account for any observed asymptotic distribution of the four states (assuming the symmetric condition $p_{CD} = p_{DC}$) . Hence the four parameters x, y, z, and w are *a forteriori* sufficient. Indeed we have more parameters than we need for predicting the asymptotic distribution. Therefore the observed distribution is not sufficient to estimate the parameters.

If we obtain the values of x, y, z, directly from the actual frequencies represented by them (counting all instances of transitions

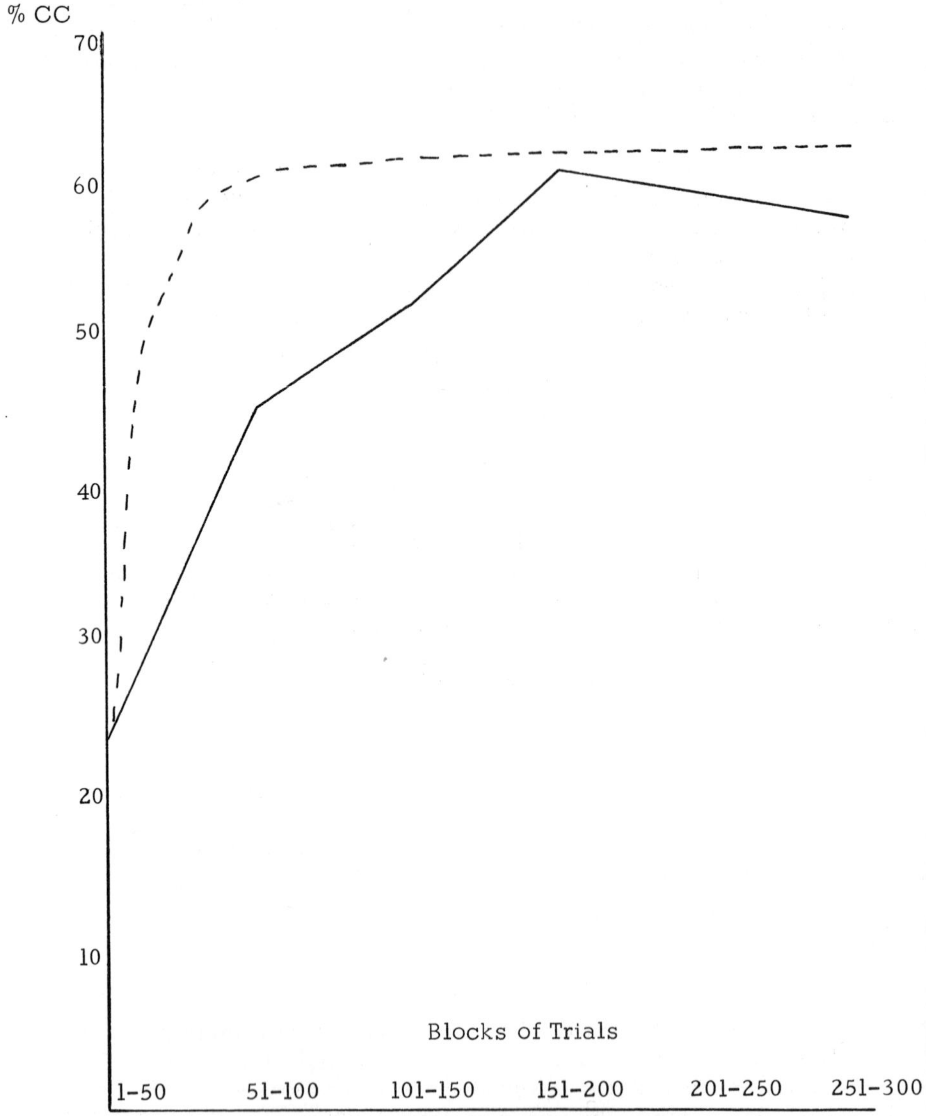

Figure 1. Solid line: actual time course of average p_{CC} .
Dotted line: theoretical time course in an equivalent <u>stationary</u> Markov process.

over the entire process) and substitute these values into equations (4), the latter will reduce to a tautology (regarding $p_{CD} = p_{DC} = 1/2[p_{CD}$ (observed) + p_{DC} (observed)]). However, we can put our model to a real test if we compare time courses of p_{CC} and p_{CD} predicted by the stationary Markov model with the observed time courses. The comparison between the predicted and observed time courses of p_{CC} is shown in Figure 1.

It is reasonable to suppose that the discrepancy is due to the fact that x, y, z, and w are subjected to dynamics of their own, ignored in the stationary Markov process. Not only does the individual have propensities, but these propensities typically change as a result of the individual's experiences. Stochastic learning theory suggests a model to describe these changes.

Suppose that on a given play, an individual is characterized by a certain propensity x. As a result of what happened on that play, this propensity may change, and the simplest assumption is that the new propensity x' is a linear function of the old, namely

$$x' = \alpha x + (1 - \alpha)\lambda \quad , \tag{28}$$

where α and λ are independent parameters $0 \leq \alpha \leq 1$; $0 \leq \lambda \leq 1$. (Bush and Mosteller, 1955). The parameters α and λ depend on what happened on the play in question, i.e., to what extent the propensity represented by x was reinforced or inhibited. In our representation of the situation 16 different events may happen, namely on the play in question the system may pass from any of four states to any of four states. Thus, in principle, we may be dealing with 16 pairs of parameters α and λ related to each of the four propensities or 128 parameters in all. If our theory is to be developed hand in hand with experiment, the prospect of estimating 128 parameters is not a cheerful one. Drastic simplifications will now be proposed in order at least to display a possible mathematical model which introduces learning into the situation.

Suppose first that a change in a propensity will occur only when the system is in a "relevant" state. That is to say, a change in the propensity to cooperate after having cooperated and been rewarded will be assumed to occur only after the system has been in state CC. If the system was in some other state, we shall assume that x remains the same. Similarly the relevant state for y are p_{CD} and p_{DC}, the same for z, while the relevant state for w is only p_{DD}.

This simplification reduces the number of events that can effect a change in x from 16 to 4. Next let us suppose that x will increase if cooperation has been rewarded or if non-cooperation has been punished and will decrease if cooperation has been punished or if defection has been rewarded. Moreover we shall suppose that these changes are such that if they continued indefinitely, x would tend to 1 in the former case and to 0 in the latter. This means that the parameter λ will assume only the values 1 and 0 . Then we can write for the expected value of x'

$$
\begin{aligned}
x' = p_{CC} \Big\{ & x^2 [\alpha_x^{(1)} x + (1-\alpha_x)] + x\tilde{x}\, [\beta_x^{(1)} x] \\
& + \tilde{x} x [\beta_x^{(2)} x] + \tilde{x}^2 [\alpha_x^{(2)} x + (1-\alpha_x^{(2)})] \Big\} \\
& + (1-p_{CC})\, x
\end{aligned}
\tag{29}
$$

The first (bracketed) term within the brace represents the operator which acts on x if the transition is from CC to CC, multiplied by the probability of this transition. Since cooperation has been rewarded in this state, $\lambda = 1$. The second term represents the operator which acts if the transition was from CC to CD (the first letter always refers to the subject in question). Here cooperation was punished, hence $\lambda = 0$. The third term represents the operator which acts if the transition was from CC to DC . Here again the subject was rewarded but for defecting; hence x should decrease, and so $\lambda = 0$. Finally the last term represents the operator which acts if the transition is from CC to DD . This, too, brings about a positive increment in x, because non-cooperation has been punished.

Now we have an opportunity for further simplification, namely we can equate the two α's (i.e., the two positive reinforcement parameters) to each other and also the two β's (i.e., the two negative reinforcement parameters) to each other. Or we can equate the two direct reinforcement parameters, $\alpha_x^{(1)}$ and $\beta_x^{(1)}$ to each other and also the two indirect reinforcement parameters $\alpha_x^{(2)}$ and $\beta_x^{(2)}$ to each other. We can make an even more drastic simplification by setting all four learning parameters equal to each other. When this is done, it can be shown that x will tend toward 0.5 as a stable equilibrium. From our data (cf. Table 3 below) it appears however as if x tends toward 1. This can be achieved in a simplified model by setting $\beta_x^{(1)} = \beta_x^{(2)} = 1$, i.e., disregarding negative reinforcement. To fix ideas, let us do this and also set $\alpha_x^{(1)} = \alpha_x^{(2)} = \alpha_x$. Then equation (29) reduces, after rearrangements to

$$x' - x = p(1-\alpha_x)\,(1-x)\,(2x^2 - 2x+1) \tag{30}$$

or, assuming small increments, to the differential equation

$$\frac{dx}{dt} = p(1-\alpha_x)(1-x)\,(2x^2 - 2x + 1) \quad . \tag{31}$$

Under these conditions x always increases, tending to 1 . Other models where an unstable equilibrium for x exists can be easily constructed.

Turning to Table 3 once more and taking the cue from the decreasing trend in w, we construct a similar equation for w, disregarding positive reinforcements, i.e., setting $\alpha_w^{(1)} = \alpha_w^{(2)} = 1$. We obtain

$$\frac{dw}{dt} = -\,p_{DD}(1-\beta_w)\,2w^2(1-w) \quad . \tag{32}$$

Examining the behavior of y, as shown in Table 2, we see that a trend toward either 1 or 0 cannot be supposed. However the assumption that y = .5 may be an equilibrium value is not too much at variance with the data. We have seen that this assumption is consistent with setting $\alpha_y^{(1)} = \alpha_y^{(2)} = \beta_y^{(1)} = \beta_y^{(2)} = \alpha_y$. We do this and obtain the corresponding differential equation for y, shown in (33) .

As for z, it exhibits no discernible trend. Accordingly we make the simplest assumption, namely z = constant.

Equations (3) can also be written as differential equations in p_{CC} and p_{CD} . Summarizing, we finally propose the following system as a dynamic model for Prisoner's Dilemma. It is the simplest model consistent with a simplified stochastic learning model and a Markov process, in which the interactions between the two players are taken into account.

$$\frac{dp_{CC}}{dt} = p_{CC}(x^2 - w^2 - 1) + 2p_{CD}(yz - w^2) + w^2$$

$$\frac{dp_{CD}}{dt} = p_{CC}(x\tilde{x} - w\tilde{w}) + p_{CD}(y\tilde{z} + \tilde{y}z - 2w\tilde{w} - 1) + w\tilde{w}$$

$$\frac{dx}{dt} = p_{CC}(1-\alpha_x)(1-x)(2x^2 - 2x + 1)$$

$$\frac{dy}{dt} = p_{CD}(1-\alpha_y)(1-2y)(1-z) \tag{33}$$

$$\frac{dz}{dt} = 0$$

$$\frac{dw}{dt} = -\,p_{DD}(1-\beta_w)\,2w^2(1-w) \quad .$$

In principle equations (33) could be solved so that x, y, z, w, p_{CC} and p_{CD} could be obtained as explicit functions of t and of the parameters α_x, α_y, and β_w. We would thus have three parameters with which to fit six curves. The theoretical gain would be in the fact that having gotten at these parameters we would have gone pretty deeply into the psychological underpinnings of the process. Observing the changes of magnitude in the learning parameters, as we manipulate the independent variables (e.g. pay-offs, population samples), we could make statements related to the psychological issues as they are reflected in the learning parameters.

To see this, let us go back to our original formulation of the Markov process. Such a process is characterized by a matrix of transition probabilities. In our case the transition probabilities can be defined only formally, e.g., the probability that the system, being in state CC passes to state CD, etc. Such definitions are devoid of psychological content and so our model remains uninterpreted.

But when we pass to the parameters x, y, z, and w, the situation changes abruptly. These parameters already have a rather rich psychological interpretation. For instance x, the probability that a player having cooperated and been rewarded, cooperates the next time can be interpreted as a measure of "trustworthiness," since in the Prisoner's Dilemma situation, the temptation to defect from CC (in pursuit of the pay-off T) is always present.

Similarly y, the probability of cooperating after having been punished for cooperating can be viewed as a measure of "forgiveness".

Next z, the probability of cooperating after having been rewarded for defecting, appears as a measure of "repentance".

Finally w, the probability of cooperating after having been punished for defecting is more than an indication of "learning from experience". For in the peculiar dilemma situation, there is no sense in trying to escape from the DD trap unless one trusts the other. Hence w appears as a measure of "trust".

If only these parameters stayed put, i.e., if they were constant in a given situation, say characteristic of a given game or a given population or given conditions under which the game is played, the theory could stop right here. The theory would become descriptive at this point. Its assertions would relate x, y, z, and w (with their psychological meanings) to various conditions.

We see, however, that x, y, z, and w, do not stay put. They have a dynamics of their own. Our next level of the dynamic model, represented by equation (33) is an attempt to get at the parameters which govern the changes of x, y, z, and w. These are the learning parameters.

The learning parameters also have a straightforward interpretation. For instance, α_x (or rather $1-\alpha_x$) is a measure of the rate at which trustworthiness is learned when the other is also trustworthy. Next $(1-\beta_w)$ is a measure of the rate trust deteriorates when the other is not trustworthy. Finally $1-\alpha_y$ is the rate at which forgiveness is learned when the other repents. We assume in our model that the "repentance" propensity (or its opposite) remains constant.

It would be interesting to get at these learning parameters. But the present work has not been brought up so far. We content ourselves with examining the average values of x, y, z, and w, to see what we can learn from these about the psychology of our situation.

In our experiment, we used seven different games, shown in Figure 2.

	C	D
C	9, 9	-10, 10
D	10, -10	-1, -1

Game I.

	C	D
C	1, 1	-10, 10
D	10, -10	-9, -9

Game II.

	C	D
C	1, 1	-10, 10
D	10, -10	-1, -1

Game III.

	C	D
C	1, 1	-2, 2
D	2, -2	-1, -1

Game IV.

	C	D
C	1, 1	-50, 50
D	50, -50	-1, -1

Game V.

	C	D
C	5, 5	-10, 10
	10, -10	-1, -1

Game XI.

	C	D
D	1, 1	-10, 10
D	10, -10	-5, -5

Game XII.

Figure 2.

The pay-offs were converted to money, 1 mill per point. Each game was played 300 times in succession by 10 pairs of subjects (male University of Michigan students).

Table 1 summarizes the findings related to the over-all distributions of the states and the estimated propensities.

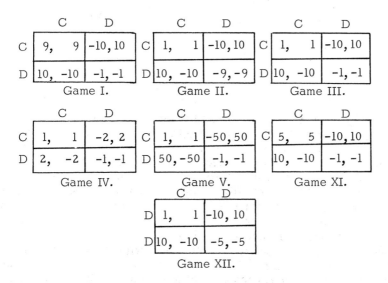

Game	x	y	z	w
I	.981	.440	.367	.161
II	.958	.414	.542	.255
III	.938	.346	.320	.187
IV	.952	.453	.377	.233
V	.970	.352	.299	.047
XI	.964	.496	.295	.195
XII	.969	.571	.211	.173

Table 1

We note first that x, y, z, and w are not related in any obvious way to the game parameters. One might expect that x would be adversely affected by the discrepancy between R and T (i.e., a measure of the temptation to defect.) From Table 1, we see, however that although x is largest in Game I, as it should be, it is next largest in Game V where the discrepancy between R and T is largest. We note also that although w is smallest in Game V, and also largest in Game II, as we would expect, it is smaller in Game XII than in XI, contrary to what we would expect.

Of course no conclusions can be drawn without estimating the significance of our estimates. Aside from this, we must keep in mind that we are examining massed data of a process in which pairs tend toward the extreme states. The high value of x in Game V may well be due to the following effect. Cooperation is most difficult to achieve in that game because of its very large T and very small (negatively large) S. Therefore only those pairs succeed in locking in on CC in Game V whose x's are very high. Since x is a contingent probability, its value may be reflecting the "selection" of the highly cooperative pairs to persist in the CC state rather than the dynamics determined by the parameters of the game directly.

Although no simple dependence of the x, y, z, and w on the game parameters can be discerned, the p's are quite simply related to these. Comparing the observed p's with the pay-off matrices we note the following (cf. Figure 3).

1. If temptation and punishment are kept constant and reward increases, p_{CC} increases (cf. Games III, XI, and I).

2. If reward and punishment are kept constant and temptation increases, while S = T, p_{CC} decreases (cf. Games IV, III, and V.)

3. If reward and temptation are kept constant and punishment increases, p_{CC} increases (cf. Games III, XII, and II.)

Figure 3a

Frequence of cooperative choices observed as a function of reward for double cooperation (R) .

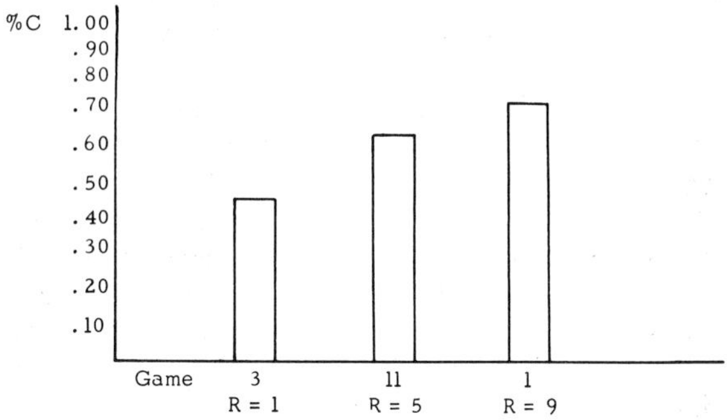

Figure 3b

Frequency of cooperative choices observed as a function of reward for single defection (T)

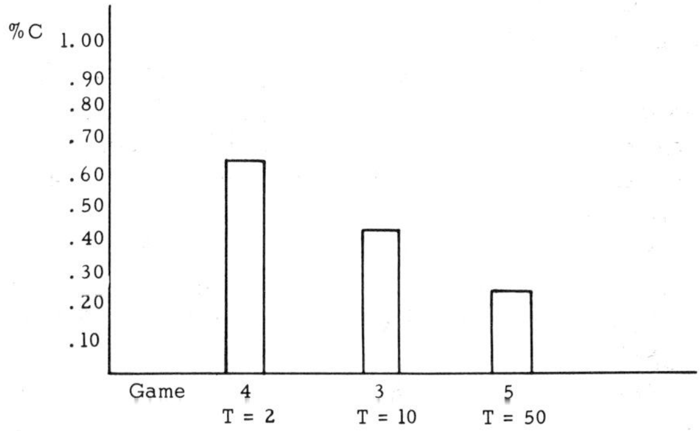

Figure 3c

Frequency of cooperative choices observed as a function of punishment for double defection (P)

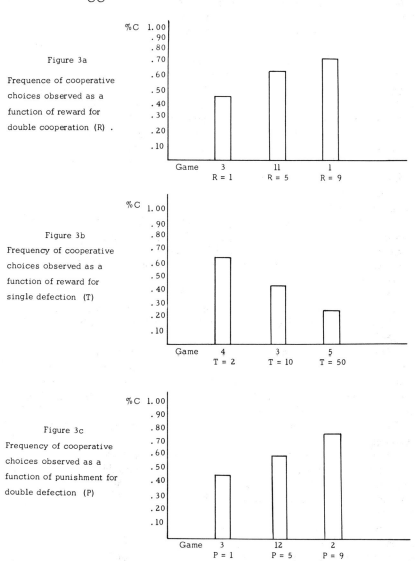

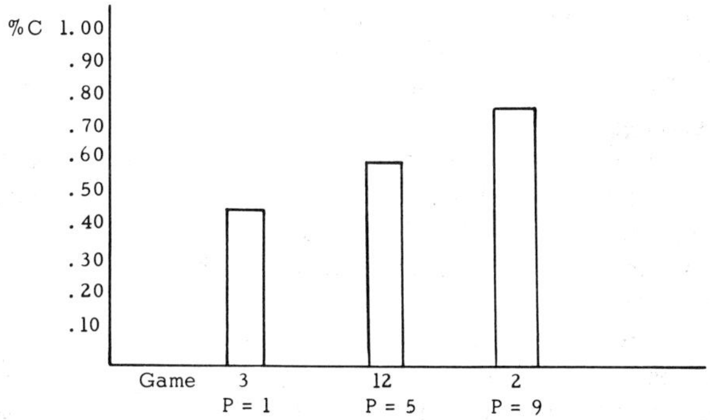

Figure 3.

These results are, of course, expected on intuitive grounds. Thus, while the possible effects of the game parameters on the average propensities, x, y, z, and w may be maskedby interdependencies or some other complications, the effects of these parameters on the over-all frequencies of cooperation are quite transparent.

However an examination of the x, y, z, and w can be instructive in view of their psychological interpretation just because they vary less than the indices of gross behavior (the frequencies of cooperation.) Let us agree to call contingent probabilities to cooperate "virtues" if they are larger than .5 and "vices" if they are smaller. In the light of those interpretations, we can conjecture something like this about the psychology of our population.

1. The population is characterized by one virtue (trustworthiness) and three vices (vengefulness, greed, and distrust.)

2. In all cases, that is, in all games, each game being represented by a different sample of the population, the numerical magnitude of trustworthiness (x) is larger than the corresponding numerical magnitude of distrust ($\widetilde{w}$) .

3. In all cases but one, the numerical magnitude of greed ($\widetilde{z}$) exceeds that of vengefulness ($\widetilde{y}$) . The one exception occurs in Game II, where greed is replaced by repentance ($z > .5$) . In this game double defection is punished more severely than in any other game (cf. Figure 1).

4. The numerical magnitudes of the propensities which make up the profile of our population arrange themselves as follows.

Trustworthiness (very high) > Distrust (high) > Greed (moderate) > Vengefulness (low).

It goes without saying that the names we have given to our contingent probabilities of response have been selected for rhetorical or mnemonic reasons only and do not constitute any serious attempt to construct numerical measures of moral qualities. Still in view of the relation of these quantities to very large numbers of small, rather spontaneous acts, their suggestive implications are not to be underestimated.

If these propensities were sufficiently constant over long sequences of plays, they would serve as indices for comparing populations or experimental conditions. Examining these values over consecutive blocks of 50 plays each (combining all games), we obtain the results shown in Table 2.

From Table 2, we conjecture that trustworthiness steadily increases; distrust very roughly increases; vengefulness roughly decreases, passing into forgiveness after about 200 plays, while greed is roughly constant.

Block of Plays	x	y	z	w
1-50	.874	.369	.338	.217
51-100	.955	.403	.324	.145
101-150	.967	.475	.291	.162
151-200	.977	.452	.372	.138
201-250	.977	.516	.359	.145
251-300	.979	.616	.328	.105

Table 2.

One suspects that statistical fluctuations begin to becloud the observations on this level of analysis. Therefore attempts to establish a dynamic theory of the propensity interactions, such as was suggested by equations (33) must either be coupled with much more massive data (to introduce more statistical stability) or with a more penetrating stochastic analysis.

On the other hand, the actual time changes in the average propensities are not large, so that the gross conclusions we have derived can be given some credence. In particular we note that along the time scale, the inequality characteristic of our "profile", namely $x > y > z > w$ holds throughout the process.

REFERENCES

1. Bush, R. R. and Mosteller, F. Stochastic Models for Learning. New York: John Wiley and Sons, 1955.

2. Deutsch, M. Trust and Suspicion. J. Conflict Resolution, 1958, 2, 265-279.

3. Deutsch, M. Trust, Trustworthiness and the F Scale. J. Abnormal & Social Psychology, 1960, 61, 138-140.

4. Luce, R. D. and Raiffa, H. Games and Decisions. New York: John Wiley and Sons, 1957.

5. Lutzker, D. R. Internationalism as a predictor of cooperation behavior. J. Conflict Resolution, 1960, 4, 426-430.

DISCUSSION PARTICIPANTS

Dr. Jacob B. Chassan
Department of Research, Hoffmann-La Roche,
Nutley, New Jersey

Dr. Bernard Harris
Mathematics Research Center, U. S. Army
University of Wisconsin
Madison, Wisconsin

Dr. Henry B. Mann
Mathematics Research Center, U. S. Army
University of Wisconsin
Madison, Wisconsin

Dr. Robert J. Taylor
Biometry Branch NCI, Robin Building,
National Institutes of Health
Bethesda, Maryland

DISCUSSION

Jacob B. Chassan. As consistent as the results appear, to what extent can you be secure that the results of the games actually measure the subjects' characteristics in true-life situations? Would this not depend upon such factors as the utility of the monetary rewards, desire to give good impressions, or just an attitude of playing games for fun, etc. ?

Anatol Rapoport. Other investigators (Deutsch, 1960; Lutzker, 1960) found correlations between the propensities of subjects to choose cooperatively and certain personality indices (F -- scale, "internationalism"). In our experiments, such correlations were not the objects of investigation.

Bernard Harris. Professor Rapoport, I should like to enquire about the extent of the monetary reward to participants.

Anatol Rapoport. The rewards were one mill per point. The total winnings or losses in a session could run up to a couple of dollars, comparable to the subjects' fees for participating in the experiment. In some of our games the rewards varied by a factor of five, the ratios of the various pay-offs remaining constant. Within that range the responses remained independent of the absolute magnitude of the rewards or punishments.

On the other hand when reward for defection only was increased together with sucker's loss (cf. Game V) cooperation was drastically reduced.

Bernard Harris. Does it not seem reasonable that a very large reward, say in the hundreds or thousands of dollars might have a profound influence in reducing the extent of cooperation between the players?

Anatol Rapoport. What the results would be if really large amounts of money were involved, I would not venture to say. Such an experiment would not be performed for ethical reasons, unless the subjects were initially "staked" with the amount they would lose, but this would not be the same as losing it out of their own pocket.

Bernard Harris. Dr. Kellogg Wilson of the Nebraska Psychiatric Institute has also been conducting experiments dealing with repeated plays of the "Prisoner's Dilemma Game". Would Professor Rapoport please comment on the relationship between the results obtained in his experiment and Dr. Wilson's experiment.

Anatol Rapoport. With regard to Dr. Wilson's work, I recall a paper by him and by Bixenstein in Behavioral Science in which various non-zero sum games, including Prisoner's Dilemma, are analyzed with respect to their strategic, motivational, and "control" characteristics. Experimental data are not given in that paper. Subsequently experiments were performed by Wilson and Bixenstein, and I recall publication in the Journal of Conflict Resolution and in the Journal of Social and Abnormal Psychology. The objectives of those experiments, as far as I recall, was to study the character of the responses as related both to imposed experimental conditions (as in our experiments) and also to the personality characteristics of the players. In particular, I recall that the behavior of men and women was compared in at least one of the papers.

Henry B. Mann. Is there an element of social conscience in your experiment which would prevent subjects from desiring advantages from somebody elses loss?

Anatol Rapoport. In our experiments, about half of the subject pairs succeeded in "locking in" on the cooperative choice. Typically this happened after about 200-250 plays. From this one cannot decide whether "social conscience" came into play or whether the subjects simply came to a tacit cooperative understanding. To test the effect of "social conscience" one would have to confine oneself to one-play sessions. This was done by Morton Deutsch (1958). The results are not indicative of any strong effect of "social conscience."

Robert J. Taylor. Have you considered experiments in which you prejudice the players with regard to their opponents degree of trustworthiness?

Anatol Rapoport. Have you considered experiments in which variables were those related to the pay-offs, to the scheduling of the games, and to the subjects' knowledge of the pay-off matrix. In one side study, we did impose a condition somewhat resembling the one you mention. Each subject believed that the other's defector's pay-off and sucker's loss were 25 times larger than his own, whereas in actuality the game was symmetrical. The effect of this distortion was rather slight but in the expected direction. One could deduce from this that the effects of the other's pay-offs on one's responses are much weaker than the effects of one's own pay-offs. But one could also deduce the operation of certain effects tending to cancel each other. The latter hypothesis suggests further experiments to separate the effects, but these were not yet performed.

CHIN LONG CHIANG

A Stochastic Model of Competing Risks of Illness and Competing Risks of Death

1. Introduction

In his journey from birth to eternity, an individual is continuously exposed to risks of illness and death. The various maladies of his time and place are in constant competition for his health and life. Statistically, illness and death are separate and different types of events. Illnesses are potentially concurrent, repetitive, and reversible, whereas death is irreversible and is an absorbing barrier. The pattern is not necessarily limited to animate beings. A mechanical object, say an automobile, is subject to many types of repairable malfunction and to complete breakdown from any of several causes.

The conventional approach to the problem of competing risks emphasizes the risks of death. Since Bernoulli's pioneering work [6], writers have studied various aspects of the problem. Among recent papers, an interesting discussion from actuarial viewpoint has been contributed by Greville [4], and a stochastic approach has appeared in Chiang [1] and [2]. Competing risks of illness, however, have so far escaped rigorous treatment, although Fix and Neyman [3], in connection with medical follow-up studies, have considered the probabilities of relapse and recovery for cancer patients.

With the consideration limited to the risks of death, only the end results of the competition can be explored. A dynamic picture of the process of competition must give equal attention to the risks of illness. This paper will present a general stochastic model of illness and death process with which we can study the competition and interaction of diseases and risks of death.

Suppose that there are r diseases operating in a human population. Due to their competition, an individual may be afflicted with any one disease or with any combination of them. As summarized in Table 1, the possible "states" of illness, defined by the combination of diseases concurrently suffered by an individual, fall into $r + 1$ mutually exclusive "sets" of states according to the concurrent presence of 0, 1, 2, ..., or r diseases: $\binom{r}{0} = 1$ state of no illness;

$\binom{r}{1} = r$ states of illness with a single disease; $\binom{r}{2} = r(r-1)/2$ states with 2 diseases, etc.; and $\binom{r}{r} = 1$ state with r diseases. The total number of states in all the sets is equal to the total possible states of illness, which is equal to 2^r; for convenience, we will designate $2^r = R$. To illustrate, if three diseases operate in a population, then $r = 3$, and there are 2^3 or $R = 8$ states of illness: these include one state of no illness, three states with a single disease, three states with two diseases, and one state with three diseases. An individual is said to be in state s_α when afflicted with the corresponding diseases; thus, a healthy person is in state s_1, while an individual affected with all the r diseases is in state s_R. An individual may leave a state at any given time either through recovery or by affliction with new diseases, and all the R states are thus transient states.

There are also R states of death d_α, similarly divided into $r + 1$ sets according to the multiplicity of causes of death (Table 2). The R states constitute a closed set in that no state outside the set may be reached from any state belonging to the set. In fact, each state itself is an absorbing barrier, since an individual arriving at state d_β from state of illness s_α will stay in d_β forever.

Consider the time interval $(0, t)$ for a given $t > 0$. At time $t = 0$, let there be N_α individuals in state s_α for $\alpha = 1, \ldots, R$; thus the quantity N_α may be referred to as the initial size of the state s_α. These N_α individuals will travel independently from one state to another. At the end of the interval $(0, t)$, after having left the original state s_α m times for $m = 0, 1, \ldots,$ a number $N_{\alpha\beta}^{(m)}(t)$ of individuals will be found in state s_β and a number $D_{\alpha\beta}^{(m)}(t)$ in state d_β for $\beta = 1, \ldots, R$. The sum

$$(1) \qquad \sum_{m=0}^{\infty} N_{\alpha\beta}^{(m)}(t) = N_{\alpha\beta}(t), \qquad \alpha, \beta = 1, \ldots, R$$

is the number of individuals in s_α at time 0 and in s_β at time t; the sum

$$(2) \qquad \sum_{m=0}^{\infty} D_{\alpha\beta}^{(m)}(t) = D_{\alpha\beta}(t), \qquad \alpha, \beta = 1, \ldots, R$$

is the number transferred from s_α to d_β in $(0, t)$. Clearly, for each α we have

$$(3) \qquad N_\alpha = \sum_{\beta=1}^{R} N_{\alpha\beta}(t) + \sum_{\beta=1}^{R} D_{\alpha\beta}(t), \quad \alpha = 1, \ldots, R.$$

Table 1. Classification of States of Illness by Multiplicity of Diseases

(r = total number of diseases)

($R = 2^r$ = total number of states)

Set of states by multiplicity of illness	Set of states S_c	State s_α	Number of states in set, $\binom{r}{c}$
State of no illness	S_0	s_1	$\binom{r}{0}$
States with single disease	S_1	s_2 . . s_{r+1}	$\binom{r}{1}$
States with two diseases	S_2	s_{r+2} . . $s_{[r(r+1)+2]/2}$	$\binom{r}{2}$
. . . .	. .	. . . . . .	. .
States with c diseases	S_c	$s_{\binom{r}{0}+\dots+\binom{r}{c-1}+1}$ . . $s_{\binom{r}{0}+\dots+\binom{r}{c}}$	$\binom{r}{c}$
. . . .	. .	. . . . . .	. .
State with r diseases	S_r	$s_{2^r} = s_R$	$\binom{r}{r}$

Table 2. Classification of States of Death by Multiplicity of Causes

(r = total number of diseases)

($R = 2^r$ = total number of states)

Sets of states by multiplicity of causes	Set of states D_c	State d_α	Number of states in set, $\binom{r}{c}$
State of death from no cause	D_0	d_1	$\binom{r}{0}$
States from single cause	D_1	d_2 . . d_{r+1}	$\binom{r}{1}$
States from 2 causes	D_2	d_{r+2} . . $d_{\frac{r(r+1)}{2}+1}$	$\binom{r}{2}$
. . . .	. . .	. . . .	. .
States from c causes	D_c	$d_{\binom{r}{0}+\ldots+\binom{r}{c-1}+1}$ . . $d_{\binom{r}{0}+\ldots+\binom{r}{c}}$	$\binom{r}{c}$
. . . .	. . .	. . . .	. .
State from r causes	D_r	$d_{2^r} = d_R$	$\binom{r}{r}$

The purpose of this paper is to derive formulas for the generating functions of $N_{\alpha\beta}^{(m)}(t)$ in terms of the eigenvalues of certain characteristic equations. The generating function and the joint probability distribution of $N_{\alpha\beta}(t)$ and $D_{\alpha\beta}(t)$, their expectations and covariance matrix, and the expected length of stay in each of the 2R states are also derived. Whenever possible, a matrix notation will be used for simplicity of presentation. A lemma regarding certain identities used in the derivation of the main results is given in the appendix.

2. Risks and Transition Probabilities

Transitions among the 2R states are governed by "risks of illness" and "risks of death," or $\nu_{\alpha\beta}$ and $\mu_{\alpha\beta}$, respectively, for $\alpha, \beta = 1,\ldots,R$. For $0 \le \tau < t$, consider an infinitesimal time element $(\tau, \tau+\Delta\tau)$. Equations (4) and (5) regarding conditional probabilities can easily be derived for τ between 0 and t.

$$(4) \qquad \nu_{\alpha\beta}(\tau)\Delta\tau + o(\Delta\tau) = \Pr\{\text{an individual in state } s_\alpha \text{ at time } \tau \text{ will be in state } s_\beta \text{ at time } \tau+\Delta\tau\}, \quad \alpha \ne \beta .$$

$$(5) \qquad \mu_{\alpha\beta}(\tau)\Delta\tau + o(\Delta\tau) = \Pr\{\text{an individual in state } s_\alpha \text{ at time } \tau \text{ will be in state } d_\beta \text{ at time } \tau+\Delta\tau\}. \quad \alpha, \beta = 1,\ldots,R .$$

Here $o(\Delta\tau)$ is a quantity such that the ratio $o(\Delta\tau)/(\Delta\tau)$ tends toward zero as $\Delta\tau$ tends toward zero. The quantities $\nu_{\alpha\beta}(\tau)$ and $\mu_{\alpha\beta}(\tau)$ are functions of time τ. In this paper it will be assumed that they are independent of τ for $0 \le \tau < t$, or that

$$(6) \qquad \nu_{\alpha\beta}(\tau) = \nu_{\alpha\beta}, \quad \alpha \ne \beta \quad \text{and} \quad \alpha, \beta = 1,\ldots,R$$

and

$$(7) \qquad \mu_{\alpha\beta}(\tau) = \mu_{\alpha\beta}, \qquad \alpha, \beta = 1,\ldots,R .$$

For notational convenience, we define

$$(8) \qquad \nu_{\alpha\alpha} = -\Big[\sum_{\substack{\beta=1\\ \beta\ne\alpha}}^{R} \nu_{\alpha\beta} + \sum_{\beta=1}^{R} \mu_{\alpha\beta}\Big], \qquad \alpha = 1,\ldots,R .$$

Since the risks $\nu_{\alpha\beta}$ and $\mu_{\alpha\beta}$ in (6) and (7) must be non-negative quantities, $\nu_{\alpha\alpha}$ must be non-positive. These risks may be summarized in the forms of the morbidity risk matrix (6a) and the mortality risk matrix (7a).

$$(6a)\qquad \underline{\underline{V}} = \begin{bmatrix} \nu_{11} & \nu_{12} & \cdots & \nu_{1R} \\ \nu_{21} & \nu_{22} & \cdots & \nu_{2R} \\ \cdot & \cdot & & \cdot \\ \cdot & \cdot & & \cdot \\ \nu_{R1} & \nu_{R2} & \cdots & \nu_{RR} \end{bmatrix}$$

$$(7a)\qquad \underline{\underline{U}} = \begin{bmatrix} \mu_{11} & \mu_{12} & \cdots & \mu_{1R} \\ \mu_{21} & \mu_{22} & \cdots & \mu_{2R} \\ \cdot & \cdot & & \cdot \\ \cdot & \cdot & & \cdot \\ \mu_{R1} & \mu_{R2} & \cdots & \mu_{RR} \end{bmatrix}$$

The strict formulation of an illness-death process requires the assumptions that no death takes place without a cause and that an individual is afflicted at the time of death with the diseases corresponding to the cause of his death. Many of the $\mu_{\alpha\beta}$ risks would then be zero. Similarly, if an individual is unlikely [with a probability of $o(\Delta\tau)$] to be afflicted with more than one disease within an infinitesimal interval $\Delta\tau$, many of the $\nu_{\alpha\beta}$ would also be zero. However, our model will be presented in a more general form, without the explicit deletion of any $\nu_{\alpha\beta}$ or $\mu_{\alpha\beta}$ risks. If certain transitions are impossible in a given case, say from s_α to s_γ or from s_β to d_δ, then $\nu_{\alpha\gamma}$ and $\mu_{\beta\delta}$ in (8) are replaced with zero. The resultant formulas will be true for the case in question in all expressions in the model. Further, the states of illness and the states of death need not be equal in number. In short, the model considered here consists of a number of transient states and a number of absorbing states, with the transitions governed by the risks defined in (4) through (8).

The fundamental quantities underlying the probability distributions of $N_{\alpha\beta}^{(m)}(t)$, $N_{\alpha\beta}(t)$, $D_{\alpha\beta}^{(m)}(t)$, and $D_{\alpha\beta}(t)$ are the transition probabilities $P_{\alpha\beta}^{(m)}(t)$, $P_{\alpha\beta}(t)$, $Q_{\alpha\beta}^{(m)}(t)$, and $Q_{\alpha\beta}(t)$. These probabilities are defined as follows:

(9) $P_{\alpha\beta}^{(m)}(t) = \Pr\{$an individual in state s_α at time 0 will leave s_α m times and be in state s_β at time $t\}$, $m = 0, 1, 2, \ldots,$ and $\alpha, \beta = 1, \ldots, R$.

(10) $P_{\alpha\beta}(t) = \Pr\{$an individual in state s_α at time 0 will be in state s_β at time $t\}$, $\alpha, \beta = 1, \ldots, R$.

(11) $Q_{\alpha\beta}^{(m)}(t) = \Pr\{$an individual in state s_α at time 0 will leave s_α m times and be in state d_β at time $t\}$, $m = 0, 1, 2, \ldots,$ and $\alpha, \beta = 1, \ldots, R$.

(12) $Q_{\alpha\beta}(t) = \Pr\{$an individual in state s_α at time 0 will be in state d_β at time $t\}$, $\alpha, \beta = 1, \ldots, R$.

These probabilities have the following relationships:

$$\sum_{m=0}^{\infty} P_{\alpha\beta}^{(m)}(t) = P_{\alpha\beta}(t), \qquad \alpha, \beta = 1, \ldots, R . \tag{13}$$

$$\sum_{m=0}^{\infty} Q_{\alpha\beta}^{(m)}(t) = Q_{\alpha\beta}(t), \qquad \alpha, \beta = 1, \ldots, R . \tag{14}$$

Since an individual in s_α at time 0 must be in one of the $2R$ states at time t, we also have

$$\sum_{\beta=1}^{R} P_{\alpha\beta}(t) + \sum_{\beta=1}^{R} Q_{\alpha\beta}(t) = 1, \qquad \alpha = 1, \ldots, R . \tag{15}$$

In matrix notation, the probabilities are written as follows:

$$\underset{=}{P}^{(m)}(t) = \begin{bmatrix} P_{11}^{(m)}(t) & P_{12}^{(m)}(t) & \ldots & P_{1R}^{(m)}(t) \\ P_{21}^{(m)}(t) & P_{22}^{(m)}(t) & \ldots & P_{2R}^{(m)}(t) \\ \vdots & \vdots & & \vdots \\ P_{R1}^{(m)}(t) & P_{R2}^{(m)}(t) & \ldots & P_{RR}^{(m)}(t) \end{bmatrix} . \tag{9a}$$

$$(10a)\quad \underline{\underline{P}}(t) = \begin{bmatrix} P_{11}(t) & P_{12}(t) & \cdots & P_{1R}(t) \\ P_{21}(t) & P_{22}(t) & \cdots & P_{2R}(t) \\ \vdots & \vdots & & \vdots \\ P_{R1}(t) & P_{R2}(t) & \cdots & P_{RR}(t) \end{bmatrix}$$

$$\underline{\underline{Q}}^{(m)}(t) = \begin{bmatrix} Q_{11}^{(m)}(t) & Q_{12}^{(m)}(t) & \cdots & Q_{1R}^{(m)}(t) \\ Q_{21}^{(m)}(t) & Q_{22}^{(m)}(t) & \cdots & Q_{2R}^{(m)}(t) \\ \vdots & \vdots & & \vdots \\ Q_{R1}^{(m)}(t) & Q_{R2}^{(m)}(t) & \cdots & Q_{RR}^{(m)}(t) \end{bmatrix}$$

$$\underline{\underline{Q}}(t) = \begin{bmatrix} Q_{11}(t) & Q_{12}(t) & \cdots & Q_{1R}(t) \\ Q_{21}(t) & Q_{22}(t) & \cdots & Q_{2R}(t) \\ \vdots & \vdots & & \vdots \\ Q_{R1}(t) & Q_{R2}(t) & \cdots & Q_{RR}(t) \end{bmatrix}$$

$$(13a)\quad \sum_{m=0}^{\infty} \underline{\underline{P}}^{(m)}(t) = \underline{\underline{P}}(t) \quad .$$

$$(14a)\quad \sum_{m=0}^{\infty} \underline{\underline{Q}}^{(m)}(t) = \underline{\underline{Q}}(t) \quad .$$

3. Generating Functions of $P_{\alpha\beta}^{(m)}(t)$

Since the N_α individuals are assumed to travel independently among the 2R states, it is sufficient to consider $N_\alpha = 1$ at time 0 in each state to derive the transition probabilities $P_{\alpha\beta}^{(m)}(t)$ and $P_{\alpha\beta}(t)$. When $N_\alpha > 1$, the probability distributions of $N_{\alpha\beta}^{(m)}(t)$ and $N_{\alpha\beta}(t)$ are simply the N_α-fold convolutions of $P_{\alpha\beta}^{(m)}(t)$ and $P_{\alpha\beta}(t)$ respectively.

To derive the transition probabilities, we introduce the generating functions

$$(16)\qquad g_{\alpha\beta}(z;t) = \sum_{m=0}^{\infty} z^m p_{\alpha\beta}^{(m)}(t), \qquad \alpha, \beta = 1,\dots,R .$$

where $|z| < 1$, and the corresponding matrix

$$(17)\qquad \underline{\underline{G}}(z;t) = \begin{bmatrix} g_{11}(z;t) & g_{12}(z;t) & \dots & g_{1R}(z;t) \\ g_{21}(z;t) & g_{22}(z;t) & \dots & g_{2R}(z;t) \\ \vdots & \vdots & & \vdots \\ g_{R1}(z;t) & g_{R2}(z;t) & \dots & g_{RR}(z;t) \end{bmatrix}$$

It may be noted that

$$g_{\alpha\beta}(1;t) = P_{\alpha\beta}(t), \qquad \alpha,\beta = 1,\dots,R ,$$

and that

$$(19)\qquad \underline{\underline{G}}(1;t) = \underline{\underline{P}}(t) .$$

Using the conventional approach, we first derive systems of the differential equations of $P_{\alpha\beta}^{(m)}(t)$ by considering the probabilities $P_{\alpha\beta}^{(m)}(t+\Delta t)$ at time $t + \Delta t$. Dirict enumerations give

$$P^{(m)}_{\alpha\alpha}(t+\Delta t) = P^{(m)}_{\alpha\alpha}(t)\left[1+\nu_{\alpha\alpha}\Delta t+o(\Delta t)\right] + \sum_{\substack{\gamma=1\\ \gamma\neq\alpha}}^{R} P^{(m)}_{\alpha\gamma}(t)\left[\nu_{\gamma\alpha}\Delta t+o(\Delta t)\right]$$

(20)

$$P^{(m)}_{\alpha\beta}(t+\Delta t) = P^{(m-1)}_{\alpha\alpha}(t)\left[\nu_{\alpha\beta}\Delta t+o(\Delta t)\right] + P^{(m)}_{\alpha\beta}(t)\left[1+\nu_{\beta\beta}\Delta t+o(\Delta t)\right]$$

$$+\sum_{\substack{\gamma=1\\ \gamma\neq\alpha,\beta}}^{R} P^{(m)}_{\alpha\gamma}(t)\left[\nu_{\gamma\beta}\Delta t + o(\Delta t)\right], \qquad \alpha,\beta = 1,\dots,R .$$

Transposing $P^{(m)}_{\alpha\alpha}(t)$ and $P^{(m)}_{\alpha\beta}(t)$, dividing through by Δt, and letting Δt approach 0, we obtain

$$\frac{d}{dt}P^{(m)}_{\alpha\alpha}(t) = \sum_{\gamma=1}^{R} P^{(m)}_{\alpha\gamma}(t)\,\nu_{\gamma\alpha},$$

(21)

$$\frac{d}{dt}P^{(m)}_{\alpha\beta}(t) = P^{(m-1)}_{\alpha\alpha}(t)\,\nu_{\alpha\beta} + \sum_{\substack{\gamma=1\\ \gamma\neq\alpha}}^{R} P^{(m)}_{\alpha\gamma}(t)\,\nu_{\gamma\beta}, \quad \alpha,\beta = 1,\dots,R .$$

Now we take derivatives of $g_{\alpha\beta}(z;t)$ in (16) with respect to t and substitute (21) in the resultant expressions to obtain the systems of differential equations for the generating function:

$$\frac{\partial}{\partial t} g_{\alpha\beta}(z;t) = \sum_{\gamma=1}^{R} g_{\alpha\gamma}(z;t)\,\nu_{\gamma\alpha},$$

(22)

$$\frac{\partial}{\partial t} G_{\alpha\beta}(z;t) = z g_{\alpha\alpha}(z;t)\,\nu_{\alpha\beta} + \sum_{\substack{\gamma=1\\ \gamma\neq\alpha}}^{R} g_{\alpha\gamma}(z;t)\,\nu_{\gamma\beta}, \quad \alpha\neq\beta,\ \alpha,\beta = 1,\dots,R.$$

For each α, (22) is a system of R linear homogeneous first-order differential equations and can be written in the form

(23)

$$
\begin{array}{l}
(D-\nu_{11})\, g_{\alpha 1}(z;t) - \nu_{\alpha 1} g_{\alpha 2}(z;t) - \ldots - z\nu_{\alpha 1} g_{\alpha\alpha}(z;t) - \ldots - \nu_{R1} g_{\alpha R}(z;t) = 0 \\
-\nu_{12} g_{\alpha 1}(z;t) + (D-\nu_{22})\, g_{\alpha 2}(z;t) - \ldots - z\nu_{\alpha 2} g_{\alpha\alpha}(z;t) - \ldots - \nu_{R2} g_{\alpha R}(z;t) = 0 \\
\quad \cdot \qquad \cdot \qquad \cdot \qquad \cdot \qquad \ldots \qquad \cdot \\
-\nu_{1\alpha} g_{\alpha 1}(z;t) - \nu_{2\alpha} g_{\alpha 2}(z;t) - \ldots + (D-\nu_{\alpha\alpha})\, g_{\alpha\alpha}(z;t) - \ldots - \nu_{R\alpha} g_{\alpha R}(z;t) = 0 \\
\quad \cdot \qquad \cdot \qquad \cdot \qquad \cdot \qquad \ldots \qquad \cdot \\
-\nu_{1R} g_{\alpha 1}(z;t) - \nu_{2R} g_{\alpha 2}(z;t) - \ldots - z\nu_{\alpha R} g_{\alpha\alpha}(z;t) - \ldots + (D-\nu_{RR})\, g_{\alpha R}(z;t) = 0
\end{array}
$$

Here the notation D indicates differentiation with respect to t. To solve (23), we introduce the characteristic equation

$$
(24) \qquad \Lambda(\alpha) = \begin{vmatrix}
(\lambda-\nu_{11}) & -\nu_{21} & \ldots & -z\nu_{\alpha 1} & \ldots & -\nu_{R1} \\
-\nu_{12} & (\lambda-\nu_{22}) & \ldots & -z\nu_{\alpha 2} & \ldots & -\nu_{R2} \\
\cdot & \cdot & \cdot & \cdot & \cdot & \cdot \\
-\nu_{1\alpha} & -\nu_{2\alpha} & \ldots & (\lambda-\nu_{\alpha\alpha}) & \ldots & -\nu_{R\alpha} \\
\cdot & \cdot & \cdot & \cdot & \cdot & \cdot \\
-\nu_{1R} & -\nu_{2R} & \ldots & -z\nu_{\alpha R} & \ldots & (\lambda-\nu_{RR})
\end{vmatrix} = 0
$$

Suppose that the characteristic equation (24) has R distinct real roots, $\lambda_i(\alpha)$ for $i = 1, \ldots, R$. From each of these roots we construct a particular solution for the system (23):

$$
(25) \qquad g_{\alpha\beta}(z;t) = a_{\alpha\beta i}\, e^{\lambda_i(\alpha) t}, \qquad \beta, i = 1, \ldots, R .
$$

The constants $a_{\alpha\beta i}$ can be determined by substituting (25) in system (23). As a result,

(26)

$$\left[\lambda_i(\alpha) - \nu_{11}\right]a_{\alpha 1 i} - \nu_{21}a_{\alpha 2 i} - \dots - z\nu_{\alpha 1}a_{\alpha\alpha i} - \dots - \nu_{R1}a_{\alpha R i} = 0$$

$$-\nu_{12}a_{\alpha 1 i} + \left[\lambda_i(\alpha) - \nu_{22}\right]a_{\alpha 2 i} - \dots - z\nu_{\alpha 2}a_{\alpha\alpha i} - \dots - \nu_{R2}a_{\alpha R i} = 0$$

$$-\nu_{1\alpha}a_{\alpha 1 i} - \nu_{2\alpha}a_{\alpha 2 i} - \dots + \left[\lambda_i(\alpha) - \nu_{\alpha\alpha}\right]a_{\alpha\alpha i} - \dots - \nu_{R\alpha}a_{\alpha R i} = 0$$

$$-\nu_{1R}a_{\alpha 1 i} - \nu_{2R}a_{\alpha 2 i} - \dots - z\nu_{\alpha R}a_{\alpha\alpha i} - \dots + \left[\lambda_i(\alpha) - \nu_{RR}\right]a_{\alpha R i} = 0$$

System (26) has a non-trivial solution $a_{\alpha\beta i}$ if the determinant of the coefficients of this system equals zero, which it does in light of the characteristic equation (24). In fact, equation (24) implies that the coefficient matrix of (26) is of rank $(R-1)$, so that the roots $a_{\alpha\beta i}$ are proportional to the cofactors $\Lambda^{(i)}_{\alpha\beta}(\alpha)$ of (24), with $\lambda = \lambda_i(\alpha)$. That is, for $\alpha = 1,\dots,R$ and $i = 1,\dots,R$,

$$a_{\alpha\beta i} = k_{\alpha i}\,\Lambda^{(i)}_{\alpha\beta}(\alpha), \qquad \beta = 1,\dots,R. \tag{27}$$

When expanded, the cofactors become

$$\Lambda^{(i)}_{\alpha\alpha}(\alpha) = \lambda_i^{R-1}(\alpha) + B_{\alpha 2}\lambda_i^{R-2}(\alpha) + \dots + B_{\alpha R}\lambda_i^{0}(\alpha)$$

$$\Lambda^{(i)}_{\alpha\beta}(\alpha) = \qquad B_{\beta 2}\lambda_i^{R-2}(\alpha) + \dots + B_{\beta R}\lambda_i^{0}(\alpha), \quad \alpha \neq \beta;\ \alpha,\beta = 1,\dots,R.$$

(28)

Here each $B_{\gamma\delta}$ is a function of $v_{\alpha\beta}: \alpha,\beta = 1,\dots,R,$ and z, but is independent of i. Therefore, the complete solutions of (22) are:

$$g_{\alpha\beta}(z;t) = \sum_{i=1}^{R} a_{\alpha\beta i}\, e^{\lambda_i(\alpha)t}$$

$$= \sum_{i=1}^{R} k_{\alpha i}\,\Lambda^{(i)}_{\alpha\beta}(\alpha)\, e^{\lambda_i(\alpha)t}, \qquad \alpha,\beta = 1,\dots,R. \tag{29}$$

The constants $k_{\alpha i}$ in (29) can be determined from the initial conditions. Since one individual is in s_α at time 0, the initial conditions are:

$$g_{\alpha\alpha}(z;0) = 1 \,,$$

(30)

$$g_{\alpha\beta}(z;0) = 0 \,, \quad \alpha \neq \beta; \quad \alpha, \beta = 1, \ldots, R \,.$$

When (29) is used, (30) becomes

$$\sum_{i=1}^{R} k_{\alpha i} \Lambda_{\alpha\alpha}^{(i)}(\alpha) = 1 \,,$$

(31)
$$\sum_{i=1}^{R} k_{\alpha i} \Lambda_{\alpha\beta}^{(i)}(\alpha) = 0 \,, \quad \alpha \neq \beta; \quad \alpha, \beta = 1, \ldots, R \,.$$

The expression

(32)
$$k_{\alpha i} = \frac{1}{\prod_{\substack{j=1 \\ j \neq i}}^{R} \left[\lambda_1(\alpha) - \lambda_j(\alpha)\right]} \,, \qquad \alpha, \ i = 1, \ldots, R$$

is easily seen to satisfy (31) if we observe the following

<u>Lemma</u>: <u>Whatever may be R distinct values</u> $\lambda_1, \ldots\ldots, \lambda_R$,

(33)
$$\sum_{i=1}^{R} \frac{\lambda_i^r}{\prod_{\substack{j=1 \\ j \neq i}}^{R} (\lambda_i - \lambda_j)} = 1 \,, \qquad r = R - 1$$

$$= 0 \,, \qquad 0 \leqq r < R - 1$$

[Lemma (33) is proved in the appendix.] Substituting (28) and (32) in (31) we have

(34)

$$\sum_{i=1}^{R} k_{\alpha i}\Lambda_{\alpha\alpha}^{(i)}(\alpha) = \sum_{i=1}^{R} \frac{\lambda_i^{R-1}(\alpha)}{\prod\limits_{\substack{j=1\\j\neq i}}^{R}\left[\lambda_i(\alpha)-\lambda_j(\alpha)\right]} + B_{\alpha 2}\prod_{i=1}^{R}\frac{\lambda_i^{R-2}(\alpha)}{\prod\limits_{\substack{j=1\\j\neq i}}^{R}\left[\lambda_i(\alpha)-\lambda_j(\alpha)\right]} + \cdots$$

$$+ B_{\alpha R}\prod_{i=1}^{R}\frac{1}{\prod\limits_{\substack{j=1\\j\neq i}}^{R}\left[\lambda_1(\alpha)-\lambda_j(\alpha)\right]}$$

$$\sum_{i=1}^{R} k_{\alpha i}\Lambda_{\alpha\beta}^{(i)}(\alpha) = \qquad + B_{\beta 2}\sum_{i=1}^{R}\frac{\lambda_i^{R-2}(\alpha)}{\prod\limits_{\substack{j=1\\j\neq i}}^{R}\left[\lambda_i(\alpha)-\lambda_j(\alpha)\right]} + \cdots$$

$$+ B_{\beta R}\sum_{i=1}^{R}\frac{1}{\prod\limits_{\substack{j=1\\j\neq i}}^{R}\left[\lambda_i(\alpha)-\lambda_j(\alpha)\right]}$$

$$\alpha \neq \beta;\ \alpha,\beta = 1,\ldots,R\ .$$

Using (33), we see that the right side member of the first equation of (34) becomes unity and that of the second equation vanishes, thus proving that (32) satisfies (31).

Substituting (32) in (29), we obtain the exact formulas for the generating functions:

$$(35)\qquad g_{\alpha\beta}(z;t) = \sum_{i=1}^{R}\frac{\Lambda_{\alpha\beta}^{(i)}(\alpha)\, e^{\lambda_i(\alpha)t}}{\prod\limits_{\substack{j=1\\j\neq i}}^{R}\left[\lambda_i(\alpha)-\lambda_j(\alpha)\right]}\ ,\qquad \alpha,\beta = 1,\ldots,R\ .$$

It may be noted that time t appears only in the exponent and that $g_{\alpha\beta}(z;t)$ is a function of z and $\nu_{\gamma\delta}$ through the cofactor $\Lambda_{\alpha\beta}^{(i)}(\alpha)$ and the characteristic roots $\lambda_i(\alpha)$.

The generating function (35) can now be used to compute the multiple transition probabilities $P_{\alpha\beta}^{(m)}(t)$ and the factorial moments, respectively, from the following relationships:

$$(36) \qquad P_{\alpha\beta}^{(m)}(t) = \frac{1}{m!}\frac{\partial^m}{\partial z^m} g_{\alpha\beta}(z;t)\Big|_{z=0}, \qquad m = 0,1,\ldots, \quad \alpha,\beta = 1,\ldots,R .$$

$$(37) \qquad E(M_{\alpha\beta}) = \frac{\partial}{\partial z} g_{\alpha\beta}(z;t)\Big|_{z=1}, \qquad \alpha,\beta = 1,\ldots,R .$$

$$(38) \qquad E\left[M_{\alpha\beta}(M_{\alpha\beta}-1)\right] = \frac{\partial^2}{\partial z^2} g_{\alpha\beta}(z;t)\Big|_{z=1}, \qquad \alpha,\beta = 1,\ldots,R .$$

Here $M_{\alpha\beta}$ is the random variable denoting the number of times that an individual leaves s_α in the interval $(0, t)$ before arriving at state s_β at time t .

In deriving the generating functions $g_{\alpha\beta}(z;t)$ it was assumed that all the R characteristic roots of equation (24) are real and distinct. If there are one or more pairs of conjugate complex roots or one or more multiple roots, the system of differential equations (22) can be solved in a similar manner, although the resulting formulas for $g_{\alpha\beta}(z;t)$ will be more complex than those given in (35).

4. Generating Functions of $Q_{\alpha\beta}^{(m)}(t)$

Let the generating function of $Q_{\alpha\beta}^{(m)}(t)$ be defined as

$$h_{\alpha\beta}(z;t) = \sum_{m=0}^{\infty} z^m Q_{\alpha\beta}^{(m)}(t), \qquad \alpha,\beta = 1,\ldots,R .$$

We wish first to express $Q_{\alpha\beta}^{(m)}(t)$ in terms of $P_{\alpha\beta}^{(m)}(t)$ and the mortality risk $\mu_{\alpha\beta}$ as defined in (5). The relationship between $Q_{\alpha\beta}^{(m)}(t)$ and $P_{\alpha\beta}^{(m)}(t)$ may be derived on the basis of two considerations. First, an individual may travel from state s_α to state d_β directly or by way of some other state s_γ for $\alpha \neq \gamma$ and $\gamma = 1, \ldots, R$ Secondly, d_β is an absorbing barrier, an individual in state d_β at time t may have reached the state at any time prior to t. For a fixed τ, $0 \leq \tau < t$, consider a time interval $(\tau, \tau + d\tau)$. According to the first consideration, the probability that an individual in state s_α at time 0 will leave the state m times and be in state d_β at time $(\tau + d\tau)$ is

$$(40) \qquad P_{\alpha\alpha}^{(m-1)}(\tau)\,\mu_{\alpha\beta}d\tau + \sum_{\substack{\gamma=1\\ \gamma\neq\alpha}}^{R} P_{\alpha\gamma}^{(m)}(\tau)\,\mu_{\gamma\beta}d\tau\,, \qquad \alpha, \beta = 1, \ldots, R\,.$$

The second consideration leads to the equation

$$(41) \qquad Q_{\alpha\beta}^{(m)}(t) = \int_0^t P_{\alpha\alpha}^{(m-1)}(\tau)\,\mu_{\alpha\beta}d\tau + \int_0^t \sum_{\substack{\gamma=1\\ \gamma\neq\alpha}}^{R} P_{\alpha\gamma}^{(m)}(\tau)\,\mu_{\gamma\beta}d\tau, \quad \alpha, \beta = 1, \ldots, R\,.$$

Substituting (41) in (39) yields

$$(42) \qquad h_{\alpha\beta}(z;t) = \sum_{m=0}^{\infty} z^m \left[\int_0^t P_{\alpha\alpha}^{(m-1)}(\tau)\,\mu_{\alpha\beta}d\tau + \int_0^t \sum_{\substack{\gamma=1\\ \gamma\neq\alpha}}^{R} P_{\alpha\gamma}^{(m)}(\tau)\,\mu_{\gamma\beta}d\tau\right],$$

$$\alpha, \beta = 1, \ldots, R\,.$$

Since $|z| < 1$, the infinite series converges uniformly in τ and we may interchange the integral and the summation sign over m and write

$$(43) \qquad h_{\alpha\beta}(z;t) = \sum_{\gamma=1}^{R}\left[\int_0^t \left\{\sum_{m=0}^{\infty} z^m P_{\alpha\gamma}^{(m)}(\tau)\right\} d\tau\right]\mu_{\gamma\beta}\,, \qquad \alpha, \beta = 1, \ldots, R\,.$$

The sum inside the braces is the generating function $g_{\alpha\gamma}(z;\tau)$ of $P_{\alpha\gamma}^{(m)}(\tau)$, as given by (35). Substituting (35) in (43) yields

(44)

$$h_{\alpha\beta}(z;t) = \sum_{\gamma=1}^{R}\left[\sum_{i=1}^{R}\int_0^t \frac{\Lambda_{\alpha\gamma}^{(i)}(\alpha)\, e^{\lambda_i(\alpha)\tau}}{\prod_{\substack{j=1\\ j\neq i}}^{R}\left[\lambda_i(\alpha)-\lambda_j(\alpha)\right]}\, d\tau\right]\mu_{\gamma\beta}\ , \quad \alpha,\beta = 1,\ldots,R\ .$$

The formula for the generating function is thus

(45)

$$h_{\alpha\beta}(z;t) = \sum_{\gamma=1}^{R}\sum_{i=1}^{R} \frac{\Lambda_{\alpha\gamma}^{(i)}(\alpha)\left[e^{\lambda_i(\alpha)t}-1\right]}{\lambda_i(\alpha)\prod_{\substack{j=1\\ j\neq i}}^{R}\left[\lambda_i(\alpha)-\lambda_j(\alpha)\right]}\,\mu_{\gamma\beta}\ , \qquad \alpha,\beta = 1,\ldots,R\ .$$

The appropriate derivatives of (45) yield the probabilities $Q_{\alpha\beta}^{(m)}(t)$ and the expected number of times that an individual will leave his original state s_α before reaching state d_β . The probabilities $Q_{\alpha\beta}^{(m)}(t)$ can also be computed through their relationship with $P_{\alpha\beta}^{(m)}(t)$ from equation (41) .

5. Formulas for $P_{\alpha\beta}(t)$ and $Q_{\alpha\beta}(t)$

Having derived the generating functions $g_{\alpha\beta}(z;t)$ and $h_{\alpha\beta}(z;t)$, we can obtain the transition probabilities $P_{\alpha\beta}(t)$ and $Q_{\alpha\beta}(t)$ by replacing z with 1 in formulas (35) and (45) . However, in many cases the transition probabilities $P_{\alpha\beta}(t)$ and $Q_{\alpha\beta}(t)$ are the major objective and should be derived directly. Further, when $z = 1$, matrix notation may be used to simplify the derivation of $P_{\alpha\beta}(t)$, which will be sketched as follows at the expense of some repetition.

Suppose that there is one individual in each state s_α at time $t=0$ for $\alpha = 1,\ldots,R$. Let the matrix of derivatives of $P_{\alpha\beta}(t)$ be

(46)

$$D\,\underline{\underline{P}}(t) = \begin{bmatrix} \frac{d}{dt}P_{11}(t) & \frac{d}{dt}P_{12}(t) & \cdots & \frac{d}{dt}P_{1R}(t) \\ \frac{d}{dt}P_{21}(t) & \frac{d}{dt}P_{22}(t) & \cdots & \frac{d}{dt}P_{2R}(t) \\ \cdot & \cdot & \cdot & \cdot \\ \frac{d}{dt}P_{R1}(t) & \frac{d}{dt}P_{R2}(t) & \cdots & \frac{d}{dt}P_{RR}(t) \end{bmatrix}$$

where D stands for differentiation with respect to t . From (23) we see that

$$(D - \underline{\underline{V}}') \, \underline{\underline{P}}'(t) = 0 \; . \tag{47}$$

Here $\underline{\underline{V}}'$ is the transpose of the morbidity risk matrix [described by (6a)], and $\underline{\underline{P}}'(t)$ is the transpose of $\underline{\underline{P}}(t)$. The corresponding characteristic equation is

$$\Lambda = |\lambda \underline{\underline{I}} - \underline{\underline{V}}'| = 0 \; , \tag{48}$$

where $\underline{\underline{I}}$ is an $R \times R$ unit matrix. Let λ_i for $i = 1, \ldots, R$ be the characteristic roots of (48) . For each λ_i, we have a particular solution

$$\underline{\underline{P}}(t) = \underline{\underline{A}}^{(i)} e^{\lambda_i t} \tag{49}$$

where

$$\underline{\underline{A}}^{(i)} = \begin{bmatrix} a_{11i} & a_{12i} & \ldots & a_{1Ri} \\ a_{21i} & a_{22i} & \ldots & a_{2Ri} \\ \cdot & \cdot & \cdot & \cdot \\ a_{R1i} & a_{R2i} & \ldots & a_{RRi} \end{bmatrix} \tag{50}$$

must be determined. Substituting (49) in (47) and dividing out the nonvanishing scalar factor $e^{\lambda_i t}$, we obtain

$$(\lambda_i \underline{\underline{I}} - \underline{\underline{V}}') \, \underline{\underline{A}}^{(i)\,'} = \underline{\underline{0}} \; . \tag{51}$$

By virtue of (48), (51) has a nontrivial solution with roots $a_{\alpha\beta i}$ proportionate to the corresponding cofactors $\Lambda_{\alpha\beta}^{(i)}$ of

$$\underline{\underline{\Lambda}}^{(i)} = (\lambda_i \underline{\underline{I}} - \underline{\underline{V}}') \; , \tag{52}$$

that is,

$$a_{\alpha\beta i} = k_{\alpha i} \Lambda_{\alpha\beta}^{(i)} \, , \qquad \alpha, \beta = 1, \ldots, R \; . \tag{53}$$

If all the R characteristic roots λ_i of (48) are real and distinct, then the complete solution of (47) is

$$\underline{\underline{P}}(t) = \sum_{i=1}^{R} \underline{\underline{A}}^{(i)} e^{\lambda_i t} \tag{54}$$

with the elements of $\underline{\underline{A}}^{(i)}$ given by (53). The scalars $k_{\alpha i}$ can be determined by the initial condition. Since there is one individual in each state s_α at time 0, the initial condition is

$$\underline{\underline{P}}(0) = \underline{\underline{I}} \tag{55}$$

and (54) becomes

$$\sum_{i=1}^{R} \underline{\underline{A}}^{(i)} = \underline{\underline{I}} \ . \tag{56}$$

Substituting (53) in (56), expanding $\Lambda_{\alpha\beta}^{(i)}$ in a polynomial of λ_i as in (28), and using formula (33) (see lemma in appendix), we obtain

$$k_{\alpha i} = \frac{1}{\prod_{\substack{j=1 \\ j\neq 1}}^{R} (\lambda_i - \lambda_j)} , \qquad \alpha = 1, \dots, R \ . \tag{57}$$

which is independent of α. From (53), (54), and (57) we have the desired solution of (47):

$$P_{\alpha\beta}(t) = \sum_{i=1}^{R} \frac{\Lambda_{\alpha\beta}^{(i)} e^{\lambda_i t}}{\prod_{\substack{j=1 \\ j\neq i}}^{R} (\lambda_i - \lambda_j)} , \qquad \alpha, \beta = 1, \dots, R \ . \tag{58}$$

Solution (58) is of course identical to (35), with $z = 1$.

The transition probabilities $Q_{\alpha\beta}(t)$ can be obtained either from (45), by setting $z = 1$, or through their relationship with the transition probabilities $P_{\alpha\beta}(t)$, as in formula (41). Using the same rationale as that used in arriving at (41), we have

$$Q_{\alpha\beta}(t) = \int_0^t \sum_{\gamma=1}^{R} P_{\alpha\gamma}(\tau)\, \mu_{\gamma\beta}\, d\tau , \qquad \alpha, \beta = 1, \dots, R \ . \tag{59}$$

Substituting (58) in (59) and integrating give the formula for $Q_{\alpha\beta}(t)$:

(60) $$Q_{\alpha\beta}(t) = \sum_{\gamma=1}^{R} \sum_{i=1}^{R} \frac{\Lambda_{\alpha\gamma}^{(i)}(e^{\lambda_i t} - 1)}{\lambda_i \prod_{\substack{j=1 \\ j \neq i}}^{R} (\lambda_i - \lambda_j)} \mu_{\gamma\beta}, \qquad \alpha, \beta = 1, \ldots, R .$$

6. Probability Distribution of $N_{\alpha\beta}(t)$ and $D_{\alpha\beta}(t)$

It was pointed out earlier that for a given α ,

(15) $$\sum_{\beta=1}^{R} P_{\alpha\beta}(t) + \sum_{\beta=1}^{R} Q_{\alpha\beta}(t) = 1, \qquad \alpha = 1, \ldots, R .$$

Having derived the formulas for $P_{\alpha\beta}(t)$ and $Q_{\alpha\beta}(t)$, we may now prove equation (15) .

Let us first compute the sum $\sum_{\beta=1}^{R} Q_{\alpha\beta}(t) = Q_{\alpha}(t)$, the probability that an individual in state s_α at time 0 will die (or enter one of the R states d_β) by time t . Using (60) yields

(61) $$\sum_{\beta=1}^{R} Q_{\alpha\beta}(t) = \sum_{\beta=1}^{R} \sum_{\gamma=1}^{R} \sum_{i=1}^{R} \frac{\Lambda_{\alpha\gamma}^{(i)} (e^{\lambda_i t} - 1)}{\lambda_i \prod_{\substack{j=1 \\ j \neq i}}^{R} (\lambda_i - \lambda_j)} \mu_{\gamma\beta}$$

$$= \sum_{i=1}^{R} \frac{(e^{\lambda_i t} - 1)}{\lambda_i \prod_{\substack{j=1 \\ j \neq i}}^{R} (\lambda_i - \lambda_j)} \left[\sum_{\gamma=1}^{R} \Lambda_{\alpha\gamma}^{(i)} \left(\sum_{\beta=1}^{R} \mu_{\gamma\beta} \right) \right] ,$$

where, by virtue of (8) ,

(62) $$\sum_{\beta=1}^{R} \mu_{\gamma\beta} = - \sum_{\beta=1}^{R} \nu_{\gamma\beta} = \left[(\lambda_i - \nu_{\gamma\gamma}) - \sum_{\substack{\beta=1 \\ \beta \neq \gamma}}^{R} \nu_{\gamma\beta} \right] - \lambda_i ,$$

and

$$(63)\quad \sum_{\gamma=1}^{R} \Lambda_{\alpha\gamma}^{(i)} \Big(\sum_{\beta=1}^{R} \mu_{\gamma\beta}\Big) = \sum_{\gamma=1}^{R} \Lambda_{\alpha\gamma}^{(i)} \Big((\lambda_i - \nu_{\gamma\gamma}) - \sum_{\substack{\beta=1 \\ \beta\neq\gamma}}^{R} \nu_{\gamma\beta} \Big) - \sum_{\gamma=1}^{R} \Lambda_{\alpha\gamma}^{(i)} \lambda_i$$

$$= \Lambda^{(i)} - \sum_{\gamma=1}^{R} \Lambda_{\alpha\gamma}^{(i)} \lambda_i$$

$$= - \sum_{\gamma=1}^{R} \Lambda_{\alpha\gamma}^{(i)} \lambda_i$$

since $\Lambda^{(i)}$ vanishes according to (52) . Substituting (63) in (61) and cancelling out λ_i, we have

$$(64)\quad Q_\alpha(t) = \sum_{\beta=1}^{R} Q_{\alpha\beta}(t) = \sum_{i=1}^{R} \sum_{\gamma=1}^{R} \frac{\Lambda_{\alpha\gamma}^{(i)}}{\prod_{\substack{j=1 \\ j\neq i}}^{R} (\lambda_i - \lambda_j)} - \sum_{i=1}^{R} \sum_{\gamma=1}^{R} \frac{\Lambda_{\alpha\gamma}^{(i)} e^{\lambda_i t}}{\prod_{\substack{j=1 \\ j\neq i}}^{R} (\lambda_i - \lambda_j)}$$

When $\Lambda_{\alpha\gamma}^{(i)}$ is expanded to the polynomial form of λ_i and (33) and (34) are used, the first sum on the right side of (64) becomes unity, and

$$(65)\quad Q_\alpha(t) = \sum_{\beta=1}^{R} Q_{\alpha\beta}(t) = 1 - \sum_{i=1}^{R} \sum_{\gamma=1}^{R} \frac{\Lambda_{\alpha\gamma}^{(i)} e^{\lambda_i t}}{\prod_{\substack{j=1 \\ j\neq i}}^{R} (\lambda_i - \lambda_j)}, \qquad \alpha = 1, \ldots, R .$$

On the other hand, from (58) we have the probability that an individual in state s_α at time 0 will be alive at time t

$$(66)\quad P_\alpha(t) = \sum_{\beta=1}^{R} P_{\alpha\beta}(t) = \sum_{\beta=1}^{R} \sum_{i=1}^{R} \frac{\Lambda_{\alpha\beta}^{(i)} e^{\lambda_i t}}{\prod_{\substack{j=1 \\ j\neq i}}^{R} (\lambda_i - \lambda_j)}, \qquad \alpha = 1, \ldots, R .$$

Substituting (65) and (66) in (15), the equation is proved.

It follows from equations (13), (14), and (15) that for a given N_α, the random variables $N_{\alpha\beta}^{(m)}(t)$ and $D_{\alpha\beta}^{(m)}(t)$, for $m = 1, 2, \ldots,$ and $\beta = 1, \ldots, R$, have a multinomial distribution. Equation (15) alone implies that $N_{\alpha\beta}(t)$ and $D_{\alpha\beta}(t)$ have a multinomial distribution. The general properties of a multinomial distribution can be applied in each of the two cases. To avoid repetition, we consider only the cases $N_{\alpha\beta}(t)$ and $D_{\alpha\beta}(t)$; corresponding results for $N_{\alpha\beta}^{(m)}(t)$ and $D_{\alpha\beta}^{(m)}(t)$ will be obvious.

The generating function of the joint distribution of $N_{\alpha\beta}(t)$ and $D_{\alpha\gamma}(t)$, defined as

$$(67) \qquad G_\alpha(z, \zeta, t) = E\left[\prod_{\beta=1}^{R} z_{\alpha\beta}^{N_{\alpha\beta}(t)} \prod_{\gamma=1}^{R} \zeta_{\alpha\gamma}^{D_{\alpha\gamma}(t)} \,\middle|\, N_\alpha\right], \quad \alpha = 1, \ldots, R.$$

with $|z_{\alpha\beta}| < 1$ and $|\zeta_{\alpha\gamma}| < 1$, is given by

$$(68) \qquad G_\alpha(z, \zeta, t) = \left[\sum_{\beta=1}^{R} P_{\alpha\beta}(t) z_{\alpha\beta} + \sum_{\gamma=1}^{R} Q_{\alpha\gamma}(t) \zeta_{\alpha\gamma}\right]^{N_\alpha}, \quad \alpha = 1, \ldots, R.$$

The joint probabilities are

$$(69) \qquad P\left\{N_{\alpha\beta}(t) = n_{\alpha\beta},\ D_{\alpha\gamma}(t) = d_{\alpha\gamma},\ \beta, \gamma = 1, \ldots, R \,\middle|\, N_\alpha\right\} =$$

$$\frac{N!}{\prod_{\beta=1}^{R} n_{\alpha\beta}! \prod_{\gamma=1}^{R} d_{\alpha\gamma}!} \prod_{\beta=1}^{R} \left[P_{\alpha\beta}(t)\right]^{n_{\alpha\beta}} \prod_{\gamma=1}^{R} \left[Q_{\alpha\gamma}(t)\right]^{d_{\alpha\gamma}},$$

where

$$(70) \qquad \sum_{\beta=1}^{R} n_{\alpha\beta} + \sum_{\gamma=1}^{R} d_{\alpha\gamma} = N_\alpha, \qquad \alpha = 1, \ldots, R.$$

Direct computation from (68) gives the expectations:

$$(71) \qquad E\left[N_{\alpha\beta}(t) \mid N_\alpha\right] = N_\alpha P_{\alpha\beta}(t), \qquad \alpha, \beta = 1, \ldots, R,$$

$$(72) \qquad E\left[D_{\alpha\beta}(t) \mid N_\alpha\right] = N_\alpha Q_{\alpha\beta}(t), \qquad \alpha, \beta = 1, \ldots, R,$$

the variances:

$$(73) \qquad \sigma^2_{N_{\alpha\beta}(t)} = N_\alpha P_{\alpha\beta}(t)\left[1-P_{\alpha\beta}(t)\right], \qquad \alpha,\beta = 1,\ldots,R,$$

$$(74) \qquad \sigma^2_{D_{\alpha\beta}(t)} = N_\alpha Q_{\alpha\beta}(t)\left[1-Q_{\alpha\beta}(t)\right], \qquad \alpha,\beta = 1,\ldots,R,$$

and the covariances:

$$(75) \qquad \sigma_{N_{\alpha\beta}(t)} = -N_\alpha P_{\alpha\beta}(t)\, P_{\alpha\gamma}(t), \quad \beta\neq\gamma,\ \alpha,\beta,\ \gamma = 1,\ldots,R,$$

$$(76) \qquad \sigma_{D_{\alpha\beta}(t),\, D_{\alpha\gamma}(t)} = -N_\alpha Q_{\alpha\beta}(t)\, Q_{\alpha\gamma}(t),$$

$$\beta\neq\gamma,\ \alpha,\beta,\ \gamma = 1,\ldots,R,$$

$$(77) \qquad \sigma_{N_{\alpha\beta}(t),\, D_{\alpha\gamma}(t)} = -N_\alpha P_{\alpha\beta}(t)\, Q_{\alpha\gamma}(t), \quad \alpha,\beta,\gamma = 1,\ldots,R.$$

The estimators of $P_{\alpha\beta}(t)$ and $Q_{\alpha\beta}(t)$ may be derived with any of the commonly used methods of estimation. The maximum likelihood estimators are

$$(78) \qquad \hat{P}_{\alpha\beta}(t) = \frac{N_{\alpha\beta}(t)}{N_\alpha}, \qquad \alpha,\beta = 1,\ldots,R,$$

and

$$(79) \qquad \hat{Q}_{\alpha\beta}(t) = \frac{D_{\alpha\beta}(t)}{N_\alpha}, \qquad \alpha,\beta = 1,\ldots,R.$$

The variances and covariances of the estimators are equal to the corresponding variance and covariance of $N_{\alpha\beta}(t)$ and $D_{\alpha\beta}(t)$ divided by N_α^2; for example,

$$(80) \qquad \sigma^2_{\hat{P}_{\alpha\beta}(t)} = \frac{1}{N_\alpha^2}\sigma^2_{N_{\alpha\beta}(t)} = \frac{1}{N_\alpha} P_{\alpha\beta}(t)\left[1-P_{\alpha\beta}(t)\right], \quad \alpha,\beta = 1,\ldots,R.$$

7. Expected Length of Stay in Each State

An important concept associated with the present model is the expected length of time that an individual will spend in each of the 2R states during a time interval. This concept is similar to the expectation of life in the life table, and it indicates the distribution of time among the possible states in a given interval.

Let

(81) $e_{\alpha\beta}(t)$ = {Expected length of stay in s_β within interval $(0, t)$ for an individual in state s_α at time $0\}$, $\alpha, \beta = 1, \ldots, R$,

and

(82) $E_{\alpha\beta}(t)$ = {Expected length of stay in d_β within interval $(0, t)$ for an individual in state s_α at time $0\}$, $\alpha, \beta = 1, \ldots, R$.

These expected lengths can be derived directly from the corresponding probabilities $P_{\alpha\beta}(t)$ and $Q_{\alpha\beta}(t)$. By straightforward reasoning we have

$$e_{\alpha\beta}(t) = \int_0^t P_{\alpha\beta}(\tau)\, d\tau, \quad \alpha, \beta = 1, \ldots, R, \tag{83}$$

and

$$E_{\alpha\beta}(t) = \int_0^t Q_{\alpha\beta}(\tau)\, d\tau, \quad \alpha, \beta = 1, \ldots, R. \tag{84}$$

Substituting (58) and (60) in (83) and (84), respectively, and integrating the resultant expressions yield

$$e_{\alpha\beta}(t) = \sum_{i=1}^{R} \frac{A_{\alpha\beta}^{(i)} (e^{\lambda_i t} - 1)}{\lambda_i \prod_{\substack{j=1 \\ j \neq i}}^{R} (\lambda_i - \lambda_j)}, \quad \alpha, \beta = 1, \ldots, R. \tag{85}$$

and

(86) $$E_{\alpha\beta}(t) = \sum_{i=1}^{R} \sum_{\gamma=1}^{R} \frac{\Lambda_{\alpha\gamma}^{(i)} (e^{\lambda_i t} - 1 - \lambda_i t)}{\lambda_i^2 \prod_{\substack{j=1 \\ j \neq i}}^{R} (\lambda_i - \lambda_j)} \mu_{\gamma\beta} \qquad \alpha, \beta = 1, \ldots, R .$$

The sum

(87) $$e_\alpha(t) = \sum_{\beta=1}^{R} e_{\alpha\beta}(t) = \sum_{\beta=1}^{R} \sum_{i=1}^{R} \frac{\Lambda_{\alpha\beta}^{(i)} (e^{\lambda_i t} - 1)}{\lambda_i \prod_{\substack{j=1 \\ j \neq i}}^{R} (\lambda_i - \lambda_j)} , \quad \alpha = 1, \ldots, R ,$$

is the expected length of time that an individual will be alive in the interval $(0,t)$. The sum

(88) $$E_\alpha(t) = \sum_{\beta=1}^{R} E_{\alpha\beta}(t) = \sum_{\beta=1}^{R} \sum_{i=1}^{R} \sum_{\gamma=1}^{R} \frac{\Lambda_{\alpha\gamma}^{(i)} (e^{\lambda_i t} - 1 - \lambda_i t)}{\lambda_i^2 \prod_{\substack{j=1 \\ j \neq i}}^{R} (\lambda_i - \lambda_j)} \mu_{\gamma\beta} ,$$

$$\alpha = 1, \ldots, R ,$$

is the expected length of time that an individual will be dead in the interval $(0, t)$. By equation (15) and the definitions of (83) and (84), we have

(89) $$e_\alpha(t) + E_\alpha(t) = \sum_{\beta=1}^{R} e_{\alpha\beta}(t) + \sum_{\beta=1}^{R} E_{\alpha\beta}(t) = t , \quad \alpha = 1, \ldots, R .$$

which can easily be verified by direct computation from (87) and (88) .

APPENDIX

Lemma. Whatever may be distinct values $\lambda_1, \lambda_2, \ldots, \lambda_n$, (a1) $$\sum_{i=1}^{n} \frac{\lambda_i^r}{\prod_{\substack{j=1\\ j\neq i}}^{n} (\lambda_i - \lambda_j)} = 1, \qquad \underline{\text{for}}\ r = n-1$$

(a2) $$= 0\ , \qquad \underline{\text{for}}\ 0 \leq r < n-1\ .$$

Proof: Let

(a3) $$\theta_{n,r} = \sum_{i=1}^{n} \frac{\lambda_i^r}{\prod_{\substack{j=1\\ j\neq i}}^{n} (\lambda_i - \lambda_j)}$$

1. Case of $r = 0$. We wish to prove that

(a4) $$\theta_{n,0} = \sum_{i=1}^{n} \frac{1}{\prod_{\substack{j=1\\ j\neq i}}^{n} (\lambda_i - \lambda_j)} = 0\ .$$

To prove (a4), we make the common denominator

(a5) $$\prod_{i=1}^{n-1} \prod_{j=i+1}^{n} (\lambda_i - \lambda_j)$$

which is equal in absolute value to the Vandermonde determinant of order n; that is,

(a6) $$\prod_{i=1}^{n-1} \prod_{j=i+1}^{n} (\lambda_i - \lambda_j) = (-1)^N \begin{vmatrix} 1 & 1 & \cdots & 1 \\ \lambda_1 & \lambda_2 & \cdots & \lambda_n \\ \lambda_1^2 & \lambda_2^2 & \cdots & \lambda_n^2 \\ \vdots & \vdots & & \vdots \\ \lambda_1^{n-1} & \lambda_2^{n-1} & \cdots & \lambda_n^{n-1} \end{vmatrix} = (-1)^N \Delta$$

where $N = n(n+3)/2$. The numerator of $\theta_{n,0}$ [written as a single fraction with denominator (a5)] will be $\sum_{i=1}^{n} (-1)^N \Delta_{ni}$, where Δ_{ni} is the (n,i)th cofactor of Δ. The first term in the numerator, for example is

(a7)
$$\prod_{i=2}^{n-1} \prod_{j=i+1}^{n} (\lambda_i - \lambda_j) = (-1)^M \begin{vmatrix} 1 & 1 & \cdots & 1 \\ \lambda_2 & \lambda_3 & \cdots & \lambda_n \\ \lambda_2^2 & \lambda_3^2 & \cdots & \lambda_n^2 \\ \vdots & \vdots & \vdots & \vdots \\ \lambda_2^{n-2} & \lambda_3^{n-2} & & \lambda_n^{n-2} \end{vmatrix} = (-1)^{M+(n+1)} \Delta_{n1}$$

and the k-th term is

(a8)
$$(-1)^{k+1} \prod_{\substack{i=1 \\ i \neq k}}^{n-1} \prod_{\substack{j=i+1 \\ j \neq k}}^{n} (\lambda_i - \lambda_j) = (-1)^{M+(n+1)} \Delta_{nk}$$

where $M = (n-1)(n+2)/2$, and $M+(n+1) = N$. Thus we have

(a9)
$$\theta_{n,0} = \frac{\sum_{i=1}^{n} \Delta_{ni}}{\Delta} .$$

Since in the case of the Vandermonde determinant, the sum of the cofactors $\sum_{i=1}^{n} \Delta_{mi} = 0$ for $1 < m \leq n$, the numerator on the right hand side of (a9) vanishes and (a4) is proven.

2. Case of $0 \leq r \leq n-1$. Proof by induction on n. For $n=2$, we have

(a10)
$$\theta_{2,1} = \frac{\lambda_1}{\lambda_1 - \lambda_2} + \frac{\lambda_2}{\lambda_2 - \lambda_1} = 1 .$$

Assume the lemma is true for n; that is, assume

(a11)
$$\left.\begin{aligned} \theta_{n,r} &= 1 \quad \text{if} \quad r = n-1 \\ &= 0 \quad \text{if} \quad 0 \le r < n-1 \end{aligned}\right\} .$$

We wish to show that

(a12)
$$\left.\begin{aligned} \theta_{n+1,s} &= 1 \quad \text{if} \quad s = (n+1) - 1 = n \\ &= 0 \quad \text{if} \quad 0 \le s < (n+1) - 1 = n \end{aligned}\right\} .$$

By Part 1 we know that $\theta_{n+1,0} = 0$, so we can let $s = s+1$, $0 \le r \le n-1$. Since

(a13)
$$\frac{\lambda_i^{r+1}}{\lambda_i - \lambda_{n+1}} = \lambda_i^r + \lambda_i^{r-1}\lambda_{n+1} + \lambda_i^{r-2}\lambda_{n+1}^2 + \dots + \lambda_{n+1}^r + \frac{\lambda_{n+1}^{r+1}}{\lambda_i - \lambda_{n+1}} ,$$

we substitute (a13) in $\theta_{n+1,r+1}$ to obtain

(a14)
$$\theta_{n+1,r+1} = \sum_{i=1}^{n} \frac{\dfrac{\lambda_i^{r+1}}{(\lambda_i - \lambda_{n+1})}}{\prod\limits_{\substack{j=1\\ j\ne i}}^{n} (\lambda_i - \lambda_j)} + \frac{\lambda_{n+1}^{r+1}}{\prod\limits_{j=1}^{n} (\lambda_{n+1} - \lambda_j)}$$

$$= \sum_{i=1}^{n} \frac{\lambda_i^r + \lambda_i^{r-1}\lambda_{n+1} + \lambda_i^{r-2}\lambda_{n+1}^2 + \dots + \lambda_{n+1}^r + \dfrac{\lambda_{n+1}^{r+1}}{\lambda_i - \lambda_{n+1}}}{\prod\limits_{\substack{j=1\\ j\ne i}}^{n} (\lambda_i - \lambda_j)} + \frac{\lambda_{n+1}^{r+1}}{\prod\limits_{j=1}^{n} (\lambda_{n+1} - \lambda_j)}$$

$$= \sum_{i=1}^{n} \frac{\lambda_i^r}{\prod\limits_{\substack{j=1\\ j\ne i}}^{n} (\lambda_i - \lambda_j)} + \sum_{k=1}^{r} \left[\lambda_{n+1}^k \quad \lambda_{n+1}^k \sum_{i=1}^{n} \frac{\lambda_i^{r-k}}{\prod\limits_{\substack{j=1\\ j\ne i}}^{n} (\lambda_i - \lambda_j)} \right] + \sum_{i=1}^{n+1} \frac{\lambda_{n+1}^{r+1}}{\prod\limits_{\substack{j=1\\ j\ne i}}^{n+1} (\lambda_i - \lambda_j)}$$

$$= \theta_{n,r} + \sum_{k=1}^{r} \left[\lambda_{n+1}^k \cdot \theta_{n,r-k} \right] + \lambda_{n+1}^{r+1} \cdot \theta_{n+1,0} .$$

By hypothesis (a11), $\theta_{n,r-k} = 0$ for $k = 1, \ldots, r \leq n-1$, and by Part 1, $\theta_{n+1,0} = 0$. Therefore, (a14) becomes

$$\theta_{n+1,r+1} = \theta_{n,r} \quad \text{for} \quad 0 < r+1 \leq (n+1) - 1 . \tag{a15}$$

This means that assumption (a11) implies (a12) and completes the inductive proof.

REFERENCES

1. C. L. Chiang, "A Stochastic Study of the Life Table and Its Applications. III. The Follow-up Study with the Consideration of Competing Risks." Biometrics, Vol. XVII, No. 1 (1961), 57-78.

2. C. L. Chiang, "On the Probability of Death from Specific Causes in the Presence of Competing Risks." Proceedings of the Fourth Berkeley Symposium on Mathematical Statistics and Probability (edited by J. Neyman), Vol. IV, 169-180. University of California Press, 1961.

3. E. Fix and J. Neyman, "A Simple Stochastic Model of Recovery, Relapse, Death and Loss of Patients." Human Biology, Vol. XXIII (1951), 205-241.

4. T. N. E. Greville, "Mortality Tables Analyzed by Cause of Death." Record of the American Institute of Actuaries, Vol. 37 (1948), 283.

5. I. Todhunter, A History of the Mathematical Theory of Probability, New York, Chelsea, 1949.

The author would like to express his sincere appreciation to Mrs. Jean S. Strohm and Miss Helen E. Supplee for their valuable assistance during the preparation of this paper.

DISCUSSION PARTICIPANT

Dr. Lillian R. Elveback
Biostatistics Unit, Division of Epidemiology,
The Public Health Research Institute of the City of New York, Inc.
Foot of East 16
New York, New York

DISCUSSION

Lillian R. Elveback. The discussion considered only the case in which $\nu_{\alpha\beta}(\tau)$ was independent of τ. What other forms of $\nu_{\alpha\beta}(\tau)$, as a function of τ, are considered in the paper itself?

Chin Long Chiang. I have considered such forms of $\nu_{\alpha\beta}(\tau)$ for which the ratios

$$\frac{\nu_{\alpha\beta}(\tau)}{\nu_{\beta\beta}(\tau)} = r_{\alpha\beta}, \quad \alpha, \beta = 1, \ldots, R,$$

are independent of time τ. But they are not included in the present paper.

H. L. LUCAS

Stochastic Elements in Biological Models; Their Sources and Significance

1. INTRODUCTION

The sources and the significance of stochastic elements in biological models are best considered as a part of a unified, general framework within which to view mathematical models for biological phenomena. I shall display an attempt to develop such a framework, but know that the effort falls short. There certainly are some loose ends, and there are probably some inconsistencies and mistakes. I hope not very many. Some aspects of my point of view seem to be rather unorthodox, but most aspects are probably not novel.

The first main part of the paper focuses in a general way on stochastic and apparently stochastic elements of models. Attention is given to the basic nature of random and apparently random elements, to their sources and to some of the troubles they cause.

The next main part of the paper is devoted to the class of biological problems that can be encompassed in the framework of input-output systems. Correspondences between the elements of the biosystem and the elements of the mathematical system are pointed out. Stochastic elements are again considered, but the context is a little broader than in the first discussion.

The last part of the paper is devoted to a specific biological problem in the input-output class. At each step in the theoretical development, an attempt is made to match the biology and the mathematics. Finally, the effectiveness of designing and analyzing experiments within the framework of the theory is illustrated by showing some of the biological progress that has been made.

2. BACKGROUND

2.1. Kinds of Models

2.1.1. Descriptive vs. elucidative and predictive models:

In my experience, some people will state that their goal is simply to summarize or describe a set of data in a few numbers or simple relations and that they do not desire to elucidate the mechanisms of a system nor to predict future phenomena. Some other people will, however, express a desire to elucidate and to make predictions. Some people will vacillate between the two aims from one time to another. When it is stated that the goal is simply to summarize, I often argue, however, that prediction ultimately ensues and note the following:

(a) Whether the person desiring an analysis of data is at the time so interested or not, he or someone else will eventually use the summarization for predictive purposes.

(b) The summarization will be used by someone as basis for imposing forces on the pertinent system in order to move it in a direction deemed to be desirable.

For those reasons, this paper will be based on the assumption that prediction of phenomena is the ultimate goal. Prediction, to be most successful, requires models to be based on an understanding of the mechanisms of the systems involved.

2.1.2. Probabilistic vs. deterministic models:

In biology, as in most cases of science, both probabilistic and deterministic models are employed. By a probabilistic model, I mean one of the type

$$\Pr(Y \leq y) = F(\underline{\theta}; \underline{X}; y) \tag{2-1}$$

where

Y = a random variable

F = a probability distribution with argument y and column-vector parameters $\underline{\theta}$ and $\underline{X}$

$\underline{\theta}$ = a vector which is invariant over a class, K, of situations of interest.

$\underline{X}$ = a vector which varies over the class, K.

Henceforth, in this paper, I shall assume that any probabilistic elements are distributed with at least the first two moments finite.

Often we might speak of Y as a "dependent" variable, a response, a predictand or an output and $\underline{X}$ as a vector of "independent" variables, treatment factors, predictors or inputs.

For the approach I wish to take, it is convenient to write

$$Y = \mu(\underline{\theta}; \underline{X}) + \epsilon \tag{2-2}$$

where

$$\mu(\underline{\theta};\underline{X}) = \int_{-\infty}^{\infty} y\, d_y F(\underline{\theta};\underline{X};y)$$

$$= E(Y|\underline{\theta};\underline{X})$$

$$\epsilon = Y - \mu(\underline{\theta};\underline{X}) \quad ,$$

with the probability distribution for ϵ expressible as

(2-3) $$\Pr(\epsilon \le e) = F(\underline{\theta};\underline{X};y) = F[\underline{\theta};\underline{X};e + \mu(\underline{\theta};\underline{X})] \quad ,$$

where $e = y - \mu(\underline{\theta};\underline{X})$ and $E(\epsilon\,|\underline{\theta};\underline{X}) = 0$. Note that a probabilistic model has deterministic aspects, e.g. the forms of F and μ, and the values taken by the elements of $\underline{\theta}$ and $\underline{X}$.

By a deterministic model, I mean one developed with no randomness assumed. The derivation would lead to a form like

(2-4) $$\eta = \mu^*(\underline{\theta}^*;\underline{X}) \quad .$$

In (2-4), η corresponds to the expected value of the response variable, Y, in (2-2); i.e., to $\mu(\underline{\theta};\underline{X})$. Real data, of course, never exactly follow (2-4) . Deviations of actual data from the model are encompassed by writing

(2-5) $$Y = \mu^*(\underline{\theta}^*;\underline{X}) + \epsilon^* \quad ,$$

where Y is the observed response and $\epsilon^* = Y - \eta$ represents deviafrom the model. These deviations are assumed to be characterized by some cumulative density function, say,

(2-6) $$\Pr(\epsilon^* \le e^*) = F^*(\underline{\beta};\underline{X};y) \quad .$$

In F^*, the parameter $\underline{\beta}$ is used instead of $\underline{\theta}^*$ because very simple assumptions are often made about F^* . Note that $\epsilon^* = \epsilon + \mu(\underline{\theta};\underline{X}) - \mu^*(\underline{\theta}^*;\underline{X})$. Ordinarily it is assumed that $E(\epsilon^*|\underline{\beta};\underline{X}) = 0$ when fitting the deterministic model to the data, but, as indicated immediately to follow, this assumption is not always justifiable.

In practice, it sometimes happens that μ is the same form as μ^* and that $\underline{\theta}$ is the same as $\underline{\theta}^*$. In a more general context, at least, such is not always true. For example, things like means of products can occur in what corresponds to $\mu(\underline{\theta};\underline{X})$, whereas products of means occur in what corresponds to $\mu^*(\underline{\theta}^*;\underline{X})$. The discrepancy between the two approaches may be of little practical import if, for example, the variances of random variables are small enough.

2.1.3. Rational vs. empirical models:

By a rational model, I mean one which is derived in a logical way, starting from basic observational knowledge, theory and reasonable supposition about the physical components of a system and their behavior. One calls on anything he can to develop a model with really meaningful form and parameters. This definition seems to include what some people call heuristic models. In contrast, an empirical model is one chosen with little regard to the characteristics of the system but which has enough flexibility to reflect sufficiently faithfully the main features of available data. Examples of empirical models are those relating Y to $\underline{X}$ by polynomials of various sorts. In such instances the meaning of parameters may only be expressible in mathematical terms, such as derivatives of Y with respect to elements of $\underline{X}$; these may be physically quite superficial. Empirical models usually lead to bad predictions for points in X-space that are not close to the region of the data used to fit the model. On the other hand, rational models often predict very well for points in X-space that are far from the experimental region.

In practice, models have both rational and empirical aspects. Beyond a certain point, empiricism enters because of a lack of basic observational knowledge, theory or reasonable supposition. One can argue, too, of course, that any theory or supposition has an empirical (observational) basis in past experience of the investigator, his forbears or his colleagues. Best predictability is obtained by introducing as much rationality as possible into all models used.

2.2. Randomness and Pseudo-randomness

2.2.1. Stochasticism vs. determinism:

An argument which seems not to be resolvable is whether the real universe has some truly random aspects, or whether the real universe is completely deterministic. The concept of randomness may have evolved simply as a device to cope with ignorance about the causes of events. Such ignorance can certainly make some things appear to be random. It seems clear enough, however, that the real universe, if not completely deterministic, has a core of deterministic features. Such must be so; otherwise Science would be fruitless. I shall play both sides by assuming that reality has both truly random features and truly deterministic features, and that ignorance requires relegating part of the deterministic features to a third category, namely, apparently random or pseudo-random features.

In (2-2), $\mu(\underline{\theta};\underline{X})$ is deterministic and ϵ is random. In subsequent development, $\mu(\underline{\theta};\underline{X})$ will be split into clearly deterministic and pseudo-random parts.

2.2.2. True randomness:

2.2.2.1. Inherent unexplainability: To me, true randomness implies that there is no ultimate explanation or reason that a given event should occur instead of another. I don't mean that the explanation is unknown; I mean that there inherently is no explanation. In the context of (2-2), the value taken by a given realization of ϵ is a truly random event; there is no inherent explanation for why that value occurred instead of another.

2.2.2.2. An anomaly: Although one might say that truly random events are those which are completely chaotic, the notion of complete chaos seems to offend the instincts of even the most ardent probabilists. There are always some things non-random about the way random variables are viewed. In particular, the relative frequency (probability) of occurrence of different events is regarded to follow some "law." This law is given by the form and the parameters of the cumulative density function, features which are non-random.

2.2.2.3. Mutual independence: To me, true randomness implies that the occurrence of an event is not in any way conditioned by the previous or the concomitant occurrence of another event. That is, truly random events are mutually independent. It appears to be instinctively impossible to conceive of random events without introducing certain non-random features, namely, the probability law. It seems, nevertheless, possible to introduce independence of successive or concomitant events as a part of the concept of true randomness. For example, if two variables are distributed in a bivariate normal distribution, it seems possible to explain any correlation between the two variables in terms of an underlying cause common to both, or to regard as truly random only that part of the variation of one variable that is not explained by the value taken by the other variable.

2.2.2.4. Definition: In view of the above, truly random events will be defined as mutually independent with a distribution characterized by the form and the parameters of some probability distribution.

2.2.3. Pseudo-randomness:

As previously implied, pseudo-randomness is the term I shall use for the ignorance-engendered apparent randomness. The term will also be used for what is effectively the same thing, namely, apparent randomness attributable to a failure to take certain knowledge into account when building a mathematical model or when designing and interpreting an experiment. This failure often occurs. In some instances, a question of feasibility is involved; e.g., it might be too expensive to make certain measurements or to control certain variables. In other instances, oversight, carelessness or laziness are, unfortunately, the reasons.

2.2.3.1. Introduction of pseudo-random elements into the model: In practice, there will be some vector-valued transformation, $\underline{I}$, not necessarily linear, such that

$$(2\text{-}7) \qquad \underline{I}(\underline{X}) = \underline{\check{X}} = \begin{bmatrix} \underline{\check{X}}_1 \\ \underline{\check{X}}_2 \end{bmatrix} ,$$

where

$\underline{\check{X}}_1$ = vector of variables used as predictors,

$\underline{\check{X}}_2$ = vector of neglected predictors not redundant to $\underline{\check{X}}_1$,

and the mapping from $\underline{X}$-space is one-to-one onto $\underline{\check{X}}$-space. Then in place of (2-2), we write

$$(2\text{-}8) \qquad Y = \mu_1(\underline{\theta};\underline{\check{X}}_1) + V + \epsilon ,$$

where ϵ is the truly random part defined as for (2-2), V is the pseudo-random part and $\mu_1(\underline{\theta}_1;\underline{\check{X}}_1)$ is the clearly deterministic part. It is convenient to define μ_1 and V in a manner analogous to the way μ and ϵ were defined for (2-1) and (2-2). Specifically, $\mu_1(\underline{\theta}_1;\underline{\check{X}}_1)$ is defined as an average, over the class, K, of situations of interest, of $\check{\mu}(\underline{\theta};\underline{\check{X}}) = \mu(\underline{\theta};\underline{X})$, given $\underline{\theta}$ and $\underline{\check{X}}_1$. Thus,

$$(2\text{-}9) \qquad V = \check{\mu}(\underline{\theta};\underline{\check{X}}) - \mu_1(\underline{\theta}_1;\underline{\check{X}}_1)$$

and has average value zero for each value of $\underline{\check{X}}_1$. We expect the form of μ_1 to be some modification of the form of $\check{\mu}$, and we also expect the number of elements in $\underline{\theta}_1$ to be different than in $\underline{\theta}$. Note that there may be relations between $\underline{\check{X}}_1$ and $\underline{\check{X}}_2$ but that $\underline{\check{X}}_2$ is not entirely dependent on $\underline{\check{X}}_1$.

2.2.3.2. Formal definition of the clearly deterministic part: It is desirable for later discussion to examine more formally the definition just given. Let $\mathcal{X}$ be the set of $\underline{\check{X}}$ vectors occurring in the class, K, of situations noted in connection with (2-1) and (2-2). Let $\mathcal{X}_1$ and $\mathcal{X}_2$ be, respectively, the sets of $\underline{\check{X}}_1$ and $\underline{\check{X}}_2$ vectors in K. Let ϕ be a (real, non-negative) measure[a/] on the collection

[a/] At this stage the measures and the distributions considered are not probabilistic in nature. They simply describe the relative frequency of occurrence of given vectors or numbers in the class, K. Later, such measures and distributions will be viewed as being rendered probabilistic by "randomization" procedures.

of measurable subsets of $\mathcal{X}$ such that $\phi(\mathcal{X}) = 1$. And let ϕ_1 be a measure on the collection of measurable subsets of $\mathcal{X}_1$ such that $\phi_1(\mathcal{X}_1) = 1$ and $\phi_1(A) = \phi(A \times \mathcal{X}_2)$, where A is a measurable subset of $\mathcal{X}_1$, and the notation, $A \times \mathcal{X}_2$, means the Cartesian product. Note that ϕ defines the distribution of $\underline{\check{X}}$ over K or, equivalently, the joint distribution of $\underline{\check{X}}_1, \underline{\check{X}}_2$. Similarly, ϕ_1 defines the marginal distribution of $\underline{\check{X}}_1$. The conditional average, $\mu_1(\underline{\theta}_1; \underline{\check{X}}_1)$, is then defined by

$$(2\text{-}10) \qquad \int_{\mathcal{X}} \bar{\mu}(\underline{\theta}; \underline{\check{X}})\, \phi(d\underline{\check{X}}) = \int_{\mathcal{X}_1} \mu_1(\underline{\theta}_1; \underline{\check{X}}_1)\, \phi_1(d\underline{\check{X}}_1) \; .$$

I assume that the integrals exist.

2.2.3.3. Distribution of the pseudo-random part: Here we desire the distribution of $V = \bar{\mu}(\underline{\theta}; \underline{\check{X}}) - \mu_1(\underline{\theta}_1; \underline{\check{X}}_1)$, given $\underline{\theta}$ and $\underline{\check{X}}_1$. We start by finding the conditional distribution of $\underline{\check{X}}_2$ given $\underline{\check{X}}_1$. The conditional measure, $\phi_{2\underline{\check{X}}_1}$, over $\mathcal{X}_2$, given $\underline{\check{X}}_1$, is defined by

$$(2\text{-}11) \qquad \int_{A \times B} \phi(d\underline{\check{X}}) = \int_{A} \phi_{2\underline{\check{X}}_1}(B)\, \phi_1(d\underline{\check{X}}_1) \; ,$$

where A, ϕ and ϕ_1 are defined as in Section 2.2.3.2., and B is a mesurable subset of $\mathcal{X}_2$. Now let $\mathcal{V}$ be the set of values which can be taken by V. Let $\mathcal{C}_{\underline{\check{X}}_1}$ be the collection of subsets, C, of $\mathcal{V}$ such that $T^{-1}_{\underline{\check{X}}_1}(C)$ is a member of the collection of measurable subsets of $\mathcal{X}_2$. The mapping function, $T_{\underline{\check{X}}_1}$, is defined by (2-9) and maps from $\mathcal{X}_2$, given $\underline{\theta}$ and $\underline{\check{X}}_1$. Since there is a conditional measure $\phi_{2\underline{\check{X}}_1}(\mathcal{X}_2) = 1$, defined by (2-11), the mapping $T_{\underline{\check{X}}_1}$ induces the measure,

$$(2\text{-}12) \qquad \nu_{\underline{\check{X}}_1}(C) = \phi_{2\underline{\check{X}}_1}[T^{-1}_{\underline{\check{X}}_1}(C)] \; ,$$

on $\mathcal{C}_{\underline{\check{X}}_1}$ with $\nu_{\underline{\check{X}}_1}(\mathcal{C}_{\underline{\check{X}}_1}) = 1$.

2.2.3.4. Practical problems: Since $\underline{\check{X}}_2$ is unknown or unmeasured, assumptions, either ad hoc or based on previous experience, may have to be made about the form of the distribution of V, given $\underline{\theta}$ and $\underline{\check{X}}_1$. At the least, a few statistics of variation (e.g., variance components) will have to be computed from data in order to obtain an estimate of the contributions of V (hence $\underline{\check{X}}_2$) and ϵ to the variation in Y.

2.2.3.5. The path of Science: The progress of Science can be viewed as a process of diminishing the amount of pseudo-randomness that exists; i.e., as a process of reducing the dimensionality of $\underline{\check{X}}_2$. This reduces the variation in V and increases predictability. Current acceleration in the ability to explain and to predict phenomena indicates that there must be much pseudo-randomness in the universe to pursue and to explain. In other words, there must be much yet that can be identified as deterministic in the universe. If some true randomness exists, bounds on explainability and predictability of course exist.

2.2.4. Problems associated with pseudo-randomness:

It appears that the troubles stemming from pseudo-randomness can all be subsumed under the term, inference biases*. The biases come about because, at one stage or another in formulating models or in analyzing data, it is assumed that the pseudo-random variable, V, as well as the truly random variable, ϵ, are both random and are distributed in ways "representative" of the class, K, of situations of interest. It is assumed that $W = V + \epsilon$ has a probability distribution function, say,

$$\Pr(W \leq w) = G(\underline{\alpha}; \underline{\check{X}}_1; w) \quad , \qquad \text{(2-13)}$$

with $E(W|\underline{\alpha};\underline{\check{X}}_1) = 0$ and with other appropriate moments. These various assumptions often do not hold.

It is convenient to discuss the biases in three categories: prediction bias, error bias and non-independence bias. The three are not mutually exclusive concepts.

2.2.4.1. Prediction bias: Prediction bias refers to bias in the estimation of μ_1 and $\underline{\theta}_1$. Any set of data represents a selection, S, not necessarily "representative," of points from K. From S, we obtain $\hat{\mu}_1, \hat{\underline{\theta}}_1$, and use as a predictor $\hat{Y} = \hat{\mu}_1(\hat{\underline{\theta}}_1; \underline{\check{X}}_1)$. Let us assume that the number of points, n, and the number of different values of $\underline{\check{X}}_1$ in S are sufficient to estimate all elements of $\underline{\theta}_1$, everything needed about the form of μ_1 and the relation of $\nu_{\underline{\check{X}}_1}$ to $\underline{\check{X}}_1$. Let the conditional distribution of $\underline{\check{X}}_2$ given $\underline{\check{X}}_1$, in S be given by the measure $\phi^*_{2\underline{\check{X}}_1}$, and let the corresponding measure over V, given $\underline{\theta}$ and $\underline{\check{X}}_1$, be $\nu^*_{\underline{\check{X}}_1}(C) = \phi_{2\underline{\check{X}}_1}[T^{-1}_{\underline{\check{X}}_1}(C)]$. In general, $\phi^*_{2\underline{\check{X}}_1}(B) \neq \phi_{2\underline{\check{X}}_1}(B)$;

---

* Bias as used in this paper does not encompass the bias associated with using biassed estimators. That is another problem. Here attention is focused on biases stemming from the way data are taken.

hence $\nu^*_{\tilde{X}_1}(C) \neq \nu_{\tilde{X}_1}(C)$. If $\nu^*_{\tilde{X}_1}$ differs from $\nu_{\tilde{X}_1}$ in such a way that the average value of V, given $\tilde{X}_1$, in S is not zero, bias in estimation of μ_1, $\underline{\theta}_1$ will result. Such can easily happen if S be "non-representative" of K .

2.2.4.2. Error bias: Even though $\nu^*_{\tilde{X}_1}$ be such that prediction bias does not result, it can be such that the second and higher moments of V are over- or under-estimated. Any statistics computed from S to provide estimates of prediction error, say the mean value of $(Y - \hat{Y})^2$, can thus be biased if the sampling is "bad."

2.2.4.3. Non-independence bias: The occurrence of "correlation" patterns (serial, auto-, lag, intra-class, etc.) among the W points observed in S can be attributed to $\nu^*_{\tilde{X}_1}(C) \neq \nu_{\tilde{X}_1}(C)$. Such correlations are ordinarily expected if the points in S are a sequence that is ordered over time or space. If such correlations cannot be prevented or cannot be taken into account satisfactorily when fitting models to data, error bias can result, although prediction bias does not necessarily occur.

2.2.5. Randomization procedures:

In many situations, pseudo-randomness can be "turned into" very nearly true randomness by the use of formal "randomization" procedures. Randomization has been ardently advised to overcome the biases just discussed. It must be recognized that, strictly, true randomness is not attainable, because the devices used to randomize (e.g., tables of random numbers) are pseudo-random. Much comparison of empirical sampling distributions with theoretical ones has, however, been done, and the results warrant the assumption that, for all practical purposes, randomization, when possible and when properly done, generates true randomness. It will be assumed, therefore, that randomization, when it can be properly accomplished, yields true randomness.

It must be recognized that randomization of a desirable type is not always possible. This is so, for example, in time series work and for analogous work in which the time axis is replaced by one or more space dimensions. In such cases one has no recourse but to assume, at some stage of complexity of the clearly deterministic part of the model, that the remainder of the variation is generated by a (natural) random process. Since this assumption of randomness may not hold, no guarantee against bias exists in such work.

2.2.5.1. Random sampling: Let $\mathcal{Y}$ be the set of (real) values that can be taken by a variable Y . Let ψ be a relative-frequency measure on the collection of measurable subsets of $\mathcal{Y}$, such that $\psi(\mathcal{Y}) = 1$. We can define a function, F(y), such that

(2-14) $$F(y) = \psi(-\infty, y] \ .$$

$F(y)$ is then the cumulative relative-frequency distribution of Y. In random sampling, we try to arrange that a value of Y realized is a chance affair with $Pr(Y \in D) = \pi(D)$ where D is any measurable subset of $\mathcal{Y}$ and π is a probability measure on the collection of measurable subsets of $\mathcal{Y}$ such that $\pi(\mathcal{Y}) = 1$. Analogous to $F(y)$, we can define

(2-15) $$P(y) = \pi(-\infty, y]$$

in which case $P(y) = Pr(Y \leq y)$ is the probability distribution function (the sampling distribution function) for Y. Obviously, if $\pi(D) = \psi(D)$ for all D, $P(y) = F(y)$ for all y, and $F(y)$ is the sampling distribution. If $P(y) \equiv F(y)$, the sampling process is called "simple random" sampling or simply "random" sampling. I shall confine attention to this case*.

2.2.5.2. Effect of random sampling in surveys: We recall (2-8), namely,

$$Y = \mu_1(\underline{\theta}_1; \underline{\check{X}}_1) + V + \epsilon \ .$$

In surveys, $\underline{\check{X}}_1$ represents, for example, the variables that serve as a basis for stratifying, and ϵ is, I shall assume, a measurement error that is truly random with $E(\epsilon) = 0$. Interest focuses on μ_1 and V. Under random sampling within each stratum, $\phi_{2\underline{\check{X}}_1}$, see (2-11), and hence $\nu_{\underline{\check{X}}_1}$, see (2-12), become probability measures. Thus $\tilde{\mu}(\underline{\theta}; \underline{\check{X}})$, given $\underline{\theta}$ and $\underline{\check{X}}_1$ becomes a truly random variable with $E(\tilde{\mu} | \underline{\theta}; \underline{\check{X}}_1) = \mu_1(\underline{\theta}_1; \underline{\check{X}}_1)$. Also V becomes truly random with cumulative density function,

(2-16) $$Pr(V \leq v | \underline{\theta}; \underline{\check{X}}_1) = \nu_{\underline{\check{X}}_1}(-\infty, v]$$

$$= H(\underline{\theta}; \underline{\check{X}}_1; y)$$

and with $E(V | \underline{\theta}; \underline{\check{X}}_1) = 0$.

---

* I shall have no reason to consider the matter of sampling with vs. without replacement. Sampling with replacement will be assumed on the grounds that, when sampling without replacement is done, sample size is small relative to population size.

2.2.5.3. Randomization in experiments: Let $\underline{\check{X}}_1$ correspond to the levels of controlled variables (treatment factors, blocking factors, etc.) that obtain during the course of an experiment. Let $\underline{\check{X}}_2$ correspond to other factors that characterize or affect the experimental units during the experiment. Note that $\underline{\check{X}}_2$ can include the levels of the treatment factors that obtained prior to placing the units on experiment and can also include pre-experimental measurements on the response variable. Let Y, however, represent response while on experiment. In this context, $\underline{\check{X}}_1$ can be regarded as having taken the same pre-experimental value, $\underline{\xi}_1$, for all units. Random allotment then "guarantees" that $\underline{\check{X}}_2$ is a truly random variable and is identically distributed for all $\underline{\check{X}}_1$ with common probability measure, $\phi^*_{2\underline{\xi}_1}$. Random allotment does not, however, guarantee that $\nu^*_{\underline{\check{X}}_1}(C)$, the probability measure induced on $C_{\underline{\check{X}}_1}$, given $\underline{\theta}$ and $\underline{\check{X}}_1$, will be the same for given C at all $\underline{\check{X}}_1$. This is because $\underline{\check{X}}_1$ and $\underline{\check{X}}_2$ can interact. Because of the way $\mu_1(\underline{\theta}_1;\underline{\check{X}}_1)$ is defined, $E(V|\underline{\theta};\underline{\check{X}}_1) = 0$ will hold for all $\underline{\check{X}}_1$, but otherwise the distribution of V can vary with $\underline{\check{X}}_1$. For example, as is well known, the variance can depend on treatment. This fact does not imply bias, however, unless it is disregarded in analyzing the data. Randomization permits unbiassedness for a class of experimental units for which the sample of units at hand is a "representative" sample. If it is intended to make inferences about a wider class of units, however, bias can result even though randomization of the available units is practiced.

2.2.6. Some other matters:

2.2.6.1. Effective non-randomness: It may happen that some elements of $\underline{X}$ can be regarded to be truly random variables. For example, the values taken by a given realization of those elements might be generated by a (natural) random process. Nevertheless, it may also be that the realized values can be known exactly. If such variables can be taken into account in the analysis, they are effectively non-random insofar as (2-8) goes, and appear in $\underline{\check{X}}_1$.

2.2.6.2. Troubles in regression analysis: Regression analysis is used widely on data which have accumulated according to no definite plan. The data might be neither from a controlled experiment ($\underline{\check{X}}_1$ controlled) on a properly drawn sample of the class of experimental units of interest nor from a properly drawn (random or stratified random) sample of the class of situations of interest. Thus, inferences based on regression analyses often are biased.

2.2.6.3. Covariance analysis: To discuss covariance analysis, we transform $\underline{X}$ into a vector of three parts corresponding to partitioning $\underline{\check{X}}_1$ into two parts, i.e.

$$\underline{\check{X}} = \begin{bmatrix} \underline{\check{X}}_{11} \\ \underline{\check{X}}_{12} \\ \underline{\check{X}}_{2} \end{bmatrix}$$

Here, $\underline{\check{X}}_{11}$ corresponds to the treatment factors, and $\underline{\check{X}}_{12}$ corresponds to the covariables (i.e., observed factors characterizing experimental units prior to the experiment and taken into account in analysis but which are disregarded when allotment of units to treatment is made). Finally $\underline{\check{X}}_{2}$ corresponds to all other non-redundant factors (unobserved or disregarded) which distinguish the units. Note that $\underline{\check{X}}_{12}$ is rendered a random variable by the randomization process, but, since it is observed and used in the analysis, it becomes effectively non-random. For covariance analysis, (2-8) can be written as

(2-17) $$Y = \mu_1(\underline{\theta}_1; \underline{\check{X}}_{11}, \underline{\check{X}}_{12}) + V + \epsilon \ .$$

Randomized allotment of units to treatments does not guarantee against bias when covariance analysis is employed. Not only can the biases mentioned for randomized experiments occur, but, in addition, the biases potentially in regression analysis can also occur.

2.2.6.4. Observational errors: With standardized observational procedures, it seems possible always to regard observation errors to be truly random with expectation zero. An observational error in Y is thus automatically absorbed into ϵ of the model and Y becomes the observed value. The situation for observational errors on $\underline{\check{X}}_1$ perhaps needs a little examination. Let

(2-18) $$\underline{Z}_1 = \underline{\check{X}}_1 + \underline{\mathcal{Z}}_1 \ ,$$

where $\mathcal{Z}_1$ represents observational errors. Now note that we can rewrite (2-2) as

(2-19) $$Y = \mu^+(\underline{\theta}^+; \underline{Z}_1, \underline{\check{X}}_1, \underline{\check{X}}_2) + \epsilon \ .$$

We now manipulate as in Section 2.2.3.2. to obtain the conditional average of μ^+ given $\underline{\theta}^+, \underline{Z}_1$ and $\underline{X}_2$. Designate this average as $\bar{\mu}^+ (\underline{\theta}^+; \underline{Z}_1, \underline{\check{X}}_2)$ and let

(2-20) $$Y = \bar{\mu}^+ (\underline{\theta}^+; \underline{Z}_1, \underline{\check{X}}_2) + \epsilon_1 + \epsilon$$

where

$$\epsilon_1 = \overset{+}{\mu}(\underline{\theta}^+; \underline{Z}_1, \underline{\check{X}}_1, \underline{\check{X}}_2) - \overset{-+}{\mu}(\underline{\theta}^+; \underline{Z}_1, \underline{\check{X}}_2) \ .$$

Thus we see that observational errors on $\underline{\check{X}}_1$ can be absorbed into ϵ along with those on Y . This means we can return to the form of (2-8) and write

$$Y = \overset{+}{\mu}_1(\underline{\theta}_1^+; \underline{Z}_1) + V + \epsilon^+ \ , \tag{2-21}$$

remembering that now we have integrated over $\mathcal{X}$, not just $\mathcal{X}_2$, in arriving at the clearly deterministic part. A practical implication is that the whole class of situations, K, must be randomly sampled in order to avoid bias.

2.2.6.5. Further comments on bias: In work done to establish relationships between Y and $\underline{\check{X}}_1$ in a given class of currently existing situations, it is possible to avoid the bias that can stem from pseudo-randomness. Random sampling from the class of interest is always possible (although perhaps not always practical). On the other hand, it seems in general impossible to avoid bias when prediction is involved. To obtain data for fitting a prediction equation, one is limited to sampling from a currently existing subclass, K^* , of the class, K, of situations of interest. The class, K, is at best vaguely defined, because it encompasses future, unknown subclasses. Let the relative frequency measures for K be ϕ over $\mathcal{X}$ and $\phi_{2\underline{\check{X}}_1}$ over $\mathcal{X}_2$. If we randomly sample from K^* , the probability measures will be ϕ^* and $\phi^*_{2\underline{\check{X}}_1}$, and it is a good bet that they will not be equal to the counterparts for K . Thus, bias can result. Perhaps we could improve data by anticipating evolution and thereby sampling K^* with the probability measures ϕ^{**} and $\phi^{**}_{2\underline{\check{X}}_1}$, our best "guesses" of the K counterparts. Even so, lack of bias will not be guaranteed.

2.2.6.6. The real test of a model: Although biases can be moderated by well designed experiments and proper analyses, the ultimate test of the goodness of any model is how it works in the future; i.e., how well it predicts. Model building thus is an iterative or sequential process. One derives as good a model as possible. He then fits it to the best data available, making modifications of the model if it be clearly incompatible with the data. Additional data are then gathered from a broader class of situations, perhaps with additional or different X-variables observed, and the model is "tested" on them. Modifications are again made, new data are gathered, the model is again tested, etc. Note that the "better" a model is, the less the magnitudes of biases that will be encountered. The term "better" is meant to imply that the model is more elucidative of the system under study.

3. ANALYSIS OF A CLASS OF BIOLOGICAL PROBLEMS

3.1. The Basic Relation

3.1.1. A vector representation:

Many biological problems can be framed in terms of input-output systems which embrace both stochastic and deterministic elements. For mathematization, it is convenient to start with an idealized basic relation, namely

(3-1) $$\underline{\eta} = \underline{T}(\underline{\xi}) \quad ,$$

where

$\underline{\eta}$ = the column vector of output,

$\underline{\xi}$ = the column vector of input,

$\underline{T}$ = a vector valued transformation,

and $\underline{\eta}$ is uniquely determined by $\underline{T}$ and $\underline{\xi}$. This is clearly a "deterministic" relation, but can serve as the starting point for stochastization. Note that time can be one element of $\underline{\xi}$; i.e., time can be regarded as an input factor.

Each element of $\underline{\eta}$ or of $\underline{\xi}$ can be a curve of output or of input, respectively, through time. Also, some or all of the elements of $\underline{\eta}$ and some but not all of the elements of $\underline{\xi}$ can be time derivatives. In this basic formulation we regard $\underline{T}$ to be invariant. We postulate (3-1) to be a true background relation, but we shall recognize later that $\underline{\eta}$, $\underline{\xi}$ and $\underline{T}$ may never be exactly knowable, a situation which may make $\underline{\eta}$ appear not to be single-valued and may make $\underline{T}$ appear to vary even though it be invariant. Also we shall recognize subsequently that $\underline{\eta}$, $\underline{\xi}$ and $\underline{T}$ may have inherently random features.

3.1.2. The biosystem vs. the mathematical system:

3.1.2.1. Matching of elements in the two systems: At the outset a semantic or didactic problem must be overcome. It is rather natural to think of the biosystem as consisting of three distinct parts, as follows: One part is the organism (or a part of an organism or a population of organisms). Another part is input to the organism (i.e., items such as food, environmental temperature, etc.), and the third part is output from the organism (items such as work, offspring, milk, meat, etc.). There is great temptation then to match the elements of the mathematical system (3-1) as follows: The input corresponds to $\underline{\xi}$, the output to $\underline{\eta}$ and the organism to $\underline{T}$. That, however, is too simple a view. For one thing, the organism itself can be part of the input, and the organism in a changed condition can be part of the output. For another, if $\underline{T}$ is to correspond to the organism, T has to be permitted to vary from organism to organism and from time to time on the same organism. Clearly, if the organism is to be, so to speak, both input and output, and if T is to be invariant, one must think of $\underline{T}$ as a sort of universal transformation and must encompass characteristics of the organism into $\underline{\eta}$ and $\underline{\xi}$.

3.1.2.2. <u>An example</u>: To illustrate these points, consider the production of meat. Animals and feed are, along with other things, input, and the animals presumably larger and fatter, are, among many other things, output. Furthermore, a change in the kind of animals used will change the relation between feed and output, even if all other input items are fixed. This is because of differences in genetic make-up and previous history of the animals. Finally, if one examines sub-periods of a fattening period for a given group of animals, it will be found that the relation of feed to output changes, even though other input items are fixed. This is because the physiological states of the animals change as the feeding period progresses. To put meat production in the framework of (3-1), then, it is clear that variables describing kind and physiological state of animal at the start of a period of interest must be part of the input, $\underline{\xi}$, and variables describing the kind and the state of the animal at the end of the period of interest must be part of the output, $\underline{\eta}$. Only if the description of the animal part of the input is adequate can $\underline{T}$ be invariant over kind and state of animal; invariance over state implies invariance over time. Many diverse and more complicated examples could be cited.

3.1.2.3. <u>Some terms</u>: As implied earlier, the simple term, <u>organism</u>, will be taken to mean an organism, a part of an organism, a metabolic system isolated from an organism, or a population of one or more kinds of organisms. Variables describing the kind and the state of an organism and of the things leaving the organism will be called <u>internal</u> variables (synonyms are <u>intrinsic</u> and <u>endogenous</u>). Other variables involved in the system, including time, will be called <u>external</u> variables (synonyms are <u>extrinsic</u>, <u>exogenous</u> and <u>environmental</u>). External variables are those which are in no way affected by internal variables, but which can affect the internal variables. Note that some internal variables in one situation can be external variables in another, and <u>vice versa</u>.

3.1.2.4. The general formulation: In summary, for mathematization in the context of (3-1), the pertinent input and output variables must be identified. Clearly, external variables appear only as input. Some, if not all, internal variables can appear as both input and output. In order for $\underline{T}$ to be invariant from situation to situation and from time to time, some variables describing kind and state of the organism will have to appear as part of the input.

3.1.2.5. Some useful special cases: Note that kind and state of organism can sometimes adequately be summarized by measurements on things leaving the organism under standardized conditions with respect to the external variables. An example is met in dairy cattle feeding work. Milk production is an output, but pre-experimental milk production rate under standardized feeding conditions characterizes input very well with respect to kind and state of cow. Note also that there are special situations in which $\underline{T}$ can be viewed to be time-invariant and in which the organism can be regarded simply as determining the form and the constants of $\underline{T}$. These are the "steady-state" situations, which perhaps really do not exist, but which often are assumed to exist for practical purposes. Obviously $\underline{T}$ can vary from one steady-state situation to another even though it be time-invariant in a given situation.

3.2. Stochastization of the Model

3.2.1. Steps of stochastization:

We shall proceed with stochastization first by analyzing the idealized form (3-1) as it stands, introducing some random features and taking into account ignorance about the system. Then we shall introduce the ever-present observational errors. The basic relation (3-1) requires that $\underline{\eta}$ be uniquely determined by $\underline{T}$ and $\underline{\xi}$. In that context, therefore, any random features exhibited by $\underline{\eta}$ must stem from random features of $\underline{T}$ or $\underline{\xi}$. In order to introduce observational errors into the model extra elements will be added.

3.2.1.1. Random and pseudo-random elements of $\underline{\xi}$: We can partition $\underline{\xi}$ as follows:

$$(3\text{-}2) \qquad \underline{\xi} = \begin{bmatrix} \underline{\delta} \\ \underline{\rho} \end{bmatrix},$$

where

$\underline{\delta}$ = the column vector of truly non-random input,

$\underline{\rho}$ = the column vector of truly random input.

Next, we make the transformation,

(3-3)
$$\underline{I}(\underline{\xi}) = \check{\underline{\xi}} = \begin{bmatrix} \check{\underline{\delta}}_1 \\ \check{\underline{\rho}}_1 \\ \check{\underline{\delta}}_2 \\ \check{\underline{\rho}}_2 \end{bmatrix},$$

where $\underline{I}$ corresponds to $\underline{I}$ of (2-7) and

$\check{\underline{\delta}}_1, \check{\underline{\rho}}_1$ = observed input variables

$\check{\underline{\delta}}_2, \check{\underline{\rho}}_2$ = unobserved input variables.

As was pointed out in Section 2, random input variables, if observed, are effectively non-random, since they can be used as predictors. Hence, we combine observed non-random with observed random input and define

(3-4)
$$\check{\underline{\xi}}_1 = \begin{bmatrix} \check{\underline{\delta}}_1 \\ \check{\underline{\rho}}_1 \end{bmatrix}.$$

Similarly, we combine unobserved non-random with unobserved random input and let

(3-5)
$$\check{\underline{\xi}}_2 = \begin{bmatrix} \check{\underline{\delta}}_2 \\ \check{\underline{\rho}}_2 \end{bmatrix}.$$

Note that $\check{\underline{\xi}}_1$ and $\check{\underline{\xi}}_2$ correspond, respectively, to $\check{\underline{X}}_1$ and $\check{\underline{X}}_2$ of (2-7) .

3.2.1.2. Comments about $\check{\underline{\rho}}_1$, $\check{\underline{\delta}}_2$ and $\check{\underline{\rho}}_2$: A future situation may permit a measurement of $\check{\underline{\rho}}_1$ for use in the prediction of $\underline{\eta}$ even though $\check{\underline{\rho}}_1$ be random. Sometimes, however, prediction must be made prior to the time that $\check{\underline{\rho}}_1$ becomes observable. In that event, an expected value for $\check{\underline{\rho}}_1$ must replace $\check{\underline{\rho}}_1$ in (3-4), and deviations of $\check{\underline{\rho}}_1$ from expectation must be adjoined to $\check{\underline{\rho}}_2$ in (3-5) .

Because $\check{\underline{\delta}}_2$ and $\check{\underline{\rho}}_2$ are both unobserved, their effects cannot be distinguished and they are pooled into $\check{\underline{\xi}}_2$. The effects of both will be put in the pseudo-random category because they are both potential predictors. Nevertheless, there is a difference between $\check{\underline{\delta}}_2$ and $\check{\underline{\rho}}_2$. Because $\check{\underline{\delta}}_2$ is non-random, bad sampling of the class of situations of interest can lead to biases from its effects. On the other hand, $\check{\underline{p}}_2$, being random, cannot be a source of bias, regardless of the sampling scheme.

3.2.1.3. Random features of $\underline{T}$: If $\underline{T}$ has random features, $\underline{\eta}$ is not uniquely determined by $\underline{\xi}$. To take randomness of $\underline{T}$ into account, we rewrite (2-1) as

$$\underline{\eta} = \bar{\underline{T}}(\underline{\xi}) + \underline{\mathcal{R}} , \tag{3-6}$$

where

$$\bar{\underline{T}}(\underline{\xi}) = E(\underline{T} | \underline{\xi}) ,$$

$$\underline{\mathcal{R}} = \underline{\eta} - \bar{\underline{T}}(\underline{\xi}) .$$

The truly random variable, $\underline{\mathcal{R}}$, is distributed with a probability density such that $E(\underline{\mathcal{R}} | \underline{\xi}) = 0$, and having as other parameters, $\underline{\xi}$ and the parameters of the distribution of $\underline{T}$. Note that the random transformation, $\underline{T}$, can be replaced by the fixed transformation, $\bar{\underline{T}}(\xi)$, and the randomness of $\underline{T}$ can be thought of as something inherently random about $\underline{\eta}$.

3.2.1.4. Modification encompassing random and pseudo-random features of both $\underline{\xi}$ and $\underline{T}$: We write (3-6) as

$$\underline{\eta} = \check{\bar{\underline{T}}}(\check{\underline{\xi}}_1, \check{\underline{\xi}}_2) + \underline{\mathcal{R}} . \tag{3-7}$$

Then, in the manner of Section 2.2.3.2, we find the average of $\check{\bar{\underline{T}}}(\check{\underline{\xi}}_1, \check{\underline{\xi}}_2)$, given $\check{\underline{\xi}}_2$, over the class of situations of interest. Let this average be $\bar{\underline{T}}_1(\check{\underline{\xi}}_1)$. Then, we write

$$\underline{\eta} = \bar{\underline{T}}_1(\check{\underline{\xi}}_1) + \underline{V} + \underline{\mathcal{R}} , \tag{3-8}$$

where

$$\underline{V} = \check{\bar{\underline{T}}}(\check{\underline{\xi}}_1, \check{\underline{\xi}}_2) - \bar{\underline{T}}_1(\check{\underline{\xi}}_1)$$

is a pseudo-random variable unless randomization procedures can be employed to render it random.

It may happen also that we cannot observe $\underline{\eta}$, but only some, not necessarily linear, transformation, $\underline{\eta}_1$, of it. The rank of the space of $\underline{\eta}_1$ may be less than the rank of the space of $\underline{\eta}$. In this event, we write

$$\underline{\eta}_1 = \bar{\underline{T}}_{11}(\check{\underline{\xi}}_1) + \underline{V}_1 + \underline{\mathcal{R}}_1 \tag{3-9}$$

in place of (3-8).

3.2.1.5. Observational errors: From Section 2.2.6.4, it is clear that we may rewrite (3-8) as

$$\underline{Y} = \underline{\bar{T}}_1^+ (\underline{\check{X}}_1) + \underline{V} + \underline{\mathcal{R}} + \underline{\epsilon}_0 \ , \qquad (3\text{-}10)$$

where $\underline{\epsilon}_0$ encompasses the observational errors in both $\underline{Y}$ and $\underline{\check{X}}_1$ (observational errors on $\underline{\eta}$ and $\underline{\check{\xi}}_1$). The counterpart of (3-9) is

$$\underline{Y}_1 = \underline{\bar{T}}_{11}^+ (\underline{\check{X}}_1) + \underline{V}_1 + \underline{\mathcal{R}}_1 + \underline{\epsilon}_{01} \qquad (3\text{-}11)$$

3.2.1.6. Assessment of the contributions of $\underline{V}$, $\underline{\mathcal{R}}$ and $\underline{\epsilon}_0$ to the variability in $\underline{Y}$: It may sometimes not be necessary nor desirable to distinguish $\underline{V}$, $\underline{\mathcal{R}}$ and $\underline{\epsilon}_0$, because there may be no way or no need to estimate their separate contributions to the variation in $\underline{Y}$. It is possible, of course, and can be very useful, to estimate the separate contributions by proper replication at the proper levels in a hierarchial sampling or experimental plan. For example, a plan might be set up that ensures the following:

(a) For each of the several situations that will lead to a given value of $\underline{V}_1$, four sub-situations are set up,

(b) Two of the sub-situations for each $\underline{V}_1$ are characterized by one value of $\underline{\mathcal{R}}_1$, and the other two by another value of $\underline{\mathcal{R}}_1$,

(c) The two sub-situations for each $\underline{\mathcal{R}}_1$ given $\underline{V}_1$ lead to different values of $\underline{\epsilon}_{01}$.

For the example to be discussed in the last part of this paper, $\underline{\mathcal{R}}_1$ and $\underline{\epsilon}_{01}$ need not be distinguished. Thus, they will be pooled and the model to be derived will be of the form,

$$\underline{Y}_1 = \underline{\bar{T}}_{11}^+ (\underline{\check{X}}_1) + \underline{V}_1 + \underline{\epsilon}_1 \ . \qquad (3\text{-}12)$$

For each situation which leads to a given value of $\underline{V}_1$, two sub-situations, which lead to different $\underline{\epsilon}_1$, will be set up.

3.2.1.7. A point of notation: In Section 2, the notation, $\mu(\underline{\theta};\underline{\xi})$, was used for a relation, and in this section the notation, $T(\underline{\xi})$, has been used. These are equivalent. The former can be regarded to take cognizance of the fact that a transformation may be characterized in terms of its form, μ, and its parameters, $\underline{\theta}$. The μ, $\underline{\theta}$ notation is perhaps to be preferred when μ is known and only $\underline{\theta}$ is to be estimated. The presence of both μ and $\underline{\theta}$ is implied by the use of T. Using T seems preferable when both μ and $\underline{\theta}$ are unknown and need to be estimated. Such will be the case in the forthcoming example.

3.3. Comments on Autocorrelation, Lag Effects and Related Matters

In time series analysis, correlations of various lags between successive observed outputs will ordinarily be found. That is, observed output at a given time is related to the history of observed output. Some of this correlation can sometimes be explained by taking into account observed current or immediately preceding input, but very often the input history will explain as much more. It is particularly interesting to see how the correlations of observed current output to input and output history (correlations that remain after adjustment for observed current, or immediately preceding, input) can be explained.

One explanation is that the internal part of the system is changing state in a way that affects the observed output, but that some of the variables necessary to describe the pertinent aspects of current or immediately preceding state are not being taken into account. Perhaps they are not recognized or perhaps they cannot be measured. Part of the change in such variables with time can be random, part can be inherent (as in growing organisms), and part can be attributed to external variables. Whatever the cause, the following can be argued: If current output of a system shows correlation with the input and output history, then this history must be reflected in the current or immediately preceding state of the system, because current or immediately preceding state is the only physical connection between history and current performance. Hence, if all relevant aspects of current or immediately preceding state can be properly taken into account, current behavior will be explained without recourse to history.

Another explanation is that the internal part of the system is complex, spreading over a physical space of some sort, and involving perhaps feed-back mechanisms. Lags occur, therefore, because of the times required for internal transport. A "point" system might be envisaged, of course, in which lags are infinitesimal. Some biological systems (e.g., in vitro systems for studying enzymes) might safely be assumed to be point systems, but most are really not. Thus, either lags must be assumed in the model, or the system must be compartmentized finely enough so that transport times between and within compartments can be assumed to be infinitesimal.

4. AN EXAMPLE

Important practical features of the material heretofore presented can be illustrated by a problem with which I have been associated for many years. It is the problem of predicting the digestibility of feeds and of various fractions of the feeds from chemical measurements made on the feeds.

The methods of assessing chemical composition that have been prevalent for many decades yield rather large errors when predicting digestibility. Present day situations require much better prediction, and there has been much effort expended to develop improved chemical methods. Most of the work has, however, been done within a vague conceptual framework. The following development provides a sound framework within which to plan experiments, to analyze data and to assess progress as work proceeds.

4.1. The Biological Framework

4.1.1. Measurement of digestibility:

4.1.1.1. The procedure: Digestion trials are simple to conduct. From the amounts and the chemical compositions of the feed consumed and the feces voided, the digestibility of the feed and of its various fractions are computed by the formula, consumed-less-voided/consumed. Sometimes, however, recovery (voided/consumed) is computed.

Such figures are called "apparent" digestion (or recovery) coefficients because the feces contain, in addition to feed residues, some materials produced by the animal body.

4.1.1.2. Experimental errors in digestion trials: To minimize experimental errors of both the random and the bias types, the following rules are followed:

(a) The daily feeding rate is held constant,

(b) The feeding rate is set at a level equal to, or little below or a little above that which will maintain the animal's body weight,

(c) The feed of interest is supplied at the set feeding rate for a long enough time to attain essentially a steady state before starting fecal collections,

(d) Fecal collections are continued for a length of time sufficient to render innocuous the day-to-day fluctuations in fecal output.

Results on a given batch of feed are remarkably duplicable, not only on the same animal, but also on different animals of the same species and physiological state. For the principal energy-supplying fractions of feeds, it is common to observe coefficients of variation of 2-4 per cent between animals and only a little less within animals.

4.1.2. The physiology:

4.1.2.1. Orientative remarks: Although the simple term, "digestibility", has been used to characterize feeds, it is well known that the physiological processes involved fall into two classes:

(a) Those of digestion proper; i.e., things that happen to the feed while in the digestive tract,
(b) Those involved in disappearance of digestive end-products from the tract.

For the theory, it is necessary to distinguish and to analyze the two sets of processes. It is also necessary to distinguish and to characterize the "feed-residue" and the "body-source" fecal components mentioned in Section 4.1.1.1.

4.1.2.2. The digestive processes: Digestion involves four actions:

(a) Chemical reaction between feed constituents,
(b) Action of enzymes and other chemicals secreted into the tract from the body proper,
(c) Action of microorganisms living in the tract,
(d) Physical action of the tract resulting in diminution of particle size, mixing and churning.

These actions have the following effects:

(i) Chemical degradation of some materials,
(ii) Solution, emulsification and colloidal suspension of some materials,
(iii) Synthesis of some materials.

Some feed materials can escape complete digestion, some digestive end-products are the same as some materials present in the feed, and digestive end-products can include materials not present in any feeds nor in feces from any feed.

4.1.2.3. The fate of digestive end-products: The disappearance processes fall into three categories:

(a) Absorption into the body,
(b) Volatilization; e.g., passage as gas via mouth or anus,
(c) Appearance in the feces.

A given material can leave the tract via more than one channel.

4.1.2.4. Source of fecal materials: Feed residues constitute part of the feces. Body-source materials constitute the remainder and fall into two classes:

(a) Secretory materials; these are associated with and/or are necessary for the digestion of feeds (e.g., mucus and constituents of the digestive juices),
(b) Excretory materials; i.e., waste products of metabolism or excesses in the body proper for which the gut is one of the paths of elimination.

The body source materials can include materials different from those in feeds.

4.1.2.5. Associative digestibility effects: Changing the amounts of one constituent in the ration can affect the apparent digestibility (or apparent recovery) of one or more other constituents. Such interactions are known as associative digestibility effects.

4.1.2.6. Extraneous factors that affect digestibility: The apparent digestibilities of feeds and of individual chemical fractions are related to species of animal, level and frequency of feeding, physical state of the feed (e.g., ground vs. unground), and possibly to other environmental factors.

4.1.3. Chemical characterization of feeds:

4.1.3.1. Chemical fractions: A chemical fraction is the mixture of substances measured by a chemical method. A chemical fraction can be defined only operationally; i.e., in terms of the manipulations, the reagents and the other conditions employed in the chemical method. An "ideal" method defines an "ideal" fraction; i.e., a fraction which has exactly the same pertinent properties regardless of the material analyzed.

Chemical fractions ordinarily are expressed in mutually exclusive terms. To completely describe a feed, then, the sum of the chemical fractions, after proper scaling for units of measure, must be unity.

4.1.3.2. Nutritive entities: A nutritive entity is defined as a "nutritionally ideal" chemical fraction. The relevant invariant properties are the digestibility characteristics of the fraction, the absorbability and volatility of digestive end-products and the nutritive value of the absorbed end-products after entering the body. Present chemical methods for fractionating feeds do not measure nutritive entities. The "chemical" view has tended to dominate the "nutritional" view.

4.2. The Mathematical Model

4.2.1. The deterministic model:

4.2.1.1. Introductory remarks: The model will be developed in terms of nutritive entities. It will be assumed initially that the extraneous factors are fixed and that no random elements exist. The consequences of relaxing some of these conditions will be considered subsequently. Steady-state is also assumed.

4.2.1.2. The fecal identity: In view of Section 4.1.2.4, we write

$$\underline{r} = \underline{f} + \underline{\psi} + \underline{\omega} \tag{4-1}$$

where

$\underline{r}$ = the matrix of amounts of nutritive entities in the feces,
$\underline{f}$ = the matrix of amounts of fecal nutritive entities which are feed residues,
$\underline{\psi}$ = the matrix of amounts of fecal nutritive entities secreted into the tract,
$\underline{\omega}$ = the matrix of amounts of fecal nutritive entities excreted into the tract.

All amounts are per unit of feed consumed. The matrices are all n x 1, with n just large enough to include all nutritive entities needed to describe any feed, feces or contents of the digestive tract. There is not necessarily a unique such set of n, but it is legitimate to assume that all such sets of n are linear transformations of each other.

4.2.1.3. The feed residue: In view of Sections 4.1.2.3. and 4.1.2.4., we write

$$\underline{f} = (\underset{\sim}{I} - \underset{\sim}{\nu} - \underset{\sim}{\alpha})\ \underset{\sim}{\delta}\,\underline{c} \tag{4-2}$$

$$= \underset{\sim}{\rho}\,\underline{c}\ ,$$

where

$\underline{c}$ = the n x 1 matrix describing feed composition ($\underline{\lambda}'\ \underline{c} = 1$, where $\underline{\lambda}$ is a vector of appropriate scaling factors),
$\underset{\sim}{\delta}$ = the n x n matrix of digestion coefficients (δ_{ij} = the fraction of jth nutritive entity converted to the ith entity),
$\underset{\sim}{\alpha}$ = the n x n diagonal matrix of absorption coefficients,
$\underset{\sim}{\nu}$ = the n x n diagonal matrix of volatility coefficients,
$\underset{\sim}{I}$ = the n x n identity matrix,
$\underset{\sim}{\rho} = (\underset{\sim}{I} - \underset{\sim}{\nu} - \underset{\sim}{\alpha})\ \underset{\sim}{\delta}$ = the n x n matrix of recovery coefficients.

4.2.1.4. The basic digestibility identity: Substituting (4-2) into (4-1) yields

$$\underline{r} = (\underset{\sim}{I} - \underset{\sim}{\nu} - \underset{\sim}{\alpha})\ \underset{\sim}{\delta}\,\underline{c} + \underline{\psi} + \underline{\omega} \tag{4-3}$$

$$= \underset{\sim}{\rho}\,\underline{c} + \underline{\mu}\ ,$$

where

$\underline{r}$ = apparently recovered nutrients per unit of feed,
$\underline{\mu} = \underline{\psi} + \underline{\omega}$ = combined body source (metabolic) materials per unit of feed.

The two body source materials are combined here for simplicity. To take factors such as feeding level and size of animal into account, $\underline{\psi}$ and $\underline{\omega}$ must be kept separated.

Some people may prefer to write the identity in terms of apparently digested (or absorbed) nutrients; i.e.,

$$\underline{d} = \underline{c} - \underline{r} = (\underset{\sim}{I} - \underset{\sim}{\rho})\, \underline{c} - \underline{\mu} \tag{4-4}$$

$$= \underset{\sim}{\Delta}\, \underline{c} - \underline{\mu}\ .$$

Note that (4-3), or, if one prefers, (4-4), corresponds to (3-1).

4.2.1.5. Parameters vs. observables: The items identified by Greek letters in (4-3) and (4-4) will be called "parameters" in order to distinguish them from the observables, $\underline{c}$, $\underline{r}$ and $\underline{d}$. Note that the "parameters" can in reality be functions of $\underline{c}$.

4.2.1.6. Associative digestibility effects: For the present purposes, associative effects will be said to exist if (4-3) is nonlinear in $\underline{c}$. That is, if $\underset{\sim}{\rho}$ is a function of $\underline{c}$ or if $\underline{\mu}$ is any nonlinear function of $\underline{c}$. This definition excludes some effects encompassed by nutritionists under the term associative effects, namely, those stemming from non-zero elements off the principal diagonal of $\underset{\sim}{\delta}$ (and $\underset{\sim}{\rho}$ and $\underset{\sim}{\Delta}$).

4.2.2. Introduction of stochastic elements:

4.2.2.1. Experimental error: Experimental error is here defined to be the variance between trials on the same batch of feed but on different animals when extraneous factors are fixed as closely as possible to certain arbitrary levels. Contributing to experimental error are:

(a) Between-animal variations in the parameters of (4-3) and (4-4),

(b) Day-to-day fluctuations in fecal output (trial error),

(c) Errors in weighing and sampling of feed and feces, and errors causing non-repeatability in the determination of a given chemical fraction of a given sample of feed.

To parallel the development in Section 3, we shall first take (a) into account. Next we shall introduce the fact that the chemical fractions measured are not nutritive entities. Then we shall take (b) and (c) into account.

4.2.2.2. Between-animal variations in the parameters of (4-3) and (4-4): To take (a) into account, we change (4-3) to read

$$\underline{r}_u = \bar{\underset{\sim}{\rho}}\, \underline{c} + \bar{\underline{\mu}} + [\underset{\sim}{\rho}_u\, \underline{c} + \underline{\mu}_u] \tag{4-5}$$

for the $\underline{u}$th animal. Here, $\bar{\underset{\sim}{\rho}}$ and $\bar{\underline{\mu}}$ represent, respectively, $E(\underset{\sim}{\rho}|\underline{c})$ and $E(\underline{\mu}|\underline{c})$ for the class of animals involved. Thus $\underset{\sim}{\rho}_u$ and $\underline{\mu}_u$ are deviations for the $\underline{u}$th animal from the average animal, with $E(\underset{\sim}{\rho}_u|\underline{c}) = \underset{\sim}{0}$ and $E(\underline{\mu}_u|\underline{c}) = 0$. Note that (4-5) corresponds to (3-6) .

4.2.2.3. Variation introduced by failure of chemical fractions to be nutritive entities: We shall let $\underline{r}_1$ and $\underline{c}_1$ be, respectively, the fecal materials per unit of feed and the feed composition when the chemical fractions measured are not nutritive entities. Note that $\underline{\lambda}_1' \underline{c}_1 = 1$ just as $\underline{\lambda}' \underline{c} = 1$. To say that the chemical fractions are not nutritive entities is to say that $\underline{r}$ and $\underline{c}$, respectively, determine unique $\underline{r}_1$ and $\underline{c}_1$, but that the converse is not true. This means that the rank of the vector space generated by $\underline{r}_1$ and $\underline{c}_1$ is less than the rank for $\underline{r}$ and $\underline{c}$. Thus, if the rank for $\underline{r}$ and $\underline{c}$ is $m \leq n$, we write for the $\underline{v}$th feed,

$$\underline{r}_{1v} = \underset{\sim}{L}\,\underline{r}_v \tag{4-6}$$

$$\underline{c}_{1v} = \underset{\sim}{L}\,\underline{c}_v \ ,$$

where $\underset{\sim}{L}$ is a matrix with rank $k < m$, and $\underset{\sim}{L}$ is not a function of $\underline{r}$ or $\underline{c}$ but only of the chemical method. The matrix $\underset{\sim}{L}$ is subject to the restriction, $\underline{\lambda}_1' \underset{\sim}{L} = \underline{\lambda}'$. We then write

$$\underline{c}_v = \underset{\sim}{L}^{-1*}\,\underline{c}_{1v} + \underline{\phi}_v \ , \tag{4-7}$$

where

L^{-1*} = a conditional inverse of $\underset{\sim}{L}$; $\underline{\lambda}'\underset{\sim}{L}^{-1*} = \underline{\lambda}_1'$,

$\underline{\phi}_v$ = discrepancy in relating $\underline{c}$ to $\underline{c}_1$ for the $\underline{v}$th feed; $\underline{\lambda}'\underline{\phi}_v = 0$.

Now an $\underset{\sim}{L}^{-1*}$ exists such that, averaging over all feeds, $E(\underline{\phi}_v) = \underline{0}$. Substituting in (4-5) yields

$$\underline{r}_{1vu} = \bar{\underset{\sim}{\rho}}_{11}\underline{c}_{1v} + \bar{\underline{\mu}}_1 + \underline{\phi}_{1v} + \underline{\eta}_{1vu} \ , \tag{4-8}$$

which corresponds to (3-9), with $\bar{\underset{\sim}{\rho}}_{11}\underline{c}_{1v} + \bar{\underline{\mu}}_1 = \underset{\sim}{L}(\bar{\underset{\sim}{\rho}}\underset{\sim}{L}^{-1*}\underline{c}_{1v} + \bar{\underline{\mu}})$ corresponding to $\bar{\underline{T}}_{11}(\underline{\xi}_1)$, $\underline{\phi}_{1v} = \underset{\sim}{L}\,\bar{\underset{\sim}{\rho}}\,\underline{\phi}_v$ corresponding to $\underline{V}_1$, and $\underline{\eta}_{1v} = \underset{\sim}{L}(\underset{\sim}{\rho}_u L^{-1*}\underline{c}_{1v} + \underset{\sim}{\rho}_u\underline{\phi}_v + \underline{\mu}_v)$ corresponding to $\underline{\mathcal{R}}_1$.

4.2.2.4. Trial and measurement errors: To take (b) and (c) into account, we introduce the trial error, $\underline{\tau}_{1vu}$, the pooled errors of weighing, sampling and chemical non-repeatability for the feed, $\underline{\zeta}_{1vu}^{(c)}$, and for the feces, $\underline{\zeta}_{1vu}^{(r)}$, and write

$$\underline{r}_{1vu}^{+} = \bar{\underline{\rho}}_{11}^{+} \underline{c}_{1v}^{+} + \underline{\phi}_{1v} + \underline{\epsilon}_{1vu} \tag{4-9}$$

for the $\underline{u}$th animal on the $\underline{v}$th feed. In (4.9), which corresponds to (3-12), $\bar{\underline{\rho}}_{11}^{+} \underline{c}_{1v}^{+} + \bar{\underline{\mu}}_{1}^{+}$ corresponds to $\bar{\underline{T}}_{11}^{+}(\underline{\breve{X}}_{1})$, $\underline{\phi}_{1v}$ is defined as for (4-8), and $\underline{\epsilon}_{1vu} = \eta_{1vu} + \tau_{1vu} - \bar{\underline{\rho}}_{11}\underline{\zeta}_{1vu}^{(c)} + \underline{\zeta}_{1vu}^{(r)}$, the experimental error, corresponds to $\underline{\epsilon}_{1}$.

4.2.4.4. Comments about $\underline{\phi}_{1v}$ and $\underline{\epsilon}_{1vu}$: Actual data show it is safe to assume that $\underline{\epsilon}_{1vu}$ is a truly random vector, with $E(\underline{\epsilon}_{1vu}) = \underline{0}$ and $E(\underline{\epsilon}_{1vu}\underline{\epsilon}'_{1vu}) = \underset{\sim}{U}$ for all v. If a set of feeds under study is a sample drawn randomly from all feeds, $\underline{\phi}_{1v}$ is also a random vector with $E(\underline{\phi}_{1v}) = \underline{0}$ and $E(\underline{\phi}_{1v}\,\underline{\phi}'_{1v}) = \underset{\sim}{V}$, say. In experimental work, there is often an arbitrary choice of feeds. Thus, it seems preferable to consider $\underline{\phi}_{1v}$ simply as "discrepance." It is the pseudo-random component of the model. For practical purposes, however, we might wish to assume it to be random. In this context, then, a good frationation procedure would show $\underset{\sim}{V} \simeq \underset{\sim}{0}$, but a poor one, $\underset{\sim}{V} > \underset{\sim}{0}$.

4.3. Uses of the Framework and the Model

4.3.1. Testing of chemical procedures:

If digestion trials are run in duplicate on a suitable variety of feeds and some "smooth" relationship between $\underline{r}_{1}^{+}$ and $\underline{c}_{1}^{+}$ is fitted to the data, then the mean square of residuals from the fit will estimate $\underset{\sim}{V}^{+} = 2\underset{\sim}{V} + \underset{\sim}{U}$. The mean square between duplicates will estimate $\underset{\sim}{U}$. A good fractionation scheme is one such that

$$\hat{\underset{\sim}{V}} = \frac{\hat{\underset{\sim}{V}}^{+} - \hat{\underset{\sim}{U}}}{2}$$

is acceptably small. Certain other criteria coming from the theory are also useful; e.g.: $\underline{\mu} \geq \underline{0}$, $\underline{0} \leq \underline{1}'\underset{\sim}{\rho} \leq \underline{1}'$, $\underset{\sim}{0} \leq \underset{\sim}{\rho} \leq \underline{1}\,\underline{1}'$, $\underline{0} \leq \underline{1}'\underset{\sim}{\Delta} \leq 1$ and $-\underline{1}\,\underline{1}' \leq \underset{\sim}{\Delta} - \underset{\sim}{I} \leq \underset{\sim}{0}$. Failure of $\bar{\underline{\mu}}_{1}^{+}$, $\bar{\underline{\rho}}_{11}^{+}$ and $\bar{\underset{\sim}{\Delta}}_{11}^{+}$ to meet these same restrictions is evidence that a fractionation scheme needs improvement.

4.3.2. Testing for associative effects:

If associative effects are negligible then the relationship of $\underline{r}_1^+$ to $\underline{c}_1^+$ is expected to be linear; otherwise, the relationship is non-linear. Important curvilinearity can, of course, be masked if $\underset{\sim}{V}$ or $\underset{\sim}{U}$ are large enough.

4.3.3. Some illustrative results:

4.3.3.1. The source of the data: A large number of digestion trials have been run at Raleigh on four species of forage: Alfalfa, Sericea Lespedeza, Tall Fescue and Weeping Lovegrass. Each species has been harvested at 8-12 stages of maturity in one or two seasons of the year for two or more years. A few trials have been run on synthetic diets.

4.3.3.2. Some statistical results: Although some rather complicated statistical analyses have been done, the main points of interest are brought out by the results of studies on the simple relations of d_i to c_i, see (4-4), for a few chemical fractions. These results for the pooled data on Alfalfa and Tall Fescue are shown in the following table. About 70 feed samples covering a wide range for each c_i are involved.

Chemical fraction	$\hat{V}_{ii}$	$\hat{U}_{ii}$	$\bar{\mu}_i^+$	$\bar{d}_i^*$
Crude protein (6.25 x nitrogen content)	.10	.27	>0 **	13.3
Carbohydrate fractionation--Method A:				
Crude fiber	10.2	1.6	<0	16.5
Nitrogen-free extract	10.3	1.7	<0	30.2
Carbohydrate fractionation--Method B:				
Cellulose	9.3	.9	0	19.6
Lignin	.26	.24	0	.3
Other carbohydrates-B	5.9	.8	<0	26.8
Carbohydrate fractionation--Method C:				
Hot-water-soluble reducing substances	.000	.005	0	4.4
4% H_2SO_4-soluble reducing substances	1.42	.28	0	8.7
72% H_2SO_4-soluble reducing substances	4.9	1.0	0	16.3
Lignin	.26	.24	0	.3
Other carbohydrates-C	3.7	1.6	>0	17.0

* average value of d_i in the data.

** >0 means the data showed clearly that $\bar{\mu}_i^+ > 0$.
<0 " " " " " " " < 0 .
0 " " " " " " " $\simeq 0$.

4.3.3.3. Comments: The results with Alfalfa and Fescue for crude protein indicate that chemical fraction to be fairly satisfactory. Upon including data for the other forage species, however, it has been found that further refinements are needed to characterize the nitrogenous fraction of feeds. Method A for carbohydrate fractionations is seen to be a very poor one; the values of $\hat{V}_{ii}$ are very large compared to $\bar{d}_i$; also $\bar{\mu}_i^+ < 0$. Method B, representing a "chemists" view, shows only a small improvement. Method C, which simply fractionates according to degree of resistance to chemical attack, is a substantial improvement, but the values of $\hat{V}_{ii}$ for the 72% H_2SO_4 and for the "other-carbohydrate" fractions are still undesirably large. Work to improve the fractionation methods is, therefore, continuing.

5. ACKNOWLEDGEMENTS

The author is greatly indebted to one of his colleagues, Professor H. R. van der Vaart and to one of his graduate students, Mr. C. A. Rohde, for help with much of the mathematical content of this paper and for their spending a great amount of time in discussion of the ideas involved. At the same time, the author wants it clearly known that he must take the blame for all mistakes, ambiquities and other signs of incompetence.

The author is also greatly indebted to his colleagues, Miss Mary Ann Cipolloni and Dr. W. W. G. Smart, for gathering and processing the digestibility data presented in this paper. Dr. R. G. Petersen also helped in the final stages of the processing.

Contribution from the Biomathematics Training Group of the Institute of Statistics, Raleigh Section, and supported in part by U. S. Public Health Service Grant 2G-678 from the Division of General Medical Sciences of the National Institutes of Health.

DISCUSSION PARTICIPANT

Dr. Irwin D. J. Bross
Director of Biostatistics
Roswell Park Memorial Institute,
Buffalo, New York

DISCUSSION

Irwin D. J. Bross. I should like compliment Dr. Lucas on his excellent presentation. It provides a first rate example of how stochastic models (or, as I would rather put it, stochastic languages) are of real value in biological research. By means of his ingenious stochastic language, Dr. Lucas was able to provide a remarkably clear and simple characterization of a complicated experimental situation in animal nutrition.

We have here an interesting illustration of the following point: Whether we come up with a sensible -- or a silly -- answer to a given question will often depend on what language we use to discuss the question. Thanks to his stochastic language, Dr. Lucas can speak realistically and precisely to the question: What can be done to reduce the variation due to failure of chemical fractions to be nutritive entities? He can get to an answer by an empirical evaluation of fractionalization methods A, B and C, so he comes out with helpful advice on this important -- and typical -- methodological issue.

On the other hand if the same question is discussed in the usual chemical language, the "obvious" answer is: Use fancier and more elaborate chemical techniques because these "must" get us closer to the nutritive entities. But the empirical results contradict this "obvious" answer. They suggest that this "obvious" advice merely sends the investigator off on a wild goose chase. So here we have a nice demonstration of what can be accomplished with a stochastic language -- at least when the speaker is as fluent as Dr. Lucas.

Henry L. Lucas. Dr. Bross is very kind indeed, and I thank him very mucn. Had time permitted, I should like to have presented a variety of examples in which the stochastic framework of Sections 2 and 3 has been effective.

INDEX